P9-BZO-780

LIFE SERIES

DISCOVER GOD'S CREATION

Science/Health, Series B

Ronald W. Ritterskamp, Editor
Daniel J. Wyrick, Editor

Produced under the auspices of the
Office of Education
North American Division
of the
General Conference of Seventh-day Adventists

Pacific Press® Publishing Association
Nampa, Idaho
Oshawa, Ontario, Canada

©1993 by the Office of Education
North American Division of the
General Conference of Seventh-day Adventists
Silver Spring, Maryland 20904

All Rights Reserved

CONTENTS

UNIT I

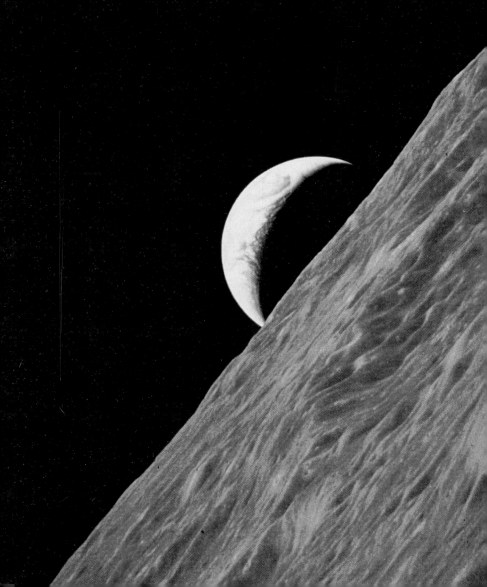

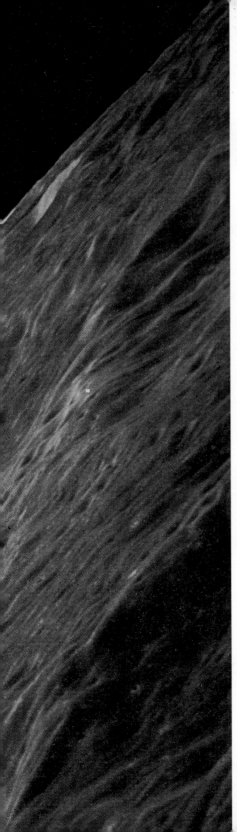

EARTH'S STRUCTURE

INTRODUCTION

Where did Earth come from? Where did the universe come from? What existed before the "beginning"? Scientists have many theories, but no proof, to answer these questions. Their theories of Earth's origin differ from one another. What is accepted today may not be accepted tomorrow.

No theory is as lasting or as exciting as the Bible record of what happened. Look at Genesis chapter 1 in your Bible. There it says that our Master Designer formed Earth and all that is in it by saying, "Let there be . . ." and it was so. Not only was it so, but, "it was good."

This unit will provide a wealth of information about Earth science and will expand your thinking about Earth and the God who created it. And remember, God made you! "And it was very good" (see Genesis 1:31).

CHAPTER TITLES

Earthrise from the moon.

CHAPTER 1

WHY STUDY SCIENCE?

INTRODUCTION

Many new products and technologies have resulted from the American space program. Out in space, some satellites help forecast our weather, while others transmit telephone calls and television programs. Closer to home, smoke detectors, cordless drills and screwdrivers, freeze-dried foods, and grooves in the highways are all spinoffs of space technology. Even certain types of sunglasses are the result of space science. As long as scientists continue to study how things work and why things happen the way they do, new products and technologies will be developed that will make our lives easier and more productive.

What is science? Why study it? What skills do scientists use? In this chapter you will explore answers to these questions. And you will develop some of the skills necessary to study the world around you.

SECTION TITLES

Many products have resulted from the American space program.

1–1 THE WHYS OF SCIENCE

VOCABULARY
science
technology

OBJECTIVES

- Explain what science is.
- Identify reasons for studying science.
- Analyze how science and technology have made life better.

Throughout history people have asked, "Why does this happen?" and, "How does that work?" To answer these questions, people have explored and examined, observed and experimented. This process of asking questions and looking for answers is what we call **science**.

What scientists discover increases our understanding of the world. Some scientists study frogs to learn how they hibernate. Some develop new varieties of corn and wheat. Some study sound, light, water, flight, and pollution. Still others study delicate butterflies, flowers, and snakes (fig. 1–1).

Scientists have also developed new **technologies**, or applications of scientific principles, that have improved our lives. Newly designed machines allow us to do things that were thought impossible, such as flying to the moon. Discoveries in medicine have increased our health and life expectancy (fig. 1–2).

Fig. 1–1 Scientists study animals to learn about them.

Fig. 1–2 Discoveries of scientists have improved medicines.

Science has enabled us to develop and use Earth's resources to benefit our lives. Scientific discoveries have led to new technology in the areas of communication and transportation. This has helped produce our telephones, televisions, and computers. Transportation has improved from horse and buggy to airplanes and space travel.

But today researchers are concerned that there are too many people and too few resources. Scientists, working with new technologies, are helping to find ways to preserve what is left on Earth. They are studying how we can conserve natural resources such as oil, trees, soil, and water. They are helping us find new ways to deal with the waste we produce and to restore land destroyed by fires and floods.

Fig. 1–3   Students learn by doing.

You can begin your study of science today. You can learn the skills that will help you observe and discover (fig. 1–3). Maybe one day you will uncover new mysteries and answers to long-asked questions.

REVIEW IT

1. What is science?
2. Why do people study science?
3. In what ways has science benefited you?

1-2 METHODS OF SCIENCE

VOCABULARY
characteristic
observation

OBJECTIVES

- Define **observation**.
- Explain why observation is important.
- Identify characteristics looked for during observation.

Look at these two drawings (fig. 1–4). They look quite similar, but there are a least ten differences between them. Can you find the differences?

For thousands of years people watched birds fly, always wishing that they, too, could fly. Some people tried to fly by making themselves a set of "wings" and tried flapping into the air. Later, the Wright brothers looked at bird flight and decided that the shape of the wings, not the flapping, was the basis of flight. Their success came after they added an engine to a properly shaped pair of wings.

Looking at something carefully and recording what you see, like the Wright brothers did, is called **observation**. This has always been an important scientific skill because it is the way we first learn about things.

Imagine that you just got a puppy (fig. 1–5). Immediately you would notice the puppy's size, its color, and its wagging tail. Soon afterward, you would discover its wet tongue and its sharp teeth and toenails. Of course, you

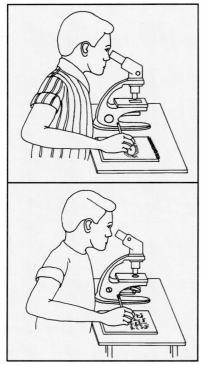

Fig. 1–4 Find the differences between the two pictures.

Fig. 1–5

TRY THIS 1–2A: The Burning Candle

Materials:

birthday candle   quart jar lid
matches

Procedure:

1. Light a candle and drip some wax onto the bottle cap. Place the candle into the wax and hold it until it sticks to the bottle cap.
2. Light the candle.(CAUTION: keep your hair or other flammable items away from the flame.)
3. Watch the candle carefully. Write down everything you observe about the candle and what it is doing. For example, your list could start:
   1. The candle is _____ color.
   2. It is burning.
   Try to make a list of at least 30 different observations before the candle burns all of the way down. You may have a few items to write after the candle stops burning.
4. Afterward, share your observations with classmates and your teacher.
   - Which of your observations are similar to those on other students' lists?
   - Which of your observations are different?

would discover the fluffiness of its fur and the softness of its ears. Within an hour or two you would find out if it liked water or milk, dry food or canned food. You would observe everything about it as you watched and played with it.

When scientists observe things, they look for and write down distinguishing features or **characteristics**—such things as color, size, shape, texture, smell, and sound. Speed, mass, volume, and temperature are other characteristics scientists look for when they are observing.

You can improve your observation skills by practicing. Look at any object and begin to observe it. Remember that good observation includes not only looking for the distinguishing characteristics, but also making a careful record of what you see.

REVIEW IT

1. What is observation?
2. Why is observation important in science?
3. List some characteristics looked for when observing.

11

TRY THIS 1–2B: The Disappearing Sugar Cube

Materials:

cold water   plastic cups (clear) – 2
hot water   sugar cubes

Procedure:

1. Before following step 2, predict how long you think it will take a sugar cube to dissolve in hot and cold water. Record your two predictions below.

   PREDICTION: _____ hot water _____ cold water

2. Place one sugar cube in a cup of hot water.
3. Time how long it takes for each sugar cube to dissolve.
4. Place the other sugar cube in a cup of cold water.
5. Repeat step 3.
   - How accurate were your predictions?
   - If your prediction was different from what you observed, explain why you think you missed the actual answer.
   - How could the experiment be changed to observe something different?

Dear Friend,

The other day I was talking with some students about falling objects. I explained that, contrary to popular belief, a large rock and a small rock fall at the same speed. They didn't believe me.

This morning I gathered several of the university students to see my experiment. I climbed the famous Tower of Pisa and dropped two weights, one light and one heavy. The weights fell side by side and hit at precisely the same moment, with *one* resounding THUD!

The students saw the weights hit but said they would not believe it because Aristotle said heavier weights fall faster than lighter ones. Why won't they accept the fact that Aristotle was wrong? It's probably because the Church of Rome supports Aristotle's teachings. Maybe they are fearful of being proven wrong. Maybe I shouldn't disprove what they believe. How can Aristotle keep them from believing what they just saw?

Sincerely, Galileo Galilei

1-3 MEASUREMENT

OBJECTIVES

- Define **measurement**.
- Explain why measurement is important.
- Distinguish between measurement of lines, volume, and mass.

VOCABULARY
mass
measure
volume
weight

To be useful, observation must be accurate and understandable. Measuring accurately helps make this possible. To **measure** something means to find out how much there is of it. We can measure the length, width, and height of an object. We can measure its volume, mass, and temperature. Even the speed an object travels or the rate at which things occur can be measured.

Hundreds of years ago, people measured things with body parts, such as a foot, forearm, or handspan. But since people were different sizes, the units of measure differed from one person to the next. To clear up the confusion, kings and rulers tried to set standards, but, unfortunately, the standards changed from region to region. For example, during the time of the Saxon kings in England, the standard for the yard was the length of the ruling king's sash. If the king was slim, the yard was short. If the king was plump, the length of the yard grew!

To solve this problem, scientists got together and standardized all units of measure. This eliminated confusion and allowed for accurate measurements.

Scientists most commonly measure lines, volume, and mass. But whatever you are measuring, the measurement must include a number and a unit.

MEASUREMENT OF LINES (fig. 1–6)

Measuring lines lets us determine length, width, height, and distance. Metersticks, tape measures, and rulers can be used to measure lines. Units used in measuring lines include miles, meters, feet, and centimeters.

Fig. 1–6 Tape measures are used in measuring height.

13

TRY THIS 1–3A: Barefoot Rulers

Materials:
none needed

Procedure:
1. Have everyone remove his or her shoes. Each student will measure the length of the classroom using his or her own feet.
2. Have each student write down the length of the room in his or her "feet."
3. Compare answers.
   - Why is there a difference in answers?
   - How can you overcome the confusion of having a variety of answers?
   - Why do all scientists use the same units of measurement?

Fig. 1–7   What is the volume of the box?

DID YOU KNOW?

One pound of gold (373 gm) is lighter than one pound of feathers (454 gm). Gold is measured in Troy pounds made up of 12 Troy ounces; the standard pound is made up of 16 ounces.

MEASUREMENT OF VOLUME (fig. 1–7)

Volume refers to how much space something occupies. It can be used to describe solid objects, liquids, and even gases. You can determine the volume of a solid by simply multiplying length times width times height. To measure the volume of a liquid, use a measuring cup or graduated cylinder. Units used in measuring liquid volume include gallons, liters, quarts, milliliters, ounces, and cups.

MEASUREMENT OF MASS

Weight and mass are often thought of as being the same thing, but they are different. **Weight** is a measure of how hard something is being pulled by gravity. **Mass** refers to how much matter an object contains. The mass of something can be determined by using a scale or balance. Units used in determining mass include kilograms (kē´ lō gramz), grams, and milligrams (mil´ i gramz).

Remember the puppy? You were so excited about the puppy that you went to school and told all of your friends about its fur, tongue, and sharp teeth. Your friends shared your excitement and asked you many questions. But when someone asked you what size and how heavy the puppy was, you were unable to answer.

That night you decided to measure your puppy while you held him. First, you got a meterstick and found out he was 20 cm (8 in) tall and 35 cm (13 in) long from his

TRY THIS 1–3B: Books and Marbles

Materials:
  graduated cylinder (100 ml)   meterstick
  marbles 6–10

Procedure:
1. Measure the height, width, and thickness of your science book in centimeters. Determine the book's volume by multiplying the three measurements together. Record your answer.
   • How would you measure the volume of your classroom?
2. Fill the graduated cylinder about half full of water. Read how much water is in the cylinder (at the meniscus). Place all of the marbles into the water and read the new water height. Record the volume of the marbles (volume = change of water height).
   • Name three irregularly shaped objects that could be measured like the marbles.
   • How could you measure the volume of a candy cane and not get it wet?

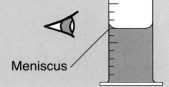

	Volume
Book	cubic cm
Marbles	ml

cubic cm = ml
1 cm x 1 cm x 1 cm = 1 ml

Meniscus

Fig. 1–8 A puppy's length increases as he grows.

nose to the tip of his tail (fig. 1–8). To measure his mass, you got the bathroom scale and discovered he weighed 1.5 kg (3.3 lbs). You wrote down the measurements, and the next day at school you were ready with answers to the many questions you had been asked.

REVIEW IT

1. What does it mean to measure something?
2. Why is measurement important to science?
3. What is the difference between volume and mass?
4. What units are used in measuring lines, volume, and mass?

RESEARCH IT
Contact an airline pilot to see how many different things pilots must measure as they fly airplanes.

CLASS ACTIVITY 1–3: Meters, Meters Everywhere

Question: What is the difference between meters, centimeters, and millimeters?

Materials:
meterstick

Procedure:
1. Observe your meterstick and compare it to the one drawn below. Diagram A shows the meterstick. Diagram B shows the meterstick expanded to show the centimeter markings. There are 100 cm in a meter. Diagram C shows 1 cm enlarged so you can see the smallest measures, called millimeters (10 mm = 1 cm). There are 1000 millimeters in a meter.

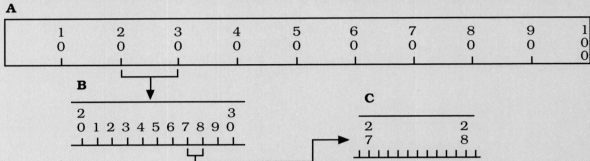

2. After studying the meter, centimeter, and millimeter markings, use the meterstick to measure each item below. Record your measurements in the chart. (Note: be sure to measure to the nearest whole unit.)

Data:

ITEM	m	cm	mm
Width of door			
Height of door			
Width of your desk			
Your own height			
Width of textbook			
Height of this paper			

Questions:
1. A meter equals how many centimeters? millimeters?
2. Which items were easy to measure in meters?
3. Why were some items easier to measure in millimeters?
4. Why is using a unit such as a meter or centimeter better than using something like the length of your foot or arm?

Conclusion: Write 3–5 sentences about what you learned from this activity.

1–4 DATA

OBJECTIVES

- Define **data**.
- Explain why data is important.
- Identify methods of displaying data.

VOCABULARY
chart
data
graph

When scientists observe and measure, they collect information called **data**. Data is usually in the form of facts and numbers. Your imaginary puppy is a source of lots of data. For instance, 35 cm long, 1.5 kg, four feet, two ears, and one tail are facts or data about the puppy.

Let's imagine that you want some more detailed data about your puppy. You decide to keep track of his growth for six months (fig. 1–9). Each month you measure him and record the data in a chart like the one shown below. A **chart** is a way to arrange data so it can be read easily. In a chart, observations and measurements are put into rows and columns.

DID YOU KNOW?
Computers store data. Some computer systems can hold enough data to fill 27 million pages of a daily newspaper.

PUPPY GROWTH CHART

Age (months)	Height (cm)	Length (cm)	Mass (kg)
2	20	35	1.5
3	23	40	2.3
4	30	46	4.0
5	34	52	6.2
6	41	63	7.9

Fig. 1–9   A chart helps to organize data so that it can be understood better.

Charts display data words and numbers. At times it is necessary to organize the data in a different form. **Graphs**, such as the one shown below, display data in picture form. Figure 1–10 uses bars to show how much your puppy grew each month. On the left is his height in centimeters. Across the bottom is his age in months. Study the graph to see how the numbers from the chart are organized.

PUPPY GROWTH

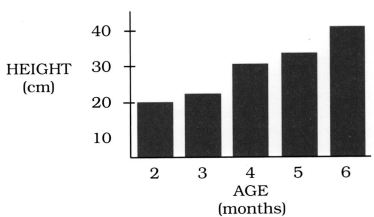

Fig. 1-10 A graph shows data in picture form.

TRY THIS 1–4: Making a Graph

Materials:
metric ruler   pencil

Procedure:
1. Use the length and mass data from the Puppy Growth Chart (fig. 1–9) and draw two bar graphs like the example given in this section. Remember to title your graphs. The left side and bottom of each graph must be labeled. Be sure to include the units (Hint: the Puppy Growth Graph had units of **centimeters** and **months**.)

REVIEW IT

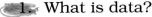

1. What is data?
2. Why is data important?
3. What is the difference between a chart and a graph?
4. How are charts and graphs useful?

CLASS ACTIVITY 1–4: Footwear Faire

Question: What shoe color is most common?

Materials:
shoes, assorted

Procedure:
1. Have everyone in class remove one shoe and place it in a row in the front of your classroom.
2. Count the number of right- and left-footed shoes. Record this number.
3. Count the number of each basic color of shoe and record this data below.
4. Graph the data on the graphs below. Remember to title each graph and label the bottom and left-side lines of each graph and give the proper units.

Data:

Foot	Number
Right	
Left	

Color	Number
Black	
Brown	
Red	
White	
Other	

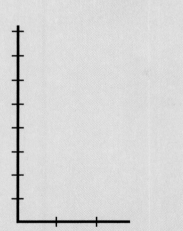
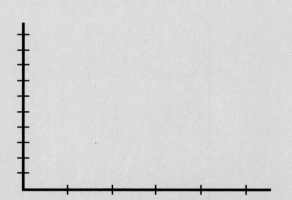

Questions:
1. Were there equal numbers of right and left shoes? Why?
2. Would the graphs be different if your class had done this activity yesterday? Why?
3. Why was the "Other" group the size it was?

Conclusion: Write 3–5 sentences about what you learned from this activity.

1–5 THE MICROSCOPE

OBJECTIVES

- Explain the use of microscopes.
- Identify the basic parts of the microscope.

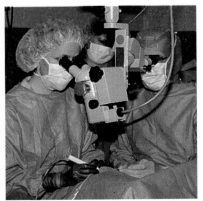

Fig. 1–11 Doctors use microscopes to do delicate surgery.

When we collect data on items that are easily seen, we observe and measure with rulers, graduated cylinders, and watches. But some items are too small to see with our eyes. In those cases we need a magnifying glass or microscope. **Microscopes** are instruments that enlarge the appearance of very small objects. They help us collect data that would otherwise go unseen.

Microscopes are used by engineers to study metals, by doctors to do surgery, and by food inspectors to check the purity of food (fig. 1–11). In the field of electronics, microscopes are needed to observe tiny parts used in computers and watches. Police use microscopes in studying things such as fingerprints, hair, blood, and fabric. Lab technicians study blood under a microscope. Microscopes can even be used to read Bibles printed on a single dot.

TRY THIS 1–5: MicroWorlds

Materials:

feather	newsprint
human hair	pond water
microscope	

Procedure:

1. Tear a small piece of newsprint from a page of the newspaper. Place it on the stage and look at it with the lowest-power objective lens. Draw what you see.
2. Continue to use the low-power lens and observe the hair and feather. Draw what you see.
3. Place a drop of pond water on a slide. Cover it with a cover slip. Observe the water for several minutes. Draw or write about what you see.
   - What did you observe about the newsprint under the microscope?
   - What was interesting about the feather or hair when observed under the microscope?
   - Did you see anything alive in the pond water?
   - Do you think drinking pond water would be a good idea? Why?

The diagram (fig. 1–12) shows a typical classroom microscope with the various parts labeled. If your school has a microscope, ask your teacher to show you how to use it.

A microscope is a very delicate instrument; handle it properly. When you carry it, place one hand under the base, and use your other hand to hold the arm. When it is time to put the microscope away, remember to cover it with a dust cover.

Microscope Identification

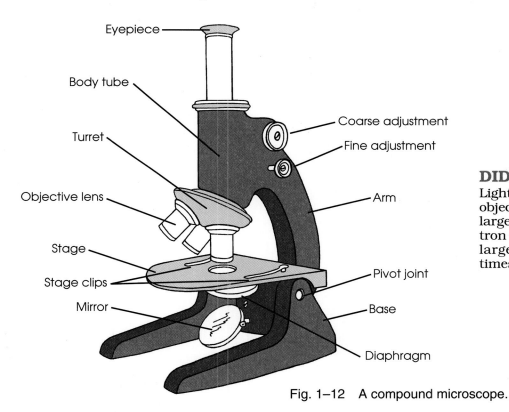

Eyepiece
Body tube
Turret
Objective lens
Stage
Stage clips
Mirror
Coarse adjustment
Fine adjustment
Arm
Pivot joint
Base
Diaphragm

Fig. 1–12   A compound microscope.

DID YOU KNOW?
Light microscopes can make objects look 400–1000 times larger than they are. Electron microscopes can enlarge things one million times.

REVIEW IT

1. How do microscopes help scientists?
2. What are the main parts of the microscope?
3. Through which parts does the image travel to get to your eye?

CHAPTER 1 WRAP-UP

SKILLS DEVELOPMENT

THINKING SKILLS: CLASSIFYING

Earth science involves geology, meteorology, oceanography, hydrology, and astronomy. Below is a list of words related to the study of Earth science that can be classified into these five areas of Earth science. Use the symbols to indicate how you would classify each word.

A = astronomy
G = geology
H = hydrology

M = meteorology
O = oceanography

1. O Arctic Ocean
2. H artesian spring
3. M barometer
4. M blizzard
5. M cold front
6. A constellation
7. G continent
8. O deep ocean floor
9. G earthquake
10. G fossil
11. H geyser
12. H glacier
13. H ground water
14. M high-pressure center
15. H lake
16. G lava
17. A lunar eclipse
18. G mid-ocean ridge
19. G mine
20. G mineral
21. A moon
22. O ocean basin

23. O ocean currents
24. O ocean waves
25. G petroleum
26. M prevailing winds
27. M rain gauge
28. M relative humidity
29. G rock
30. O sea water
31. A solar eclipse
32. A solar system
33. A stars
34. H stream runoff
35. A sun
36. O surf zone
37. A telescope
38. M thunderstorm
39. H tributaries
40. G volcano
41. H water cycle
42. H watershed
43. H water table
44. M weather map

QUESTIONS AND PROBLEMS

1. Scientists have developed many things that have improved life and made it easier. List at least five examples of such things in your classroom.
2. What is the first step of science?
3. What characteristics of a football would best describe it to someone else? Explain.
4. Why is it an advantage to use the metric system of measurement?
5. Most observable characteristics can be measured; some cannot. Name three characteristics that cannot be measured.
6. Compare the volume and mass of a carton of milk and a box of cereal.
7. How would you measure the volume of air in a balloon?
8. Explain how you should carry a microscope.
9. What is the difference between a telescope and a microscope?
10. What is the purpose of the mirror on a microscope?

RESEARCH

1. Find out the type of information gathered by the U.S. Census Bureau. Write a report on your findings.
2. Make a series of posters that could be used to teach younger students about various types of charts and graphs and how to read them.
3. Use an almanac or similar book to discover the number of gold, silver, and bronze medals that have been won in the winter or summer Olympics by the United States or Canada in the last 10 years. Chart and graph the data you research. Make an oral presentation to your class.
4. Design an attractive bulletin board that displays and explains microscopes.
5. Observe a sunset and write a detailed account of the changes that take place over a 30-minute period. Include sights, sounds, smells, etc. Prepare a written report of your observations, and include visual aids. (CAUTION: Do not look directly at the sun.)

REVIEW

HIGHLIGHTS

1. Science is the process of asking questions and looking for answers.
2. People study science to improve life.
3. Science has improved our lives by inventing products that help us live longer and more comfortably.
4. Observation involves carefully looking at something and identifying its distinguishing characteristics.
5. Observation is the first step of science.

6. Characteristics observed in scientific study: size, mass, volume, color, shape, texture, smell, taste, sound, speed, and temperature.
7. Measurement is used to determine how much of something there is.
8. Measurement makes observations more accurate and more easily understood.
9. Measurement of lines enables us to determine length, width, height, and distances. Measurement of volume allows us to measure how much space is occupied by an object. Measurement of mass enables us to determine how much matter is contained in an object.
10. Data is facts and numbers collected by observation and experimentation.
11. Data is what we study to discover the answers to questions.
12. Data can be displayed in charts and graphs, which make it easier to read and understand.
13. Microscopes allow us to observe things that we cannot see with the unaided eye.
14. The parts of the microscope are identified in the diagram on page 19.

VOCABULARY LIST

characteristic	mass	science
chart	measure	technology
data	microscope	volume
graph	observation	weight

PRACTICE
Multiple Choice. Choose the best answer.
1. Which is not a characteristic useful in observation?
   a. size
   b. beauty
   c. color
   d. sound
2. Which unit is used to measure volume?
   a. second
   b. inch
   c. gram
   d. liter
3. Which of these processes are important to science?
   a. asking questions
   d. recording data
   c. observing
   d. all of these
4. What is the first step of science?
   a. observing
   b. measuring
   c. talking
   d. recording data
5. What part of the microscope should be held when carrying it?
   a. the eyepiece
   b. the arm
   c. the body tube
   d. the stage

6. Why are microscopes useful?
   a. identify medicines
   b. amplify sound
   c. make things easier to see
   d. bring distant things up closer
7. What is the volume of a block that is 4 cm wide, 6 cm long, and 1 cm high?
   a. 11 cu cm
   b. 24 cu cm
   c. 26 cu cm
   d. 30 cu cm
8. Which is longer than a meter?
   a. 245 g
   b. 103 cm
   c. 2.5 L
   d. 996.45 mm
9. Which displays data in picture form?
   a. graph
   b. table
   c. chart
   d. all of these
10. Which is a reason for studying science?
   a. to develop new inventions
   b. to make life easier
   c. to produce new medicines
   d. all of these

Matching. Match each word with its definition or description.
1. organizes data into rows and columns
2. looking for characteristics
3. to determine how much of something
4. asking questions and looking for answers
5. helps us see tiny things
6. the amount of matter an object contains
7. organizes data in a picture form
8. a feature of something
9. the amount of space an object occupies
10. facts and numbers that are collected

a. characteristic
b. chart
c. data
d. graph
e. mass
f. measure
g. microscope
h. observation
i. science
j. volume

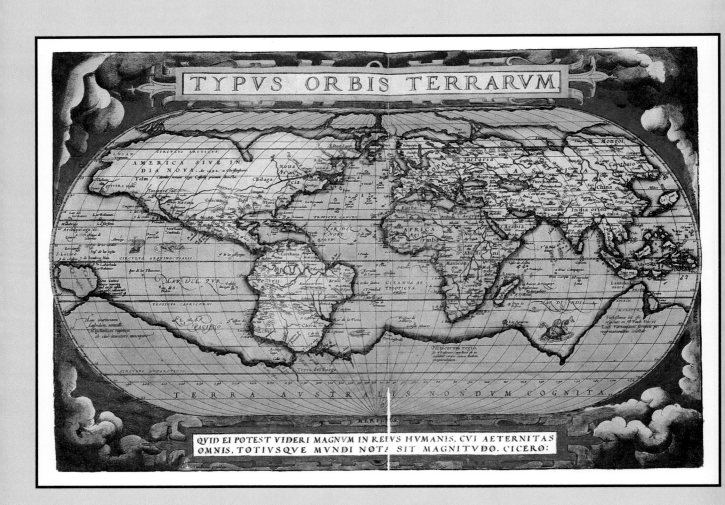

CHAPTER 2

PHYSICAL GEOLOGY

INTRODUCTION

This map doesn't look much like the map of North America you are used to seeing, does it? It was drawn in the sixteenth century and is not very accurate. When it was drawn, much of Earth's surface was still unexplored. As explorers sailed around this continent, they made exciting discoveries about its shape and where rivers were located. These discoveries helped geographers better understand what Earth was like and enabled them to draw more accurate maps.

Maps, however, show only Earth's surface features. What would we find if we drilled a hole through Earth? In this chapter you will explore Earth's surface features and what it is like on the inside.

SECTION TITLES

2–1   Earth's Features
2–2   Earth's Movements
2–3   Earth's Layers
2–4   Earth's Forces
2–5   Earth's Topography

A world map drawn in the sixteenth century.

2–1 EARTH'S FEATURES

OBJECTIVES

- Identify Earth's characteristics.
- Identify important features of Earth's surface.

Earth is the fifth largest of the nine planets in our solar system (fig. 2–1). Even though it is the third closest planet to the sun, Earth is still nearly 150 million km (93 million mi) from the sun. The Creator placed Earth just the right distance from the sun to support life. If it were any closer, living things could not survive because of the hot, dry conditions. If Earth were farther from the sun, plants and animals would freeze in the frigid environment.

DID YOU KNOW?
Earth weighs about 6,500, 000,000,000,000,000,000 tons!

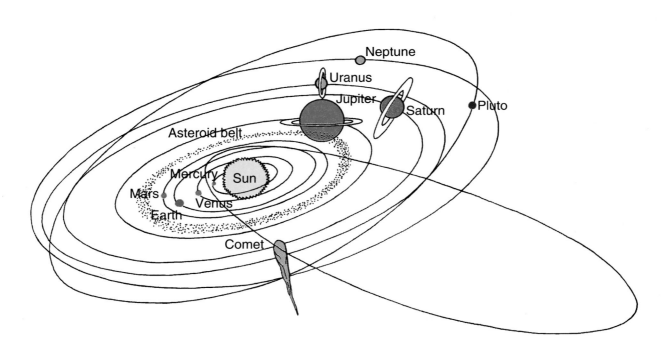

Fig. 2-1   Our solar system is made up of one sun, nine planets, and dozens of moons.

While Earth may look like a perfect **sphere** (sfir), or ball, it is not. It is flattened at the North and South poles and bulges slightly at the equator (fig. 2–2). Geologists, Earth scientists, believe this flattening is caused by the spin of Earth on its axis.

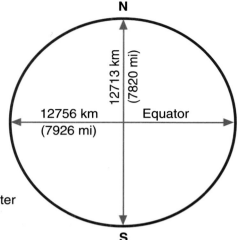

Fig. 2-2   Earth has a greater diameter at the equator because of its spin.

TRY THIS 2–1: A Bulging Middle

Materials:

construction paper   pencil
hole punch   scissors
metric ruler   transparent tape

Procedure:
1. Cut two strips of construction paper 3 cm x 40 cm (1 1/4 in x 16 in).
2. Cross the strips of paper at the center so that they are arranged at right angles. Tape the strips at the center as shown.
3. Bring the four ends of the strips together so that they overlap and form a sphere. Tape the ends of the strips together.
4. Punch a hole through the center of the overlapping ends.
5. Push a standard pencil about 5 cm (2 in) through the hole.
6. Hold the pencil between your palms and move your hands back and forth to make the sphere spin as shown.
    • What happens to the sphere's center when it spins? Why?
    • What would happen if the sphere were to spin faster?
    • How is Earth like this sphere?

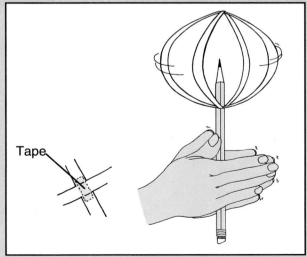

Earth's diameter, or the distance through Earth, is about 12 000 km (8000 mi). The average distance around Earth, or its circumference, is about 40 000 km (25,000 mi).

Fig. 2–3 summarizes other important features about Earth's surface.

Fig. 2–3

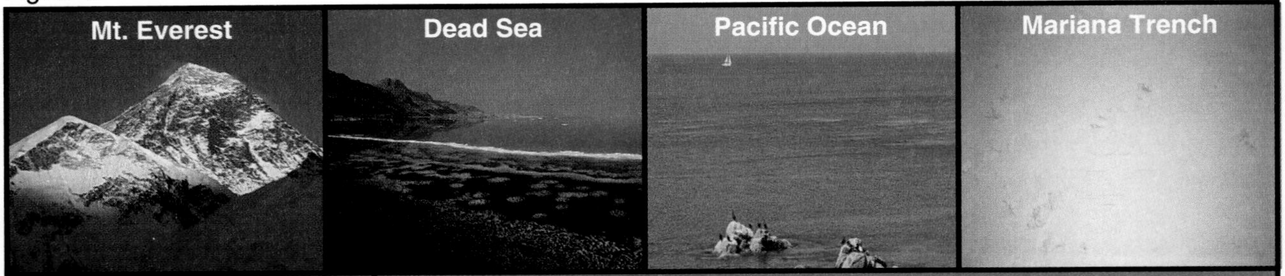

| Mt. Everest | Dead Sea | Pacific Ocean | Mariana Trench |

FEATURE	LOCATION
Highest point	Mt. Everest, located on the border of India and Tibet, rises about 8 800 meters (29,000 ft) above sea level.
Lowest point	Earth's lowest point on dry land is the shore of the Dead Sea, located between Israel and Jordan. This lake's shoreline is about 400 m (1300 ft) below sea level.
Largest ocean	Oceans cover 70 percent of Earth's surface. Of this area, one-third is covered by the Pacific Ocean.
Deepest point	The Mariana Trench, a submarine canyon, is more than 11 km (7 mi) deep. This deep gorge is located off the coast of the Philippines in the Pacific Ocean.

REVIEW IT

1. Earth lies between which two planets?
2. In what ocean is the Mariana Trench?
3. How do scientists know that Earth is not perfectly round?

2–2 EARTH'S MOVEMENTS

OBJECTIVES

- Identify Earth's movements.
- Distinguish between rotation and revolution.

VOCABULARY

axis
equator
orbit
revolution
rotation

Can you really sit still on Earth? While it may appear that you are stationary, you are taken along with Earth in its four different movements.

MOVEMENT 1. Movement 1 is Earth's **rotation**, or spin, on its axis. Earth rotates from west to east around an imaginary line, the **axis**, that passes through the center of Earth (fig. 2–4). At the top of the axis is the North Pole. At the bottom lies the South Pole. The **equator**, another imaginary line, circles the earth halfway between the two poles. At the equator Earth spins at a rate of about 1 600 km/hr (1000 mi/hr). The closer you live to the equator, the faster you move. The closer you are to either pole, the slower you move (fig. 2–5). It takes about 24 hours for Earth to make one complete rotation. Earth's spin gives us our day-and-night cycle and affects our weather, the wind, and the tides.

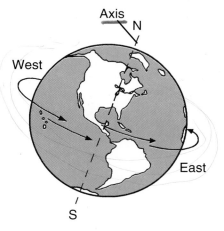

Fig. 2-4 Earth rotates around its axis from west to east.

Rotational Speed

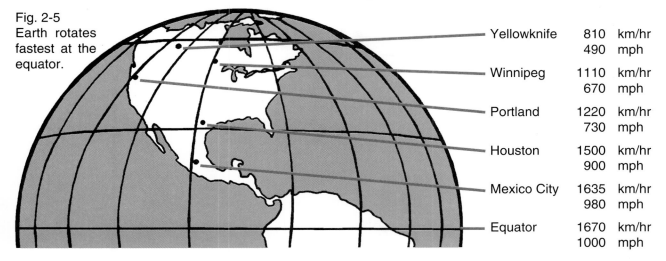

Fig. 2-5 Earth rotates fastest at the equator.

	km/hr	mph
Yellowknife	810	490
Winnipeg	1110	670
Portland	1220	730
Houston	1500	900
Mexico City	1635	980
Equator	1670	1000

RESEARCH IT
Find out the rotational and orbital speeds of the other eight planets in our solar system.

MOVEMENT 2. Movement 2 is Earth's **revolution** around the sun. Earth revolves in its **orbit** around the sun about 100 000 km/hr (67,000 mi/hr). Because Earth is tilted on its axis, the northern and southern hemispheres are tilted toward or away from the sun at different times of the year, resulting in the cycle of seasons (fig. 2–6).

Fig. 2-6   The tilt of Earth's axis and its movement around the sun cause our seasons.

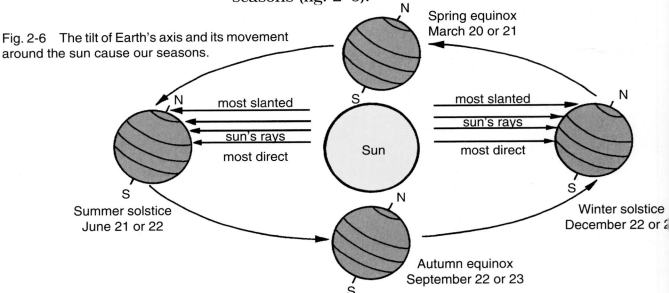

MOVEMENT 3. Our solar system travels around the center of the Milky Way Galaxy at an approximate rate of 900 000 km/hr (600,000 mi/hr).

MOVEMENT 4. The galaxy hurtles through the universe about 1 600 000 km/hr (1,000,000 mi/hr).

As you can see, even though you feel you are sitting still, you aren't! You will learn what keeps you from falling off Earth at these speeds when you study Earth's forces in Section 2–4.

REVIEW IT

1. How is Earth moving in space?
2. Which of Earth's movements results in the seasons?

CLASS ACTIVITY 2–2: Seasons Model

Question: What causes Earth's seasons?

Materials:
- bond paper
- flashlight
- metric ruler
- protractor
- scissors
- straight pins
- styrofoam ball
- transparent tape
- wood skewer

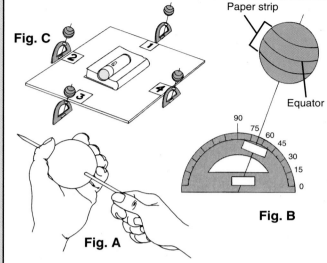

Fig. C

Paper strip

Equator

Fig. B

Fig. A

Procedure:
1. Run the wood skewer (axis) through the ball (fig. A).
2. Measure the diameter and circumference of the ball.
3. Cut a strip of paper the length of the ball's circumference and a width that is 1/3 the ball's diameter (diameter = circumference divided by 3). Attach the strip of paper to the ball (fig. B).
4. Tape the axis to the protractor (fig. B).
5. Tape four pieces of tape to your desk and label them (fig. C).
6. Set the flashlight on a book (fig. C).
7. Place your model in position 1. Be sure it is at right angles to the edge of the desk.
8. Determine and record which season is represented by position 1. Also record the correct description of the sun's angle in reference to the Northern Hemisphere.
9. Repeat steps 7 and 8 at positions 2, 3, and 4 (fig. C). Rotate the flashlight so that it points to each new position.

Data:

POSITION	SUN'S ANGLE			SEASON		
	Low	Moderate	High	Winter	Spring/Fall	Summer
1						
2						
3						
4						

Questions:
1. At what position does Earth's Northern Hemisphere have the longest night? The longest day?
2. Why is it cooler in the Northern Hemisphere when Earth is in position 1 than it is when Earth is in position 3?
3. Are there distinct seasons at the equator? Explain.
4. What would happen if Earth had no tilt?
5. What factors cause Earth's seasons?

Conclusion: Write 3–5 sentences about what you learned from this activity.

2–3 EARTH'S LAYERS

VOCABULARY
core
crust
magma
mantle
plate

OBJECTIVES

- Identify the layers of Earth.
- Compare and contrast the layers of Earth.

Geologists study earthquakes to learn about Earth's interior. Because earthquake waves travel at differing speeds through different materials, they can give scientists a glimpse of what the inside layers of Earth are made of.

DID YOU KNOW?
Scientists believe that the core of Earth has a temperature of 5000° C (9000° F).

Geologists have discovered that Earth is somewhat like a baseball (fig. 2–7). Just as a baseball is made of a cover, a wrapping, and a central core, Earth has a crust, mantle, and core. These layers did not happen by accident but were designed by the Creator to be part of Earth.

Parts of Earth

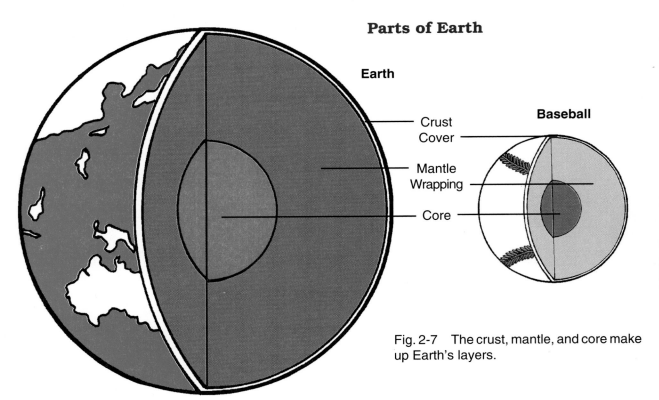

Earth

Crust
Cover

Mantle
Wrapping

Core

Baseball

Fig. 2-7   The crust, mantle, and core make up Earth's layers.

CRUST. The **crust** is the thin outer layer of Earth that corresponds to the cover of the baseball. The crust is made of dirt and rock and is mostly covered by oceans (fig. 2–8). The crust is 4–70 km (3–40 mi) thick and is the thinnest of Earth's layers. Because we live on the crust, we know more about it than we do about the other layers.

When you dig down through the crust, you find that the deeper you go, the warmer it gets. This heat is caused by the weight of the crust pressing down and by processes taking place deep within Earth. Miners feel this heat as they travel down deep mine shafts. This heat causes the oil from 650 m (2,000 ft) deep oil wells to be more than 34° C (100° F).

The crust is broken into large pieces called **plates** (fig. 2–9). The plates under the ocean are thinner than the plates that make up the continents.

Fig. 2-8 Earth looks bluish from space because of large oceans.

Earth's Plates

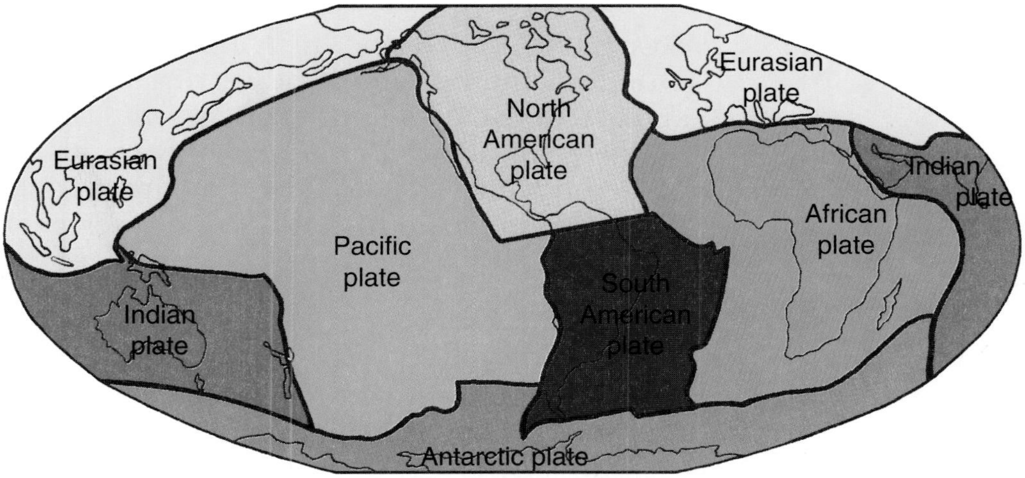

Fig. 2-9 Earth's crust is made up of seven major plates.

MANTLE. In the early 1900s a Yugoslavian scientist discovered that earthquake waves changed speed as they traveled through different kinds of rock layers. His discovery helped geologists learn about Earth's mantle.

The **mantle**, the thickest of the three layers, is about 2 900 km (1800 mi) thick and makes up about four-fifths of Earth's volume. It corresponds to the wrapping of the baseball. Because of intense heat created by the weight of the crust and radioactive processes, the mantle is made of melted rock called **magma**. The lava of volcanoes comes from this magma (fig. 2–10).

Fig. 2-10 Lava is magma pushed up to the surface from the mantle.

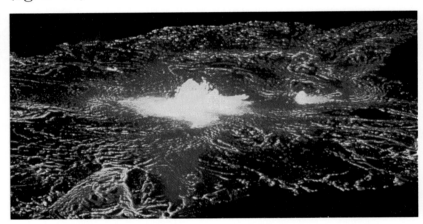

CORE. Earth's **core**, the innermost layer, makes up a little less than one-fifth of Earth's volume. It corresponds to the cork center of the baseball and has a diameter of about 7 000 km (4400 mi). The core is made up of two parts. The outer core is thought to be made of molten iron. Within the outer core lies the solid and very heavy inner core, the center of Earth.

REVIEW IT

1. If you could drill a well completely through Earth, list in order the layers you would pass through on your way to the other side.
2. How is the mantle different from the crust?

2–4 EARTH'S FORCES

OBJECTIVES

- Analyze the effect of Earth's gravity.
- Analyze the effect of Earth's magnetism.

VOCABULARY
gravity
magnetism
magnetosphere
mass

Gravity can be defined as the pull of matter on matter. You probably know that the force of gravity keeps you from flying off Earth's surface. But did you know that gravity also pulls your pencil toward your book, and that both pull on you (fig. 2–11)? Gravity acts between any two objects because every object has mass. But, as in the case of the pencil and the book, sometimes the pull is so slight you don't notice it.

The gravity of a planet or moon depends on the amount of matter it contains, or its **mass**. The greater the mass, the greater the gravity. The moon has one-sixth of Earth's mass; therefore, it has one-sixth of Earth's gravity. Because weight is a measure of the pull of gravity, you weigh more on Earth than you would on the moon. For example, if you weigh 45 kg (100 lbs) on Earth, on the moon you would weigh about 7.5 kg (17 lbs). On a large planet such as Jupiter, gravity is so strong that you would weigh over 116 kg (232 lbs)!

Another force of attraction that affects Earth is **magnetism**. Magnets such as the one in fig. 2–12 have a north and south pole. Like a bar magnet,

Fig. 2-11 All objects attract one another.

Fig. 2-12 All magnets have a north and south pole.

DID YOU KNOW?
If you move with the spin of Earth, gravity has less effect on you. At the equator, a 20,000 ton ocean liner moving east at 20 knots weighs about 3 tons less than if it were sailing to the west.

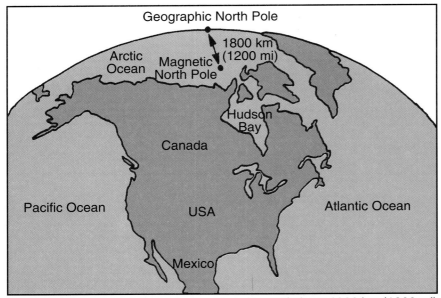

Fig. 2-13 Earth's magnetic north pole is located about 1800 km (1200 mi) from its geographic North Pole.

Fig. 2-14 Iron filings show the magnetic field of a magnet.

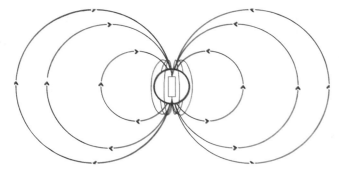

Fig. 2-15 Earth has its own magnetic field.

Earth also has a magnetic north and south pole. These magnetic poles are not in the same location as the geographic North and South poles. The magnetic north pole is located near Hudson Bay, Canada; whereas the geographic North Pole is 1800 km (1200 mi) away (fig. 2–13).

In fig. 2–14 you can see the pattern metal filings make around a bar magnet, showing its magnetic field. Like the magnet, Earth has a magnetic field, called the **magnetosphere** (mag nət´ ō sfir), surrounding it (fig. 2–15). This magnetic field deflects some of the sun's dangerous radiation. For centuries people have used Earth's magnetism to navigate by the aid of a compass. God has also given many animals the ability to use Earth's magnetic field for navigation in their yearly migrations.

REVIEW IT

1. What is weight?
2. What is one benefit of the magnetosphere?

38

2–5 EARTH'S TOPOGRAPHY

OBJECTIVES

- Describe the topographical features of Earth.
- Explain how points on Earth's surface are located.

What makes each landscape in the picture different? The plants, climate, and soil are all important factors. But perhaps most important is the shape of the land, or the **topography** (tə päg´ re fē). Four main features create the land's shape: mountains, hills, **plateaus** (pla tōs´), and plains (fig. 2–16).

Fig. 2-16   Mountains (left) are higher and more rugged than hills (right).

MOUNTAINS are greatly elevated sections of Earth's crust. To be classed as mountainous, land must be over 600 m (2000 ft) high. Mountains often occur in series called **chains**. The Rocky Mountains of North America make up one such chain. The Mid-Atlantic Ridge is another chain of mountains. This mountain chain runs along the bottom of the Atlantic Ocean.

HILLS are similar to mountains but lower in elevation. Hills are usually less steep and less jagged than mountains.

VOCABULARY
chain
International Date Line
latitude
longitude
meridian
parallel
plateau
Prime Meridian
topography

RESEARCH IT
Research to discover how Mount Olympus on Mars compares to Mt. Everest on Earth.

Fig. 2-16 Plateaus (left) are high, flat areas; plains (above) are low, flat areas.

Fig. 2-17 An address identifies where you live.

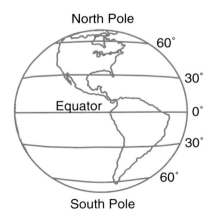

Fig. 2-18 Latitude lines identify how far north or south of the equator something is located.

PLATEAUS are flat elevated lands. They may cover thousands of square kilometers, such as the Colorado Plateau. When rivers cut through plateaus, they form broad valleys and steep-sided canyons.

PLAINS are level low-lying lands. Plains lie between mountain ranges and along the coasts of continents. They usually have rich soil, excellent for farming.

Your home has an address (fig. 2–17). Just as your address helps other people find where you live, so two sets of imaginary lines, called latitude and longitude, help locate specific places on Earth. These lines form a grid that allows any point on Earth to be given a numbered location.

LATITUDE. Lines that run parallel to the equator, or **parallels**, help to determine latitude. The **latitude** of a place tells its distance north or south of the equator and is measured in degrees.

The equator is given a value of 0 degrees because it is the starting point for measuring latitude (fig. 2-18). The poles are given a value of 90 degrees.

Points lying north of the equator have north latitudes; those south of the equator have south latitudes. In fig. 2–19 you will see that Philadelphia, Pennsylvania, lies at 40 degrees north latitude. What is the latitude of Winnipeg, Manitoba? Houston, Texas?

LONGITUDE. The lines that run from pole to pole are called **lines of longitude**, or **meridians**. They are used to locate points from east to west. If you were at one of the poles, you could put your foot on all the meridians (fig. 2–20). Like latitude, longitude is measured in degrees.

There is no geographical starting point for longitude, so it was decided that an imaginary line running through Greenwich, England, would be used. This line is called the **Prime Meridian** and has a value of 0 degrees. Meridians running east and west of the Prime Meridian meet at the 180-degree meridian, called the **International Date Line**. It lies in the Pacific Ocean and determines what day it is. If you are traveling west and cross the date line, you move forward one day. You move back one day when you travel east across this imaginary line.

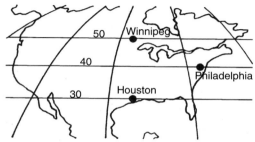

Fig. 2-19 Winnipeg is farther north than Philadelphia or Houston.

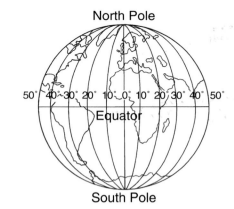

Fig. 2-20 Longitude lines identify how far east or west of the Prime Meridian something is located.

TRY THIS 2–5: The Great Mineral Search

Materials:
  Try This 2–5 Special Master R35

Procedure:
  1. Use the latitude and longitude provided for each mineral deposit to find where each is located. Mark each location by writing the number on the map in the correct location.
  2. Write the name of the state or province where each deposit is located.
     • Which state or province has the most mineral deposits?
     • What topographical feature is often associated with mineral deposits?

REVIEW IT

1. How is a plateau different from a plain?
2. How are hills and mountains different?
3. How are latitude and longitude used to locate places on Earth?

CHAPTER 2 WRAP-UP
SKILLS DEVELOPMENT

THINKING SKILLS: USING TOPOGRAPHIC MAPS

Earth scientists must be able to use maps. One kind of map they use is the topographic map. A topographic map shows the shapes and features of Earth's surface. The topographic map below shows a view of a mountain from the top. The lines on the map are called contour lines. These lines show the height of the land. On this map the distance between each line represents 200 m. You can tell the steepness of the land by how close together the contour lines are. The closer together the lines are, the steeper the land.

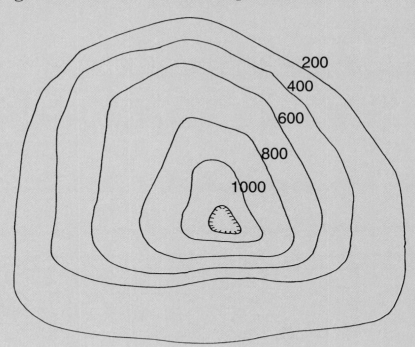

1. What do the contour lines on the topographic map show?
2. How far apart are the contour lines?
3. What is the elevation at the top of the mountain?
4. Why are the contour lines closer on one side of the mountain than the other?

QUESTIONS AND PROBLEMS

1. Why is Earth not perfectly round?
2. What would life on Earth be like if Earth were closer to the sun? farther from the sun?
3. Where would you rotate faster, in Quito, Ecuador, or in Toronto, Canada? Explain.
4. What would happen to our seasons if Earth were not tilted on its axis?
5. True or False. Earth's crust varies in thickness. Explain.
6. How did scientists discover Earth's mantle?
7. Everything that has mass has gravity. Which has more gravity, a ping-pong ball or a golf ball? Why.
8. Which poles are directly on top of and at the bottom of Earth, the magnetic poles or geographical poles?
9. What is the difference between a plateau and a plain?
10. What is the latitude and longitude of the city or town where you live?
11. Why is the International Date Line drawn in the ocean?

RESEARCH

1. Write a biographical report on the scientist who first discovered Earth's mantle.
2. Use a grid similar to latitude and longitude to identify the location of students in each classroom in your school. Make a bulletin board or poster that displays your work.
3. Investigate the International Date Line and Prime Meridian to discover why and how they were created. Present an oral report of your findings.
4. Construct a cross-section color diagram that shows Earth's layers. Provide labels and a brief description of each layer.
5. Draw a cross-section map of the United States that shows major topographical features. Provide labels for your map.

REVIEW

HIGHLIGHTS

1. Earth's features include its shape, circumference, diameter, rotation, and distance from the sun.
2. Earth is slightly oval because of the bulge at the equator.
3. Earth has four different movements: spinning on its axis, revolving around the sun, moving through space with the solar system, and moving through space with the galaxy.

4. Rotation is the spinning of Earth on its axis. Revolution is the complete path of Earth around the sun.
5. The three layers of Earth are the crust, the mantle, and the core.
6. The crust is the thin outer layer of Earth, the mantle is the layer that lies just beneath the crust, and the core is the innermost layer of Earth.
7. Gravity is the force or pull of Earth on matter. Magnetism is a force of the magnetic field surrounding Earth. This magnetic field also protects us from dangerous radiation.
8. Topography is the shape of the surface of Earth, which includes mountains, hills, plateaus, and plains.
9. Points on Earth's surface can be located by latitude, lines that run parallel to the equator, and longitude, lines that run from the North Pole to the South Pole. These lines are measured in degrees.

VOCABULARY LIST

axis	longitude	parallel
chain	magma	plate
core	magnetism	plateau
crust	magnetosphere	Prime Meridian
equator	mantle	revolution
gravity	mass	rotation
International Date Line	meridian	topography
latitude	orbit	

PRACTICE
Multiple Choice. Choose the best answer.
1. How many kilometers is Earth from the sun?
   a. 29 billion
   b. 150 million
   c. 1.5 million
   d. 250 thousand
2. Which best describes the shape of Earth?
   a. a ball that is pushed in on the sides
   b. a ball that is perfectly round
   c. a ball that bulges in the middle
   d. a football
3. In which direction does Earth rotate?
   a. north to south
   b. south to north
   c. east to west
   d. west to east

4. Which movement results in our day and night?
   a. Earth's movement through the solar system
   b. Earth's revolution
   c. Earth's rotation
   d. none of these
5. How long does it take for Earth to make one complete revolution?
   a. 1 day   c. 1 month
   b. 1 week   d. 1 year
6. Which layer is made up of dirt and rock?
   a. the crust   c. the outer core
   b. the mantle   d. the inner core
7. The material that comes out of volcanoes originates in what layer?
   a. the crust   c. the outer core
   b. the mantle   d. the inner core
8. Which has the greatest effect on an object's gravity?
   a. its weight   c. its speed
   b. its mass   d. its position
9. Why is the magnetosphere important?
   a. it creates Earth's climate
   b. it creates Earth's magnetism
   c. it protects Earth from sunlight
   d. it protects Earth from radiation
10. Where is longitude measured from?
    a. the Prime Meridian   c. the equator
    b. the International Date Line d. Paris, France

Matching. Match each word with its definition or description.
1. The shape of the land   a. core
2. Used to determine latitude   b. equator
3. Starting place for measuring longitude   c. plates
4. The pull of matter on matter   d. parallels
5. Elevated land above 600 m (2000 ft)   e. gravity
6. Inner layer of Earth   f. Prime Meridian
7. Large sections of Earth's crust   g. topography
8. Imaginary line through Earth   h. axis
9. Path Earth follows around the sun   i. orbit
10. Starting place for measuring latitude   j. mountains

CHAPTER 3

THE MOVING CRUST

INTRODUCTION

In Iceland there is a canyon that formed as its sides were pushed apart. Some people believe that it took millions of years for this to happen. Many creationists believe that the canyon formed much more rapidly—since the Flood—and not over millions of years. It is important to understand that both evolutionists and creationists study the same facts and use the same processes to examine geological events. The difference is in the conclusions they draw.

In this chapter you will study the theories of continental drift, sea-floor spread, and plate tectonics.

SECTION TITLES

A spreading canyon in Iceland.

3–1 CONTINENTAL DRIFT

VOCABULARY
continental drift theory
Pangea

OBJECTIVES

- Describe Pangea.
- Describe the continental drift theory.
- Analyze evidence that supports the theory of continental drift.

For thousands of years, people believed that the surface of Earth had always been the same. But as people explored Earth more thoroughly, they discovered new facts that showed Earth had changed.

As maps were drawn more accurately, some people began to think that the continents had changed position. From the new maps, it looked as if the edges of some continents fit together like a jigsaw puzzle. About 1800, Alexander Von Humboldt found mountains in South America matching mountains in Africa. Humboldt believed that the continents had become separated by erosion. Later, people began to believe that the continents had somehow moved apart.

In 1912, Alfred Wegener, a German scientist, suggested that long ago the continents were joined in one large landmass. He called this landmass **Pangea** (pan jē´ ə) (fig. 3–1). According to Wegener, Pangea split

Pangea

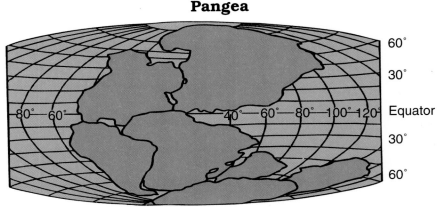

Fig. 3-1 Wegener's Pangea.

DID YOU KNOW?
Pangea is made up of the Greek words that mean "all earth." The water that surrounded Pangea was called Panthalassa, which means "all sea."

48

into what we call continents. Once split, the sections drifted to where they are today. Wegener based his **continental drift theory** on several ideas:

1. The coastlines and mountains of Africa and South America looked as if they fit together like a jigsaw puzzle.
2. Fossils found on the African continent matched those found in South America.
3. Tropical plants were found frozen in the ice of Antarctica.

Wegener's ideas were interesting, but he could not explain how or why the sections had split and drifted apart. The answers to these questions came in the late 1960s, when geologists began to explore the ocean floor.

DID YOU KNOW?
North of the equator 40 percent of the total area is covered by continents. South of the equator, only 20 percent of the area is covered by continents.

TRY THIS 3–1: It Fits

Materials:

construction paper	Special Master R59
scissors	transparent tape

Procedure:
1. Cut out the continents on the Special Master.
2. Try different ways to fit the continents together so that one large continent (Pangea) is formed. Make sure the edges of the continents fit closely together.
3. When you have decided how the continents should fit, glue or tape them to the construction paper.
4. Write the name of each continent on the appropriate puzzle piece.
   - The rock and fossils on the coastline of B should match those on the coastline of what other part of Pangea?
   - The rock and fossils on the coastline of G should match those on the coastline of what other part of Pangea?
   - In what direction did each of the following parts of Pangea move to get to their present position?

   Continent G _____   Continent C _____
   Continent D _____   Continent B _____

REVIEW IT

1. What was Pangea?
2. What does the continental drift theory state?
3. Why is it believed that South America and Africa were once joined together?

3–2 SEA-FLOOR SPREAD

VOCABULARY
midocean ridge
pillow lava
rift valley
sea-floor spread
sonar
trench

OBJECTIVES

- Describe sea-floor spreading.
- Explain the importance of sea-floor spread to continental drift.

Sonar came into use during World War II as a device to locate submarines. **Sonar** transmits sound waves that bounce off objects. By recording the time it takes for sound waves to travel out and bounce back, scientists can determine how far away an object is (fig. 3–2). After the war, scientists used sonar to measure the depth of the ocean, allowing geologists to draw more accurate maps of the ocean floor.

As geologists charted the ocean floor, they discovered new features (fig. 3–3). Long, narrow canyons called **trenches** were found in the deepest parts of the ocean. Geologists also discovered details about an underwater mountain range called the **midocean ridge** that circles Earth much like the seam of a baseball. Running down the center of this ridge is a narrow valley called a **rift valley**. Scientists discovered that this area was warmer than the surrounding areas. They also found **pillow**

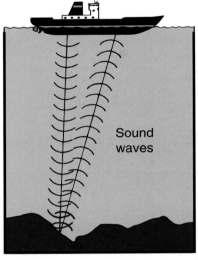

Fig. 3-2 Scientists use sound waves to map the ocean floor.

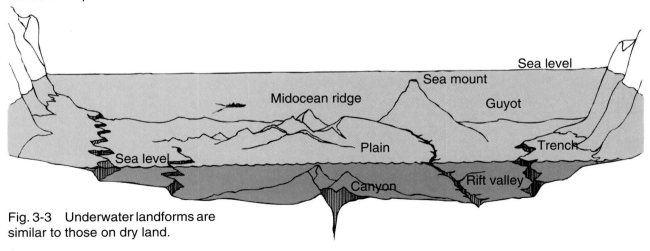

Fig. 3-3 Underwater landforms are similar to those on dry land.

lava in the rift valley, which forms when molten rock cools underwater (fig. 3–4).

These discoveries led to the theory of **sea-floor spread**. According to this theory, magma from the mantle pushes up and out at the rift valley. This upward movement of the magma causes the sea floor on either side to spread out (fig. 3–5). As the magma pushes out, it pushes the sea floor apart on either side and forms new ocean floor. This continuing process causes the continents to move farther apart.

Fig. 3-4   Pillow lava forms only underwater.

Midocean Ridge

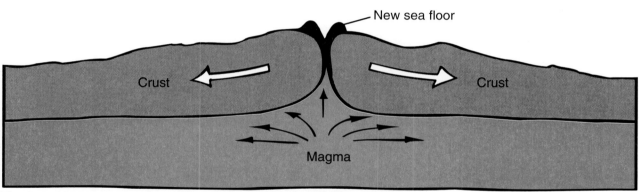

New sea floor

Crust

Crust

Magma

Fig. 3-5   Upward movement of magma causes the sea floor to spread.

The theory of sea-floor spread is supported by the study of ocean sediments. Geologists have found less sediment on the newly formed ocean floor near the center of the rift valley than they have on the older areas of ocean floor.

RESEARCH IT
Find out why Earth isn't getting larger even though the continents are spreading apart at the midocean ridges.

REVIEW IT

1. What is sea-floor spread, and how is it caused?
2. Why is sea-floor spread important to the idea of moving continents?

3–3 PLATE TECTONICS

VOCABULARY
colliding boundary
convection current
plate
plate tectonic theory
plume
sliding boundary
spreading boundary

OBJECTIVES

- Describe the theory of plate tectonics.
- Explain how convection currents and plumes cause plates to move.
- Distinguish between the types of plate boundaries.

The theory of sea-floor spread explained how the continents could have moved, but not why. Additional information came from studying volcanoes and earthquakes. Geologists found patterns when they began to mark maps where volcanoes were located and where earthquakes had occurred. One of these patterns was named the "Ring of Fire." The Ring of Fire is formed by hundreds of volcanoes that circle the Pacific Ocean (fig. 3–6). This ring is an area of intense volcanic and earthquake activity. Patterns such as this show that Earth's surface is divided into sections, or **plates**.

Ring of Fire

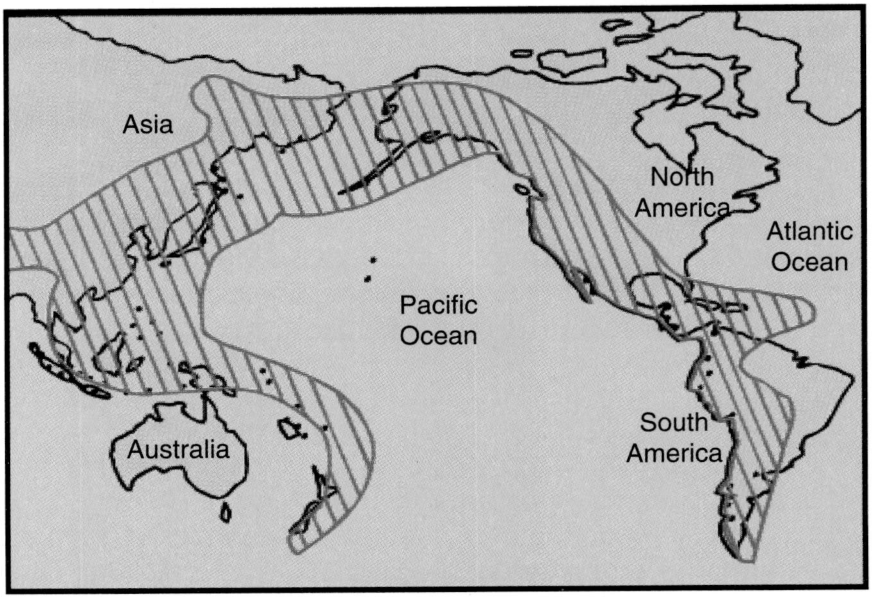

Fig. 3-6   The Ring of Fire circles the Pacific Ocean.

This discovery helped scientists explain why the continents moved. This explanation, called the **plate tectonic** (tek tän´ ik) **theory**, states that Earth's crust is broken into seven major plates, each a different size and thickness (fig. 3–7). Geologists believe that the plates float on Earth's liquid mantle. These plates are often named for the continents they support. For example, Canada and the United States lie on the North American plate.

DID YOU KNOW?
Earth is not solid. Just as the tides in the ocean rise and fall each day, the continents rise and fall each day as much as six inches.

Earth's Plates

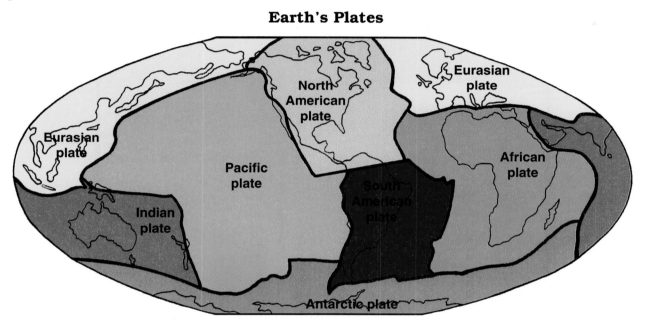

Fig. 3-7   Earth's plates vary in size and thickness.

At the midocean ridge, the plates move apart about 3–5 cm (1–2 in) per year. This movement is caused by two forces. The first, **convection** (kən vek´ shən) **currents**, is created by the motion of liquids and gases. As a liquid or gas is heated, it rises; as it cools, it sinks. Geologists believe convection currents occur inside Earth. These currents cause magma to rise at the midocean ridge and push the plates apart.

The second force thought to move plates is plumes. **Plumes** are columns of hot magma that rise from the mantle. As a plume rises, it spreads out below the plate, cools, "locks" onto the plate, and pulls the plate along with it as it continues to move (fig. 3–8). If a plume breaks through the crust, it forms a volcano. As the plate continues to move, the opening in the crust moves away from the plume, and the volcano stops erupting. Geologists believe that the Hawaiian Islands were formed in this way.

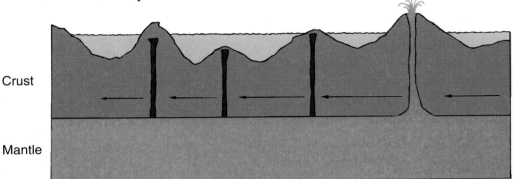

Crust

Mantle

Fig. 3-8   One plume may have created all the Hawaiian Islands.

Where the edges of the plates come together, they form three kinds of boundaries: spreading, sliding, and colliding, (fig. 3–9).

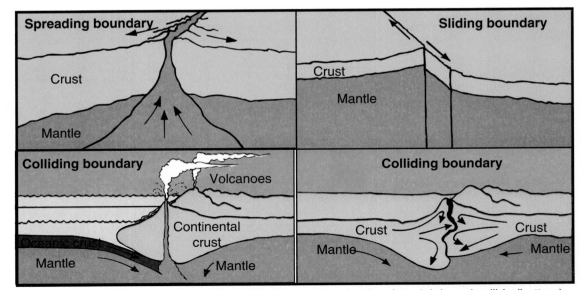

Fig. 3-9   Boundaries spread apart (top left), slide past each other (top right), and collide (bottom).

54

SPREADING BOUNDARIES. These boundaries are often identified by large, spreading valleys. The Great Rift Valley of northeastern Africa, like the valley in the midocean ridge, is formed as two plates are pushed apart by the upward movement of magma (fig. 3–10).

Fig. 3-10   The Rift Valley in Africa.

COLLIDING BOUNDARIES. Colliding boundaries occur when two plates are pushed together. When two continental plates collide, mountain ranges are often formed. The Himalayas in Asia are formed in this way (fig 3-11). When a continental plate collides with an oceanic plate, the heavier oceanic plate slips below the lighter continental plate and is absorbed back into the mantle. Ocean trenches and volcanoes occur in these areas. The Andes Mountains of South America and the Cascade Mountains of North America are volcanic mountains formed in this way.

Fig. 3-11   The Himalayas in Tibet.

SLIDING BOUNDARIES. These boundaries, such as the San Andreas fault in California, occur where plates slide past each other (fig. 3–12). Instead of sliding smoothly, the plates pull on each other, causing tension to build up. When the plates slip suddenly, this tension is released in an earthquake.

Fig. 3-12   The San Andreas fault in California.

REVIEW IT

1. According to the plate tectonic theory, what are Earth's plates floating on?
2. What are convection currents, and how do they affect Earth's plates?
3. Which type of boundary is associated with the midocean ridge? Mountain building?

CLASS ACTIVITY 3–3: Where Does It Go?

Question: How do Earth's plates fit together?

Materials:
scissors
Special Master R63
Special Master R65
transparent tape

Procedure:
1. Carefully cut out the pieces on R63.
2. Assemble the pieces together like a jigsaw puzzle. Be sure that the edges fit tightly together.
3. Once you have decided how you think the pieces fit together, glue or tape them to R65.
4. Use one of the names below to label each plate (puzzle piece).
   African Plate
   Antarctic Plate
   Pacific Plate
   Australian-Indian Plate
   Eurasian Plate
   North American Plate
   South American Plate
5. Color the boundary of each plate using the key below.
   Colliding boundaries = Red
   Separating boundaries = Green
   Sliding boundaries = Blue

Questions:
1. Name two plates that are moving apart. Name two plates that are moving together.
2. On which plate do you live?
3. The mid-Atlantic ridge marks what type of boundary?
4. What type of boundary is marked by ocean trenches?
5. How are these tectonic plates different from the pieces of Wegener's Pangea?

Conclusion: Write 3–5 sentences about what you learned from this activity.

3–4 BIBLICAL PERSPECTIVE

OBJECTIVE

- Explain how plate tectonics corresponds with the Bible record.

Creation scientists, like evolution scientists, believe that the theories of sea-floor spread and plate tectonics explain how and why Earth's crust has moved in the past and continues to move.

Because plates are now moving slowly, many evolutionists believe that the plates have always moved slowly. At today's speed, it would have taken 200 million years for South America and Africa to have moved so far apart.

Some creation scientists believe the continents have moved to where they are today in the time since Creation and that long periods of time do not agree with the Bible record.

Genesis 1 records that God created the dry land and seas on the third day. It is possible that He created the dry land in the form of Pangea. During the Flood, however, great changes happened on Earth. Many creationists believe that the violent events during the Flood and geological changes since the Flood explain how Earth's plates moved apart much more rapidly than they are observed moving today (fig. 3–13).

Fig. 3-13   Tremendous forces of the Flood caused dramatic changes in Earth's crust.

REVIEW IT

1. According to many creationists, when would the continents have split from Pangea?

CHAPTER 3 WRAP-UP
SKILLS DEVELOPMENT

THINKING SKILLS: SEQUENCING

Read each of the statements below carefully. Put a 1 before any statement that refers to the theory of continental drift. Put a 2 before any statement that refers to the theory of plate tectonics. Once you have marked each statement, write a brief paragraph on each theory, putting each set of statements in the proper order.

1. _____ Wegener's theory was supported by the finding of similar rocks and fossils in South America and Africa.
2. _____ These areas are far from the poles, so they must have been closer to one of the poles at some time in the past.
3. _____ When the plates move, the oceans or continents above the plates move also.
4. _____ Wegener proposed that the continents are still moving apart.
5. _____ The landmass broke apart, forming several small continents.
6. _____ Movements of the mantle may cause the plates to move.
7. _____ Some of the plates carry the oceans; others carry the continents.
8. _____ In 1912, Alfred Wegener proposed that all the continents were once part of one large landmass.
9. _____ The plates seem to be floating on the upper mantle, the layer just beneath Earth's crust.
10. _____ The crust of Earth is made up of seven large sections called plates.
11. _____ In addition, certain land areas showed evidence of having been covered by ice in the past.

Continental drift theory. _____

_____

_____

_____

_____

Plate tectonic theory. _____

_____

_____

_____

_____

QUESTIONS AND PROBLEMS

1. How do scientists know that Earth is not hollow?
2. What evidence suggests that Africa and South America were joined at one time?
3. What did Wegener's continental drift theory fail to do?
4. How did World War II help scientists learn about the oceans?
5. What evidence suggests that the ocean floor is spreading in some areas?
6. How do convection currents cause plates to move?
7. What type of plate boundary does the San Andreas fault of California mark?
8. What are plumes, and what do they do?
9. Describe the various types of plate boundaries, and identify the type of features associated with each.
10. How do most creation scientists explain the plate tectonic theory?

RESEARCH

1. Draw a large map of the world. Draw in the mountain ranges that correspond to areas where plates collide. Label and color the mountain ranges so they can be easily identified.
2. Survey 10 adults and 10 high-school students to discover whether they believe in moving plates and the reasons for their beliefs. Construct a graph that displays your findings, and present a report to the class.
3. Investigate how scientists measure the movement of Earth's plates. Present an oral report that includes visual aids on your research.
4. Construct a bulletin board that shows Earth's seven plates. Be sure to label each plate and use arrows to show the direction each moves.
5. Write a biographical report on meteorologist Alfred Wegener's life and accomplishments. Include information on how his interest in weather led him to hypothesize about continental drift.

REVIEW

HIGHLIGHTS

1. Some scientists believe that at one time all the continents were joined as a single landmass called Pangea.
2. The continental drift theory states that Pangea split apart into continents that drifted to their present locations.
3. The continental drift theory is supported by coastlines and topography of Africa and South America, fossils found on different continents, glacial deposits in rocks near the equator, and tropical plants found frozen in Antarctica.

4. Sea-floor spread occurs when magma from the mantle pushes up and out at the rift valleys under the ocean.
5. Continental drift theory describes the separating of the continents by the sea floor spreading apart.
6. Plate tectonics identifies seven major plates of Earth, each floating on liquid material. Some plates are gradually moving apart while others are moving together.
7. The plate movements are caused by convection currents of hot liquid material as it rises, separates, and sinks under the land crust.
8. Spreading boundaries are boundaries where the plates are spreading apart; colliding boundaries are boundaries where the plates are coming together. Sliding boundaries occur where the plates slide past each other.
9. Geological features that mark plate boundaries are rift valleys, ocean ridges and canyons, mountain ranges, and fault lines.
10. Some creationists believe that Earth may have been created in the form of Pangea and that the violent action of the Flood at the time of Noah separated the landmass.

VOCABULARY LIST

colliding boundary	pillow lava	sea-floor spread
continental drift theory	plate	sliding boundary
convection current	plate tectonic theory	sonar
midocean ridge	plume	spreading boundary
Pangea	rift valley	trench

PRACTICE
Multiple Choice. Choose the best answer.
1. Which is responsible for plate movement?
   a. volcanoes   c. convection currents
   b. earthquakes   d. all of these
2. Wegener developed what theory?
   a. plate tectonics   c. evolution
   b. sea-floor spread   d. continental drift
3. Which does not suggest that Earth's plates have moved?
   a. the Ring of Fire
   b. mountains on Africa and South America that are similar
   c. the depth of the Pacific Ocean
   d. coastlines that appear to fit together
4. Which theory explains how the continents have moved?
   a. plate tectonics   c. continental drift
   b. sea-floor spread   d. all of these

5. Which is/are created by the heating and cooling of liquids and gases?
   a. plumes
   b. convection currents
   c. pillow lava
   d. continental drift
6. What name do scientists give to Earth's original landmass?
   a. Rift
   b. Pangea
   c. Guyot
   d. Atlantis
7. Which feature is not associated with colliding boundaries?
   a. trenches
   b. rift valley
   c. mountains
   d. volcanoes
8. The San Andreas fault lies near what type of plate boundary?
   a. spreading boundary
   b. sliding boundary
   c. colliding boundary
   d. sinking boundary
9. When do many creationists believe that most plate movement took place?
   a. before Creation
   b. during Creation
   c. before the Flood
   d. during the Flood
10. Which feature would be associated with a spreading boundary?
    a. a rift valley
    b. volcanoes
    c. a trench
    d. all of these

Matching: Match each word with its definition or description.
1. located at the midocean ridge
2. mountains created by colliding plates
3. formed when lava cools underwater
4. underwater mountain range
5. uses reflected sound waves
6. sections of Earth's crust
7. columns of hot magma
8. location of the Great Rift Valley
9. forces plates apart
10. deepest part of the ocean

a. midocean ridge
b. Africa
c. plates
d. Himalayas
e. rift valley
f. trench
g. plumes
h. magma
i. sonar
j. pillow lava

CHAPTER 4

VOLCANOES AND EARTHQUAKES

INTRODUCTION

Most changes in Earth's crust happen slowly. Some, however, happen quickly. Surtsey (sərt´ sē), an island off the coast of Iceland, formed in just a few weeks during 1963 as a result of a violent volcanic eruption. But volcanoes are not the only events that cause rapid changes. Swift changes also happen during earthquakes. In 1906, movement occurred along the San Andreas fault that caused the land on either side of the fault to shift more than 5 m (16 ft). What causes volcanoes and earthquakes? Can they occur anywhere? You will explore these questions as you study this chapter.

SECTION TITLES

4–1 Volcanoes
4–2 Earthquakes
4–3 Earthquake Waves

Surtsey, a volcanic island off the coast of Iceland.

4–1 VOLCANOES

VOCABULARY
cinder cone
composite volcano
cone
crater
fissure
lava
pipe
shield volcano
vent
volcano

OBJECTIVES

- Explain how volcanoes form.
- Describe the features of volcanoes.

Volcanoes are formed when magma, the melted rock of Earth's mantle, pushes up through the crust onto the surface. Volcanoes form both on land and in the middle of oceans, usually near the boundaries of Earth's plates. The Ring of Fire is a region of heavy volcanic activity that surrounds the Pacific Ocean. Scientists discovered this area by marking the locations of active volcanoes.

Anatomy of a Volcano

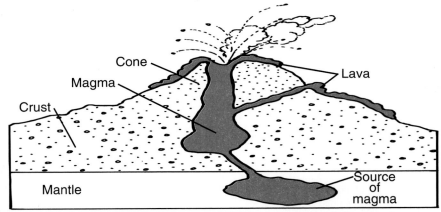

Fig. 4-1   Volcanoes form where magma breaks through the crust.

Figure 4–1 shows the parts of a volcano. The **vent** is an opening in Earth's crust. A volcano can have many different vents. From the vent, a tube or **pipe** serves as a pathway from the mantle to the crust and allows the magma to move up and out of the vent. **Lava** is magma that reaches the surface. Lava can be thin and almost watery, or thick like cookie dough, depending on the kind of minerals in the lava (fig. 4–2). As lava cools, it crystallizes to form rock (fig. 4–3). When lava cools quickly, it has a smooth texture such as obsidian (əb sid´ ē ən). Coarse

Fig. 4-2   Lava may be runny or thick, depending on the minerals that make it up.

64

rocks form when lava cools slowly. Sometimes gasses create "foamy" lava that cools into rocks called scoria (skôr´ ē ə) and pumice (pum´ is).

Volcanoes differ in the size of their eruptions and the type of material they eject—lava, steam, gas, rocks, and ash. Some volcanoes discharge only steam and ash. Others release lava and ash.

Fig. 4-3 When lava cools, it forms various types of rocks—obsidian, granite, and pumice.

Volcanoes also differ in the way they erupt. In some volcanoes the lava flows out of cracks called **fissures** (fish´ ərz). These eruptions do not build mountains but form broad, spreading layers of lava (fig. 4–4). Other volcanoes build mountains as they erupt (fig. 4–5). When lava flows out of the vent and cools, a bowl-shaped **crater** often forms around the vent. As new material flows over the top, a **cone** builds up.

Fig. 4-4 Broad, spreading layers of lava flow from fissures.

Fig. 4-5 Often lava builds up to form tall volcanoes.

DID YOU KNOW?
Active volcanoes are those that have been active in the past 150 years. While all volcanoes were active at some time, most volcanoes are inactive today.

Three kinds of volcanoes form mountains: shield volcanoes, cinder cones, and composite volcanoes.

Fig. 4-6   The shield volcano, Mauna Loa, Hawaii.

SHIELD VOLCANOES are the largest type of volcano. They are broad with gently sloping sides (fig. 4–6). They do not have violent eruptions; lava flows out slowly. The Mauna Loa volcano, perhaps the largest active volcano on Earth, is a shield volcano.

Fig. 4-7   The cinder cone, Paricutin, Mexico.

CINDER CONES are the smallest type of volcano, usually less than 300 m (1000 ft) high. They form when pieces of lava blow out of a volcano's vent (fig. 4–7). Unlike shield volcanoes, cinder cones have very steep sides. In 1943, Paricutin, a volcano in Mexico, erupted. In the first day, a cone 40 m (130 ft) high formed, and within five days it was over 100 m (300 ft) high. Two years later, the volcano was more than 400 m (1300 ft) high.

COMPOSITE VOLCANOES, such as Mount St. Helens, have alternating layers of lava and ash. Lava quietly flows out for a time. When the lava stops flowing, a plug forms in the vent. In this condition, the volcano may stay inactive for many years. When it again becomes active, there is no place for magma and steam to go. As pressure within the volcano builds, there is an explosion that blows out the plugged vent. Such eruptions release tremendous power. The eruption of Mount St. Helens blew away most of the mountain's north side (fig. 4–8).

Fig. 4-8   The composite volcano, Mount St. Helens, Washington, before the May 1980 eruption (top) and after the May 1980 eruption (bottom).

Volcanic eruptions have had a dramatic impact on Earth's surface and on the lives of people. One of the largest volcanic eruptions ever recorded was that of Mount Vesuvius (və sōō´ vē əs) in Italy, about 80 years after the death of Jesus (fig. 4–9). A huge black cloud of dust and rocks exploded out of this volcano. The hot cloud quickly smothered 16,000 residents of Pompeii, a city about 10 km (6 mi) away from the vent. As the rock, dust, and hot gases continued to rain down, another 4000 people lost their lives. Dust from the volcano eventually covered the city to a depth of 6 m (20 ft).

DID YOU KNOW?
So much pumice was released onto the ocean's surface from the eruption of Krakatoa in 1883 that sailors were able to walk 3 km (2 mi) from their ship to the shore on top of the pumice raft.

Fig. 4-9 The eruption of Mount Vesuvius in Italy destroyed the city of Pompeii.

RESEARCH IT
Why is Mount Krakatoa famous? Report on your findings.

TRY THIS 4–1: Locating Volcanoes

Materials:
Special Master R83

Procedure:
1. Use the latitudes and longitudes provided to locate each volcano listed in the chart. Mark the number of each volcano on the appropriate place on the map.
   - What ocean has volcanoes that stretch north and south along its midpoint?
   - Along what coast is there a chain of volcanoes?
   - What geologic feature is located near the volcanoes you marked on the map?
   - What other geological activity occurs in the same regions as these volcanoes?
   - According to your map, which state or province has the greatest number of volcanoes?

REVIEW IT

1. How are volcanoes formed?
2. Why do shield volcanoes form differently from cinder cones?

4-2 EARTHQUAKES

VOCABULARY

earthquake
epicenter
fault
focus
normal fault
strike-slip fault
thrust fault
tsunami

OBJECTIVES

- Explain how earthquakes are caused.
- Distinguish between the types of earthquake faults.
- Identify what a tsunami is.

Earthquakes are shock waves resulting from sudden movements in Earth's crust (fig. 4–10). They have occurred throughout the history of the world. Scientists estimate that worldwide, over 800,000 earthquakes occur each year. While most earthquakes are too small to be felt, they can be detected by special equipment.

Fig. 4-10 The force of earthquakes causes tremendous damage.

Fig. 4-11 The snap of a dry stick is similar to an earthquake.

Geologists have discovered that earthquakes often happen near boundaries of plates and at **faults**, or cracks, in the plates. As plates move, pressure builds up in the rocks along the fault. If movement stops, the energy remains stored in the rocks. If movement continues, the rocks can no longer hold their position and suddenly slip past each other. If you bend a small stick, the energy builds until the stick suddenly snaps, causing your hand and the stick to move (fig. 4–11). In a similar way, the sudden release of energy at a fault causes Earth to shake.

Unlike the snapping stick, however, only one side of the fault moves. The moving plate can either push up, slip down, or move horizontally.

There are three kinds of faults: normal faults, thrust faults, and strike-slip faults (fig. 4–12).

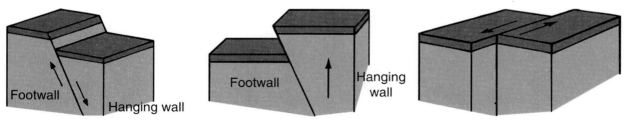

Fig. 4-12   Faults can either be normal (left), thrust (center), or strike-slip (right).

NORMAL FAULTS are those faults where the moving plate slips below the stationary plate (fig. 4–13). The fault that runs through the Rift Valley of Africa is an example of a normal fault.

THRUST FAULTS are those faults where the moving plate moves up and over the stationary plate. Chief Mountain in Montana is an example of a thrust fault (fig. 4–14).

STRIKE-SLIP FAULTS are those faults where the moving plate slides past the stationary plate. The San Andreas fault in California is a strike-slip fault (fig. 4–15).

Fig. 4-13   A normal fault.

Fig. 4-14   A thrust fault, Chief Mountain, Montana.

Fig. 4-15   The San Andreas fault, a strike-slip fault in California.

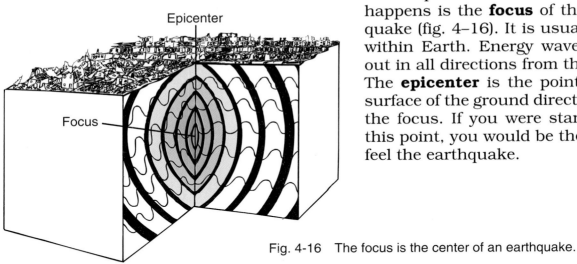

Epicenter

Focus

The point where the actual slip happens is the **focus** of the earthquake (fig. 4–16). It is usually deep within Earth. Energy waves travel out in all directions from the focus. The **epicenter** is the point on the surface of the ground directly above the focus. If you were standing at this point, you would be the first to feel the earthquake.

Fig. 4-16   The focus is the center of an earthquake.

MINIBIOGRAPHYMINIBIOGRAPHYMINIBIOGRAPHYMINIBIOGRAPHYMINIBIOGRAPHY

CHARLES RICHTER

You are sitting at your desk when you hear a low rumble that grows louder. Suddenly you feel a slight shaking in the floor. The windows rattle, and a book falls off the shelf. Hanging lights swing back and forth. It's an EARTHQUAKE!

In the 1920s scientists began to study earthquakes. Charles Richter, a physics student at Cal Tech in California, was given the job of studying the readings of seismographs to determine the epicenters of earthquakes. He had to describe the size or strength of each earthquake studied. At that time scientists used the Mercalli scale to describe earthquakes. Richter found this method was not very exact and described only how much damage an earthquake had done, not how strong it was.

Charles decided to develop a better method of measuring earthquakes. He used the seismograph readings and compared the largest surface waves of each earthquake. He used the word *magnitude* to mean the strength of an earthquake and assigned each earthquake a number from 1–10. Richter arranged his scale so a magnitude 2 earthquake was 10 times stronger than one measuring 1, a magnitude 3 was 100 times (10 X 10) stronger, and a magnitude 4 was 1000 (10 X 10 X 10) times stronger.

MINIBIOGRAPHYMINIBIOGRAPHYMINIBIOGRAPHYMINIBIOGRAPHYMINIBIOGRAPHY

If an earthquake occurs under the ocean, a large underwater shock wave called a **tsunami** (tsoo nä´ mē) usually forms. These shock waves may travel underwater at nearly 600 KPH (400 mph) across the ocean. When a tsunami reaches a coastline, it can cause large waves; some tidal waves have measured more than 40 m (130 ft) high (fig. 4–17). These very large waves destroy almost everything in their paths. Today, geologists record and track tsunamis in order to warn people of tidal waves.

Many small earthquakes can delay a large earthquake by releasing built-up energy along a fault. If this energy continues to build, a major earthquake will eventually occur. The damage caused by one large earthquake is many times greater than that caused by hundreds of smaller ones.

RESEARCH IT
Find out how strong the strongest earthquake was and what earthquake killed the most people.

Fig. 4-17   Imagine the damage a 40 m tidal wave could cause to a coastal city.

REVIEW IT

1. What causes earthquakes?
2. Name three types of faults and describe the motion associated with each.
3. Why are tsunamis dangerous?

4–3 EARTHQUAKE WAVES

OBJECTIVES

- Explain how earthquakes are located.
- Compare and contrast the types of earthquake waves.
- Describe how earthquakes are measured.

Geologists use **seismographs** (sīz´ mə grafs) to record shock waves created by earthquakes. These records help Earth scientists determine the location and size of an earthquake and how long the earthquake lasts.

A seismograph consists of a rotating drum that moves a strip of paper at a constant speed. Resting on top of the paper is a pen that draws a straight line as the paper moves beneath it. Vibrations caused by earthquake waves make the pen scribble on the paper (fig. 4–18). The scribble labeled **A** was created by a very small earthquake. Very large earthquakes cause scribbles like the one labeled **B**.

DID YOU KNOW?
More than a thousand earthquakes occurred in Denver between 1962 and 1966. During this time large amounts of liquid waste were pumped into wells. The earthquakes resulted when the liquid seeped into faults, making it easier for the rocks to slip.

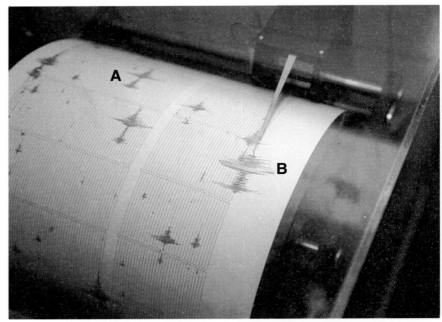

Fig. 4-18   A seismograph records movements in the crust.

Earthquakes produce three kinds of shock waves: primary waves, secondary waves, and surface waves (fig. 4–19).

Fig. 4-19   Three types of earthquake waves: P-waves, S-waves, L-waves.

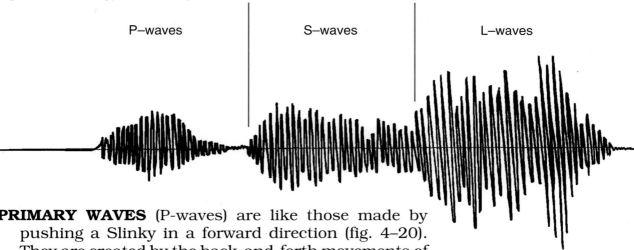

P–waves   S–waves   L–waves

PRIMARY WAVES (P-waves) are like those made by pushing a Slinky in a forward direction (fig. 4–20). They are created by the back-and-forth movements of rock that makes up the crust. Primary waves travel more than 50 000 km/hr (28,000 mph) and are the first to reach the seismograph. But although P-waves travel fast, they *do not* cause damage on Earth's surface.

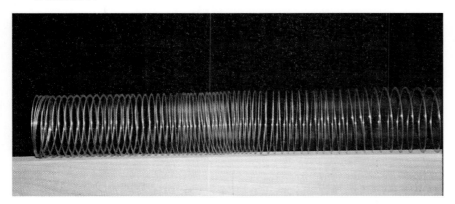

Fig. 4-20 P-waves travel through the crust in the same way waves move through a Slinky.

SECONDARY WAVES (S-waves) are created by the up-and-down movements of underground rock. S-waves are the second earthquake wave to reach the seismograph and also do not cause earthquake damage.

SURFACE WAVES (L-waves) are created on the surface. They move more slowly than the other types of waves and are created by the movement of the S-waves. L-waves are similar to the ripples created when you throw a large rock into a pond or lake. They make Earth's crust move and are the waves that cause earthquake damage (fig. 4–21).

Fig. 4-21 L-waves cause all the surface damage we see from an earthquake.

Seismographs located around the world record earthquake waves as they arrive, telling geologists how fast earthquake waves travel through Earth. Geologists

TRY THIS 4–3: And the Winner Is . . .

Materials:
none needed

Procedure:
1. Use the information on the speed of earthquake waves to answer the questions.

Wave	Speed
P-wave	6 km/sec
S-wave	4 km/sec

- The epicenter of an earthquake is at point A. How long will it take P-waves to reach the town of Hoduncun 120 km away?
- How long will it take the S-waves to reach Hoduncun?
- The same earthquake is felt in the town of Ellos 2 minutes 45 seconds after it occurred. How far is Ellos from the epicenter?

locate the epicenter of an earthquake by comparing the time it takes the primary and secondary waves to arrive at three different seismic stations (fig. 4–22).

In 1935, Charles Richter developed the **Richter scale** (rik´ tər) to measure the energy released by an earthquake. Fig. 4–23 shows a table that compares the energy of an earthquake to tons of exploding dynamite. An earthquake measuring 4 on the Richter scale is 10 times stronger than one measuring 3. An earthquake measuring 7 releases 10,000 times more energy than one measuring 3.

Earthquakes measuring 4 or less on the Richter scale are considered small. Small earthquakes occur more than 700 times per day. Large earthquakes, those measuring greater than 7 on the Richter scale, occur less frequently. Usually fewer than 20 large earthquakes happen each year throughout the world.

Geologists have tried to predict earthquakes by measuring pressure in and around a fault. So far they have been able to predict only *where* an earthquake may occur, not *when* one will strike.

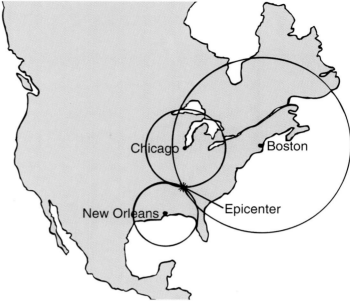

Fig. 4-22 The records of three seismic stations are used in locating earthquake epicenters.

Richter Magnitude	Equal Amount of Exploding Dynamite
0	Smallest detectable earthquake
3	8 ounces of dynamite
4	120 pounds of dynamite
5	15 tons of dynamite
6	3800 tons of dynamite
7	950,000 tons of dynamite
8	230,000,000 tons of dynamite

Fig. 4-23 This table shows the relative strengths of earthquakes.

REVIEW IT

1. How do scientists locate the epicenter of an earthquake?
2. What are three types of earthquake waves, and what are their features?
3. What is the Richter scale?

CLASS ACTIVITY 4–3: Locating Earthquakes

Question: How do scientists locate earthquake epicenters?

Materials:
drawing compass   metric ruler   Special Master R85

Procedure:
1. Three seismograph stations recorded an earthquake. Reports indicated that the quake was 1120 km from Seattle, 1120 km from Berkeley, and 840 km from Santa Fe.
2. Use the distance key provided and determine what distance you should set your compass at for 1120 km. Set your compass at this distance.
3. Draw a circle on sheet A at this setting with Seattle as the center of the circle.
4. Repeat steps 2 and 3 for both Berkeley and Santa Fe.
5. Another earthquake was recorded a few days later. Reports indicated that the epicenter of this quake was 1096 km from Santa Fe, 1376 km from Washington, D. C., and 1280 km from Atlanta.
6. Repeat steps 2–4 for this new set of data.

Data:

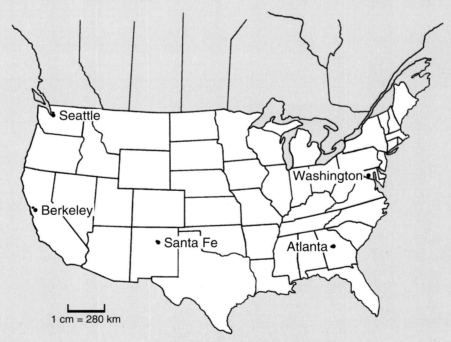

1 cm = 280 km

Questions:
1. In what state was the epicenter of the first earthquake located?
2. Where was the epicenter of the second earthquake?
3. Why must scientists have data from three seismograph stations before they can locate the epicenter of an earthquake?

Conclusion: Write 3–5 sentences about what you learned from this activity.

FRONTIERS: The Ring of Fire

The Ring of Fire is the name given to the coastal region and islands surrounding the Pacific Ocean. This area is active with volcanoes and earthquakes. The reason for this activity lies underground, hidden from view. Earth's plates are in constant motion. In some areas the plates are pushed apart. In other areas plates are pushed together.

Along the edge of the Pacific Ocean, the plates collide. The plate under the ocean slips beneath the land plate. Scientists believe that the sinking plate melts and forms new magma. This newly formed magma may push up through the crust and form a volcano. The nearly 500 volcanoes that make up the Ring of Fire show where one plate sinks below another. Colliding plates also cause earthquakes.

In 1980 Mt. St. Helens, a volcano located in the state of Washington, erupted and showed scientists the relationship between volcanoes and earthquakes. From 1975 to 1980 more than 45 earthquakes occurred on or near the mountain. In the month just before the volcano erupted, there were as many as 15 earthquakes occurring there each hour. The earthquakes culminated in a large-magnitude earthquake just as the volcano erupted.

The land in the Ring of Fire has changed in the past and will continue to change in the future. These changes will cause old volcanoes to come to life, new volcanoes to form, and earthquakes to rumble and shake the ground.

QUESTIONS:
1. Where is the Ring of Fire?
2. Why are the volcanoes so active in this area?
3. Why do so many earthquakes occur in the Ring of Fire?
4. Do plates always collide? Explain.

CHAPTER 4 WRAP-UP

SKILLS DEVELOPMENT

THINKING SKILLS: READING A TABLE

The Richter scale is used to measure the strength of an earthquake. The strength is determined on this scale by using the record of a seismograph. As the numbers increase by 1, the strength of the earthquake increases by 10.

Study the information contained in the tables below. Answer the questions.

RICHTER MAGNITUDES	EARTHQUAKE EFFECTS
0	Smallest detectable quake.
2.5–3	Generally not felt but recorded. About 100,000 such earthquakes of this magnitude occur each year.
4.5	Can cause local damage.
6.0	Destructive in a populated region.
7.0	Called a major earthquake.
7.8	San Francisco earthquake of 1906.
8.0 or greater	Great earthquakes. Cause total destruction to close population centers.

SOME MAJOR EARTHQUAKES		
Location	Date	Richter Scale Reading
Colombia	1906	8.9
San Francisco	1906	7.8
Chile	1906	8.6
China	1932	7.6
Japan	1946	8.4
Iran	1957	7.1
Morocco	1960	5.8
Alaska	1964	8.5
Nicaragua	1972	6.2
Philippines	1976	7.8
Argentina	1977	8.2
Algeria	1980	7.3
Italy	1980	7.2

1. Which earthquake listed had the greatest intensity? Which had the least?

2. Which of the earthquakes listed would not have been considered major earthquakes?

3. Which earthquake do you think probably caused the greatest damage? Explain.

4. List the earthquakes in the table in order from most intense to least intense.

5. About how many earthquakes that measure 2.5 to 3 on the Richter scale occur each year?

6. Why might a 7.5 earthquake that occurs in Afghanistan cause more damage than a 7.5 earthquake that occurs in San Francisco?

QUESTIONS AND PROBLEMS

1. What is the "Ring of Fire"?
2. When Mount Vesuvius erupted, what caused most of the deaths?
3. How are shield volcanoes different from cinder cones?
4. Why was the eruption of Mount St. Helens more violent than the eruption of the Mauna Loa volcano?
5. What is the difference between an earthquake's epicenter and its focus?
6. Why is it impossible to locate an earthquake with just one seismograph?
7. What is the Richter scale?
8. Which waves cause most of the damage associated with earthquakes?
9. What is the difference between lava and magma?
10. Do all volcanoes build mountains? Explain.
11. How do primary waves and secondary waves differ?

RESEARCH

1. Interview someone who has lived through a major earthquake. Compare his or her story with the stories written in magazines or newspapers.
2. Investigate a major volcanic eruption. Prepare an oral report that includes visual aids, and present it to the class.
3. Draw a poster-sized cutaway diagram or model that shows the features of a volcano.
4. Use a local library to investigate major North American earthquakes. Use a map of North America to show where these earthquakes have occurred. Make a bulletin board display of your findings. Include a label and brief description of each earthquake.
5. Make a list of major biblical references to earthquakes and volcanoes. Include a brief description of the context for each reference.

REVIEW

HIGHLIGHTS

1. Volcanoes result when magma pushes up through the surface of the crust.
2. A vent is an opening formed in a weak spot of Earth's crust. A tube or pipe is the pathway that the magma passes through to reach the surface.
3. A shield volcano is the largest type, having a broad shape with gently sloping sides. A cinder cone is the smallest type, usually less than 300 m (1000 ft) high with steep sides. A composite volcano is made of alternate layers of lava and ash.
4. Earthquakes are caused by sudden movements in the crust.

5. Normal faults occur when one side slips below the stationary side. Thrust faults occur when one side moves up and over the stationary side. Strike-slip faults occur when two sides slide past each other.
6. A tsunami is a high, fast-moving wave caused by an underwater earthquake.
7. Earthquakes are located by comparing the time it takes for p-waves and s-waves to arrive at three different seismic stations.
8. Primary waves are the fastest moving waves; secondary waves are the next fastest; the slowest are surface waves.
9. The Richter scale uses numbers to show the relative energy released by an earthquake.

VOCABULARY LIST

cinder cone	focus	shield volcano
composite cone	lava	strike-slip fault
cone	normal fault	surface wave
crater	pipe	thrust fault
earthquake	primary wave	tsunami
epicenter	Richter scale	vent
fault	secondary wave	volcano
fissure	seismograph	

PRACTICE
Multiple Choice. Choose the best answer.
1. Lava can be . . .
   a. watery
   b. thick
   c. foamy
   d. all of these
2. Which of these can scientists predict about earthquakes?
   a. when they will occur
   b. where they will occur
   c. how strong they will be
   d. none of these
3. Which waves created by an earthquake move the fastest?
   a. l-waves
   b. p-waves
   c. s-waves
   d. f-waves
4. Which cools quickly and has a glassy surface?
   a. obsidian
   b. lava
   c. pumice
   d. scoria
5. The largest volcanoes are generally what kind?
   a. composite volcanoes
   b. shield volcanoes
   c. cinder cones
   d. fissures

6. Which of these come out of volcanoes?
   a. steam   c. gas
   b. ash   d. all of these
7. In what type of fault does one side slide past the other?
   a. normal fault   c. strike-slip fault
   b. thrust fault   d. convergent fault
8. Small earthquakes often cause as much damage as large ones.
   a. true
   b. false
9. What type of earthquake waves are similar to those created by throwing a rock into a pond?
   a. primary waves   c. secondary waves
   b. surface waves   d. none of these
10. An earthquake measuring 5 on the Richter scale would be how many times stronger than an earthquake that measures 3?
    a. 2   c. 100
    b. 10   d. 1000

Matching. Match each word with its definition or description.
1. Paricutin is an example   a. composite volcano
2. measures earthquake waves   b. l-waves
3. travel underground   c. p-waves
4. lava flows through these cracks   d. fissures
5. tube that connects the mantle and crust   e. earthquake
6. caused by sudden movement in the crust   f. cone
7. sea wave caused by underwater earthquake   g. pipe
8. travel on the surface   h. seismograph
9. a small, steep-sided volcano   i. cinder cone
10. Mount St. Helens is an example   j. tsunami

CHAPTER 5

WEATHERING

INTRODUCTION

In recent years, city workers have reported widespread damage to public buildings, statues, and monuments, not due to vandalism or poor maintenance, but due to air pollution!

This statue has been worn away because of pollutants created by the burning of gas, oil, and coal. These pollutants combine with the air's moisture to form acids that break up, or weather, the exposed surface of the statue.

In this chapter you will investigate the forces that weather the rocks of Earth's crust and the process by which weathering produces the soil needed to support life on Earth.

SECTION TITLES

A statue showing the effects of weathering.

5–1 PHYSICAL WEATHERING

VOCABULARY

chemical weathering
erosion
physical weathering
weathering

Fig. 5–1 This layering is caused by pressure within the rock.

Fig. 5–2 Water is a major force of physical weathering.

OBJECTIVES

- Distinguish between weathering and erosion.
- Compare and contrast physical and chemical weathering.
- Identify forces of physical weathering.

Two processes that change Earth's crust are weathering and erosion. **Weathering** breaks up or changes rocks. It can be either physical or chemical. **Physical weathering** simply breaks rock into smaller pieces, while **chemical weathering** dissolves rock and changes it into new substances. **Erosion**, which will be discussed later, moves the pieces of weathered rock to new locations.

Five main forces of physical weathering are heating and cooling, internal pressure, water, wind, plants and animals.

HEATING AND COOLING, from changes in the weather, cause rocks to expand and contract. As they do, pieces break off the rock's surface.

INTERNAL PRESSURE in some rock formations makes their outer layers peel away (fig. 5–1). This often happens to granite, creating large dome formations. It can also happen in mines and quarries. As workers remove rock, pressure in the underlying rock is released, causing pieces of rock to explode outward. Miners refer to this as "flying rock."

WATER is also a force of physical weathering. When water runs into the cracks of rocks, then freezes, it expands and breaks the rock apart (fig. 5–2).

84

DID YOU KNOW?
The largest underground lake is the Lost Sea. It lies 91 m (300 ft) underground in Tennessee and covers over 1.7 hec (4.0 acres).

Fig. 5–3 Strong currents cause sand and gravel to wear depressions in rock.

In streams and rivers, water-borne sand and gravel scrape the rock that forms the bottom and sides of streams and rivers, slowly wearing the rock away. Fig. 5–3 shows a pool formed by such action.

WIND loosens and lifts away small particles of rock. Sand and small pebbles carried by strong winds create a "sandblasting" action that wears away rock surfaces. Sometimes the physical weathering caused by wind results in unusual landscapes (fig. 5–4).

Fig. 5–4 Wind carves dramatic shapes in rock.

85

Fig. 5–5   Tree roots can break apart solid rock.

PLANTS AND ANIMALS also help to break up Earth's crust. Often plant roots grow into the cracks in rock. As the roots extend into a crack, the rock is forced apart (fig. 5–5).

Animals such as ants, worms, and moles help break up the crust by burrowing in the soil, allowing water to get to the rocks below.

People also break up Earth's crust. Blasting done in mines and quarries breaks rock apart. Construction of dams and roads also helps to break up Earth's crust.

TRY THIS 5–1: Ice at Work

Materials:
aluminum foil   plastic bottle (16 oz)
dish towel   water

Procedure:
1. This activity is to be done at home.
2. Completely fill the empty soft-drink bottle with tap water.
3. Tightly cover the mouth of the bottle with aluminum foil and tape the foil securely to the neck of the bottle. (Note: Be sure that there are no air bubbles inside the bottle.)
4. Carefully set the bottle upright in the freezer where it won't be disturbed.
5. After two days take the bottle out of the freezer and observe it carefully.
   • Describe what has happened.
   • What would have happened if the top of the bottle had been capped tightly by its original cap? Why?
   • What type of weathering does this demonstrate?

RESEARCH IT

Describe what happened at Lake Peigneur, Louisiana, on November 20, 1980.

REVIEW IT

1. What is the difference between weathering and erosion?
2. What happens in chemical weathering?
3. What are the forces of physical weathering?

5-2 CHEMICAL WEATHERING

OBJECTIVE

• Describe the agents of chemical weathering.

As you have learned, physical weathering breaks rock into smaller pieces. Chemical weathering is different because it changes rock into new substances. Water, oxygen, and acid are the agents responsible for chemical weathering.

WATER acts on rock by dissolving the rock's minerals or by combining with them. Sometimes the dissolved minerals join with other minerals to form new rock. When water combines with minerals in the rock, the rock may swell, become soft, and fall apart.

OXYGEN, in water and air, combines with the minerals in rock to form **oxides** (fig. 5–6). As oxides form, the rock's surface begins to loosen, allowing oxygen to penetrate deeper into the rock. New oxides form as oxygen reacts with the rock's deeper layers. This process can continue until the rock is completely changed.

ACIDS also chemically change rocks. Some acids form when water combines with minerals in the soil. One such acid, called **carbonic acid**, breaks down limestone. In some places, large amounts of limestone have dissolved underground, leaving **caverns** or caves (fig. 5–7). Even some

acid rain
carbonic acid
cavern
lichen
oxide

Fig. 5–6 Iron oxide gives quartz (normally white) a rusty color.

Fig. 5–7 Water dissolves minerals in the ground to form underground caves such as these at Carlsbad Caverns, New Mexico.

DID YOU KNOW?
You can easily break a mushroom with your fingers, but the same mushroom can push with enough force to break through 38 cm (15 in) of pavement.

plants, such as **lichen** (lī kən), produce acids that dissolve rock (fig. 5–8).

Fig. 5–8 Lichens produce acids that dissolve rock.

RESEARCH IT
Find out where the major limestone caverns are located in the U.S. Mark these on a map.

Burning fossil fuels such as coal and oil produces gases that combine with rain and snow to form **acid rain**, which can dissolve stonework and metal in buildings.

REVIEW IT

1. What are the main agents of chemical weathering?

MINIBIOGRAPHYMINIBIOGRAPHYMINIBIOGRAPHYMINIBIOGRAPHYMINIBIOGRAPHY

Dr. Gene E. Likens

The face of a statue slowly corrodes; its eyes and nose become invisible. The decorative metal on a historic building changes color as it is silently eaten away. Fish and other aquatic organisms die in ponds and streams. Dense green forests of spruce and fir turn yellow and die. All because of acid rain and other pollution in the air.

In 1972 Dr. Gene E. Likens announced that rain in New England contained strong acids. Then acids were affecting not only buildings and statues, but waterways and forests as well. Likens and colleagues pointed out that the acids in the rain came mostly from the emissions released by power plants that burned coal and oil.

Before 1972 a few people had studied acid coming from factories. They found that people suffered more from bronchitis in areas downwind from such factories. But Dr. Likens was the first to find high levels of acid widespread throughout the environment of North America and to connect them to acid rain. Although his ideas were not accepted by many people at the time, they have since been shown to be correct.

In 1983 Dr. Likens briefed then President Ronald Reagan and his cabinet about serious problems about acid rain. Since then, many scientists have explored how acid rain affects the environment and have tried to develop solutions to this problem.

MINIBIOGRAPHYMINIBIOGRAPHYMINIBIOGRAPHYMINIBIOGRAPHYMINIBIOGRAPHY

CLASS ACTIVITY 5–2: Rock Eater

Question: How does chemical weathering affect rock?

Materials:

chalk	stopwatch
plastic cups (clear) – 2	vinegar

Procedure:
1. Fill each cup about half full of vinegar.
2. Break the chalk into two equal pieces.
3. Break one half into several smaller pieces.
4. Place the unbroken half in one cup and the pieces of the broken half into the other cup.
5. Observe the cups for five minutes. Record your observations.
6. Carefully pour off the vinegar in each cup and observe the chalk in each cup. Record your observations.

Data:

	OBSERVATION OF CHALK IN VINEGAR	OBSERVATION OF CHALK AFTER FIVE MINUTES
UNBROKEN HALF		
BROKEN HALF		

Questions:
1. What happened to the chalk as it was placed in the vinegar?
2. Was there a difference in what happened in the two cups? Why?
3. At the end of five minutes, which half of the chalk had changed more? Why?
4. Why did breaking up the half into smaller pieces change what happened?
5. Suppose you begin with a rock the size of a large beach ball. Will the rate of chemical weathering change if conditions remain basically the same? Why?

Conclusion: Write 3–5 sentences about what you learned from this activity.

5–3 SOIL

humus
parent rock
subsoil
texture
topsoil

OBJECTIVES

- Explain how soil forms.
- Describe the layers that make up soil.
- Identify the factors that influence the type of soil an area has.
- Identify the major soil types.

Weathering breaks rock into smaller and smaller pieces. Erosion moves these particles and deposits them in new locations. Soil forms as this broken rock mixes with decayed material, water, and air.

Soil is made from the bottom up as well as from the top down. Fig. 5–9 shows the layers that make up soil. Dead plant and animal material form **humus** (hyoo′ məs) at the top. At the bottom, **parent rock** weathers to form **subsoil**. When the humus from the top mixes with the subsoil from underneath, topsoil is formed. **Topsoil** is the most important layer of the soil. It provides food for plants and homes for many animals (fig. 5–10). All life on land depends on soil.

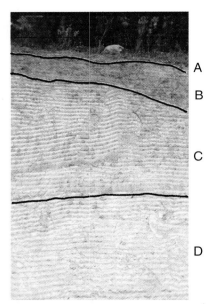

Fig. 5–9 Soil layers can be identified by their color and composition. Humus (A), topsoil (B), subsoil (C), parent rock (D).

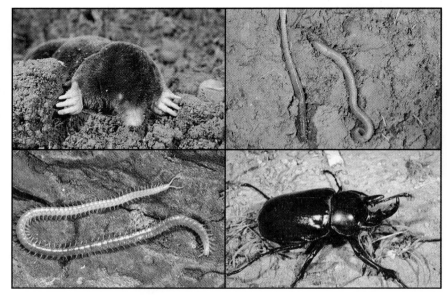

Fig. 5–10 Animals such as moles (top left), centipedes (bottom left), earthworms (top right), and beetles (bottom right) help break up the soil.

The type of soil influences the type of plants that will grow in a region. Several factors determine the type of soil an area will have, including the type of rock lying beneath the soil, the topography of the land, and the climate.

The **texture**, or size of soil particles, is also important. It determines how well the soil holds water and minerals needed by plants.

Scientists identify three kinds of soil texture: sandy, clay, and loamy. The largest particles in soil are sand; the smallest are clay. When soil is made up of mostly large particles, the soil has a sandy texture. When most of the particles are small, a clay-textured soil is created. Loamy-textured soil occurs when sand and clay are mixed evenly (fig. 5–11).

Fig. 5–11   Soil texture is determined by the particles that make it up—clay (left), loamy (center), sandy (right).

A great variety of soils make up Earth's crust. Scientists classify soil types based on location, texture, and minerals. The six basic types of soil are forest, prairie, desert, tropical, mountain, and tundra. (fig. 5–12).

Fig. 5–12 Forest soils are found in eastern North America (top left). Prairie soils cover most of central North America (top right). Tropical soil is found only in jungle areas of North America (bottom left). Dry, sandy soil makes up desert regions (bottom right).

Fig. 5–12 Mountain soils are found on the slopes of western mountains (left). Tundra soils are found in the polar regions (right).

REVIEW IT

1. How does soil form?
2. List the layers that make up the soil and describe the features of each.
3. What are three factors that affect the type of soil an area will have?
4. List the six major types of soil.

DID YOU KNOW?

One hundred years ago Iowa was covered with over 40 cm (16 in) of topsoil. Today, less than 20 cm (8 in) of topsoil covers the state. Most of the lost topsoil was washed into the Gulf of Mexico.

CHAPTER 5 WRAP-UP

SKILLS DEVELOPMENT

THINKING SKILLS: DESIGNING AN EXPERIMENT

Weathering affects various types of rocks differently. Soft rock erodes faster than hard rock. Sometimes it is difficult to determine which rock is softer than the other. Imagine you have two rock samples. Each sample is 60 cm (2 ft) long by 30 cm (1 ft) wide and 15 cm (6 in) thick. Your job is to determine which of the two samples will be eroded faster by running water. Set up an experiment that can determine the above problem.

Set up your experiment in the following way.

Question.	This is the purpose of the experiment.
Hypothesis.	A statement that can be tested.
Method.	The way you will go about testing your hypothesis.
Data.	The collection of information. This could include the measurement of how much is eroded, not eroded, and/or material collected.
Analysis.	Once the data is obtained, you must interpret the data.
Conclusion.	Once the interpretation of the data is complete, you should be able to make your final statement. In this case, you could tell which rock is the softer of the two.

QUESTIONS AND PROBLEMS
1. How do plants cause weathering?
2. What causes "flying rock"?
3. In the area where you live, which force of physical weathering do you think has the greatest effect? Explain.
4. What are three sources of acids that cause weathering?
5. Explain how oxygen causes weathering.
6. Other than weathering of statues, monuments, and buildings, what other problems are created by acid rain?
7. How does water cause chemical weathering?
8. Humus and parent rock eventually form what layer of soil?
9. Why is soil an important factor in determining the ecology of an area?
10. Why are sandy soils better for farming than clay soils?
11. What type of soil is most common in the area where you live?

RESEARCH
1. Find out where in North America the effects of acid rain are the greatest. Draw a map and color it to show the regions that are affected the most, those affected moderately, and those affected the least.
2. Make a list of crops that grow best in sandy soil, those that grow best in clay soil, and those that grow best in loamy soil. Organize your findings into a poster and present it to the class.
3. Contact a local farm bureau, department of agriculture office, or nursery to discover specific plants and animals that help to improve the quality of soil. Prepare a bulletin board that identifies your findings.
4. Visit a recent cut in a hillside or an excavation site. Take pictures or make a drawing of the soil layers that have been exposed. Label the layers and determine whether the soil is young or old. Present an oral report of your findings.
5. Make a poster that illustrates both physical and chemical weathering and the factors that cause each.

REVIEW

HIGHLIGHTS
1. Weathering is the breaking up or changing of rocks that make up the crust; erosion is the moving of the pieces of weathered rocks to new locations.
2. Physical weathering breaks rock into smaller pieces; chemical weathering dissolves rock and changes it into a new substance.
3. Forces of physical weathering include heating and cooling, internal pressure, water, wind, and plants and animals.

4. Forces of chemical weathering include the dissolving of rock by water and reaction of rock with oxygen and with acid.
5. Soil forms as weathered rock mixes with decayed material, water, and air. Soil is made from the bottom up as well as from the top down.
6. The layers that make up the soil are:
    humus—dead plants and animals
    topsoil—mixture of subsoil and humus
    subsoil—weathered parent rock
    parent rock—the bottom layer of rock
7. The type of soil an area has depends on the type of rock that lies beneath the soil, the topography of the land, the climate, and the texture or size of the soil particles.
8. There are six major soil types: forest soil, prairie soil, mountain soil, desert soil, tundra soil, and tropical soil.

VOCABULARY LIST

acid rain	humus	subsoil
carbonic acid	lichen	texture
cavern	oxide	topsoil
chemical weathering	parent rock	weathering
erosion	physical weathering	

PRACTICE
Multiple Choice. Choose the best answer.
1. Which is not a soil type?
    a. swamp
    b. desert
    c. tundra
    d. mountain
2. Which is not a soil texture?
    a. clay
    b. mud
    c. loam
    d. sand
3. Which has the least effect on the type of soil an area has?
    a. climate
    b. topography
    c. animals
    d. bedrock
4. Which is not a factor of physical weathering?
    a. internal pressure
    b. oxygen
    c. animals
    d. water
5. How do human beings cause weathering?
    a. pollution
    b. mining
    c. construction
    d. all of these

6. Water causes only physical weathering.
   a. true
   b. false
7. Which is often responsible for caverns?
   a. freezing
   b. water
   c. wind
   d. none of these
8. Which has the greatest effect on the ecology of an area?
   a. plants
   b. soil
   c. animals
   d. temperature
9. Which of these animals help to weather the crust?
   a. worms
   b. gophers
   c. ants
   d. all of these
10. Which soil type is dry and sandy?
   a. tundra soil
   b. mountain soil
   c. prairie soil
   d. desert soil

Matching. Match each word with its definition or description.
1. formed by underground weathering
2. dead plant and animal material
3. type of soil that has a reddish color
4. best soil texture for farming
5. type of soil found in the polar regions
6. soil texture that holds water best
7. causes rock to change to new substances
8. responsible for creating granite domes
9. dissolves limestone
10. causes physical and chemical weathering

a. loam
b. internal pressure
c. water
d. humus
e. clay
f. carbonic acid
g. chemical weathering
h. caverns
i. tropical soil
j. tundra soil

DGC—7

CHAPTER 6

EROSION

INTRODUCTION

Earth's crust is changed not only by weathering, but also by the forces of erosion. Unlike earthquakes and volcanoes, both weathering and erosion usually happen slowly, over longer periods of time.

While weathering breaks up rock, erosion moves the broken rock into new areas. Examine the picture. What caused this erosion? You will understand more about Earth's changing crust after you study this chapter.

SECTION TITLES

An arch in Arches National Park, Utah

6–1 EROSION CAUSED BY WATER

VOCABULARY

alluvial fan
aquifer
delta
flood plain
geyser
ground water
hot spring
load
runoff water
sinkhole

RESEARCH IT

Find out what an artesian well is.

OBJECTIVES

- Identify the features created by ground water erosion.
- Identify the features caused by runoff water erosion.
- Identify the features created by wave erosion.

Raindrops splashing on the ground can move an amazing amount of soil and rock. In a single storm, raindrops falling on an area the size of a football field can move more than 100 tons of dirt.

Ground water is precipitation, rain or melting snow, that soaks into the soil. Fig. 6–1 shows how water drains down through the soil until it reaches solid rock. There it collects into underground deposits called the **aquifer**. In some areas, water from the aquifer bubbles up through the ground in springs. In other areas, wells must be dug to tap into the aquifer.

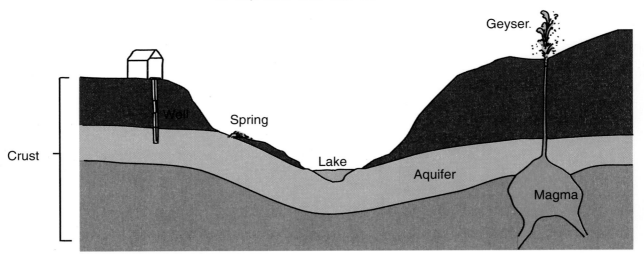

Fig. 6–1 Wells, springs, geysers, and aquifers are part of the ground water.

Erosion can occur underground. In some areas, water moves through the soil and dissolves soft rock. The dissolved minerals are carried away, leaving cracks and openings. As water continues to dissolve the rock, the cracks and openings erode into caves and caverns. Some underground caves collapse because they cannot support the weight of the ground above them. This forms a **sinkhole** (fig. 6–2). Natural erosion causes many sinkholes. Others have occurred where too much water or oil has been pumped out of the ground.

Sometimes water flows down cracks and gets deep inside Earth. If water gets near the hot magma, it heats up. Often the heated water moves up and flows out above ground to form a **hot spring** (fig. 6–3). At other times the water shoots to the surface and bursts out as a **geyser**. Some geysers are so powerful, they spray hot water and steam 120 m (400 ft) into the air.

Fig. 6–2   Sinkholes form when underground cavities collapse.

Most erosion is caused by runoff water. **Runoff water** is water that does not soak into the ground, but runs downhill to form creeks and streams. Streams combine to form rivers that eventually empty into the ocean. As runoff water moves over the land, erosion takes place.

Fig. 6–3   Hot springs form where heated water rises to the surface.

The eroded material carried by a river is called the **load**. As the river slows, boulders and gravel begin to settle out, then pebbles are deposited. Sand and mud are the last to sink to the bottom and may often form sandbars that change the path of the river (fig. 6–4). When a river overflows its banks, the load spreads over a large area called a **flood plain**.

Fig. 6–4   Sandbars and mudbars often form at mouths of rivers.

Fig. 6–5   Alluvial fans form at the foot of mountains.

Fig. 6–6   Waves erode the shoreline and form beaches.

Where rivers flow out of hills and mountains into open valleys or plains, alluvial fans form. **Alluvial** (ə lōō vē əl) **fans** are fan-shaped deposits of rocks and gravel at the base of hills or mountains (fig. 6–5).

By the time a river reaches the ocean, its load usually consists of only very fine particles. These tiny particles settle out at the mouth of the river and form a **delta**. The Mississippi River deposits an average of 80 million kg (850,000 tons) of material at its delta every day.

Ocean waves cause erosion as they hit the shore. The waves move material from one place and deposit it in another, forming different features (fig. 6–6). Ocean waves release tremendous amounts of energy that can move huge rocks. During one storm, a wave near Tillamook, Oregon, hurled a 61 kg (130 lb) boulder 30 m (99 ft) above the shore and through the roof of a building.

REVIEW IT

1. What is the aquifer?
2. How does ground water get out of the ground?
3. Why do only small particles make up the load of rivers as they near the ocean?
4. Which wave-caused features are the result of material being deposited?

DID YOU KNOW?

The Mississippi River delta extends more than 320 km (200 mi) into the Gulf of Mexico. The delta continues to grow out into the Gulf at a rate of 110 m (350 ft) per year.

6–2 EROSION CAUSED BY WIND AND GRAVITY

OBJECTIVES

- Describe the features created by wind.
- Describe the features created by gravity.

VOCABULARY
landslide

Although most erosion is caused by runoff water, wind and gravity also actively erode the land's surface.

WIND erodes the land in two ways. One way is by scooping out loose material and blowing it away. The second way is similar to sandblasting. Tiny grains of sand bombard rock surfaces and slowly wear away the softer rock (fig. 6–7).

Wind also changes the landscape by depositing material. Sand dunes form in deserts and along beaches because of the wind (fig. 6–8). Wind can move sand a great distance. For example, sand dunes on the shore of Lake Michigan move 5–7 m (16–25 ft) per year. Particles of rock and soil carried by the wind are deposited along the way or are ground into a fine powder. In some places deposits of this powdery material are several meters thick.

Fig. 6–7　Soft rock is eroded by the wind while harder material remains.

Fig. 6–8　Sand dunes are formed and shaped by wind.

DID YOU KNOW?
The largest sand dunes are in the Sahara Desert. These dunes measure nearly 5 km (3 mi) long and over 400 m (1400 ft) high.

103

DID YOU KNOW?
On August 17, 1959, a large earthquake hit Montana. The quake caused a large section of a mountain to break off and tumble into the valley below. In minutes, millions of tons of rock buried campers vacationing along the Madison River, forming a natural dam on the river.

GRAVITY caused the erosion pictured in fig. 6–9. As weathering takes place, gravity pulls the loosened material down. Rock and soil fall from cliffs or roll down steep hillsides, gradually building up at the base.

Fig. 6–9 Gravity causes rock to fall away from steep mountains and cliffs.

Not all movements of land due to gravity happen slowly. **Landslides** may occur quickly and without warning. Some landslides occur as rain soaks hillsides. Water loosens the soil and increases its weight, making the land slide down rapidly (fig. 6–10). Earthquakes can also cause landslides.

Fig. 6–10 Many landslides happen after an earthquake or heavy rain.

REVIEW IT

1. How does wind carve rock?
2. What features are caused by gravity?

CLASS ACTIVITY 6-2: Gone With the Wind

Question: What factors affect the erosion done by wind?

Materials:

graduated cylinder (100 ml)	sand
plastic cups (clear, 16 oz) – 2	scissors
plastic spoon	shoe box
potting soil	water

Procedure:

1. Use scissors to carefully punch a small hole in the end of the shoe box. Stick about 4 cm (2 in) of the straw through the hole into the box.
2. Fill one of the plastic cups with sand. Fill the other with potting soil.
3. Place a small handful of potting soil in a pile in the box about 6 cm (2.5 in) from the end of the straw.
4. Blow through the straw, directing a gentle, steady wind at the pile of soil. Continue gently blowing through the straw for about one minute. Observe and record what happens.
5. Repeat step 4. This time blow through the straw with more force to create a stronger wind. Observe and record what happens.
6 Empty the box by dumping the potting soil back into the plastic cup.
7. Repeat steps 3–6 with the sand.
8. Add about 50 ml of water to each cup, and mix each sample until it becomes uniformly moist. Repeat steps 3–6.

Data:

CONDITION	SAMPLE	OBSERVATION
Gentle wind	dry sand	
	dry soil	
Strong wind	dry sand	
	dry soil	
Gentle wind	damp sand	
	damp soil	
Strong wind	damp sand	
	damp soil	

Questions:

1. Which factor, wind speed or moisture, had the greater effect on the wind's ability to erode the pile of soil?
2. Which of the soil samples changed the most when water was added?
3. Where would wind erosion have a greater effect, in a desert region or in a grassland area? Why?

Conclusion: Write 3–5 sentences about what you learned from this activity.

6–3 EROSION CAUSED BY GLACIERS

continental glacier
erratic boulder
esker
glacial polish
kettle lake
moraine
U-shaped valley
valley glacier

OBJECTIVES

- Distinguish between continental and valley glaciers.
- Describe the features created by glaciers.

Glaciers are large masses of thick ice that move slowly over the land. They form only in very high mountains or in cold regions near the North and South poles, where the temperature never rises enough to melt the snow completely. Year after year, the snow builds up and packs into ice. Large glaciers begin to move slowly over the land, usually only a few meters per year. However, glaciers that are near the sea move much faster because the land's surface near the sea is warmer. During the summer, the Mendenhall Glacier in Alaska moves over 30 m/day (90 ft/day) (fig. 6–11)!

There are two types of glaciers: continental glaciers and valley glaciers.

Fig. 6–11 Most glaciers move slowly, but the Mendenhall Glacier moves rapidly.

Fig. 6–12 One continental glacier covers Greenland; another covers Antarctica.

CONTINENTAL GLACIERS are large enough to cover most of an entire continent (fig. 6–12). Today there are only two in the world: one covers most of Greenland; the other covers most of Antarctica. These two glaciers contain 95 percent of all the glacial ice in the world.

VALLEY GLACIERS are much smaller than continental glaciers. Over 200,000 of these small glaciers are scattered over Earth. Valley glaciers usually occur in high mountains and look like frozen rivers (fig. 6–13).

You can see the effects of glaciers throughout much of Canada and the northern United States. As glaciers move, they carve and grind away the landscape like giant bulldozers, scraping away soil and loose rock and depositing it elsewhere. Moraines (mə rānz´), eskers (es´ kərz), kettle lakes, erratic boulders, glacial polish, and U-shaped valleys all indicate where glaciers have come and gone (fig. 6–14).

DID YOU KNOW?
The Quarayaq Glacier in Greenland moves 20–24 m (65–80 ft) per day.

Fig. 6–13   Valley glaciers form in mountains and look like frozen rivers.

Fig. 6–14

MORAINES. As a glacier moves, long piles of rock and soil, called **moraines**, form along its edges. When the glacier melts, these moraines remain. Sometimes they dam rivers and form moraine lakes.

ESKERS. Water melting off the glacier forms channels beneath the ice. As water continues to flow along these channels, long, winding ridges called **eskers** form.

KETTLE LAKES. Some glaciers gouge out basins as they move. When glaciers melt, the basins fill with water to form **kettle lakes**. The state of Minnesota, called the "land of 10,000 lakes," is dotted with thousands of kettle lakes.

ERRATIC BOULDERS. As a glacier moves, it often picks up large boulders and carries them to a new location. When the glacier melts, it leaves these **erratic boulders** behind.

GLACIAL POLISH. As glaciers move over some kinds of rock, the grinding action "polishes" the surface of the rock. The rock shown above has **glacial polish**.

U-SHAPED VALLEYS. As glaciers move between mountains, they gouge out **U-shaped valleys**. Yosemite Valley in California is an example of this feature of glacial action.

Fig. 6–14 (cont.)

REVIEW IT

1. How are continental glaciers different from valley glaciers?
2. What type of glacier would most likely form U-shaped valleys?
3. What are erratic boulders?

RESEARCH IT

What is a drumlin, and how is it formed?

CLASS ACTIVITY 6–3: Slow Motion

Question: How do glaciers move?

Materials:

index card (3" x 5")
index card (4" x 6")
masking tape
paper dots – 5

plastic spoon
Prell concentrate – 1 tbsp
stopwatch

Procedure:
1. Draw marks along the edge of a 4 x 6 card. Fold the card in half lengthwise to make a V-shaped trough. Tape the trough to the 3 x 5 card (fig. A). Thoroughly tape where the two cards come together so no cracks remain.
2. Number the five paper dots 1–5.
3. Use a book or other object to prop up the open end of the trough so that the closed end forms a pocket. Squeeze about 1 oz of Prell into the trough.
4. Make sure that no movement of the Prell occurs, while your partner lines up the five paper dots in order across the Prell near the other card. (Note: If you dampen your finger, it will pick up the dots more easily.) Use a pencil to line up the dots in a straight line.
5. You are going to watch the movement of the dots and mark on the side of the trough where each dot is at 15-second intervals.
6. When ready, watch the clock and set down the open end of the trough at a given minute. Watch the movement of the dots as the Prell moves. Mark on the trough the location of each dot at each elapsed interval of 15 seconds. You will end up with four positions marked for each dot.
7. Measure and record the distance each dot traveled during each 15-second interval (measure to the nearest millimeter).

Data:

Distance Moved

Dot #	15 sec	30 sec	45 sec	60 sec
1				
2				
3				
4				
5				

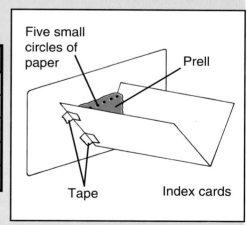

Questions:
1. Which dot moved the greatest distance? Which dots moved the least distance?
2. What part of the Prell "glacier" moved the fastest? Which part moved the slowest?
3. How would the movement of the Prell best be described?

Conclusion: Write 3–5 sentences about what you learned from this activity.

6–4 THE ICE AGE

VOCABULARY
ice age

OBJECTIVES

- Describe the evidence that supports the ice age.
- Explain a creationist's interpretation of the ice age.

Because of the many moraines, U-shaped valleys, kettle lakes, extensive glacial polish, and other evidences of glacial activity, scientists believe that glaciers once covered much of North America, Asia, and Europe (fig. 6–15). They believe these huge glaciers formed during a time when Earth's climate was much colder than it is today. They call this time the **ice age**, but they do not agree on when or how it happened.

Many scientists believe there were several ice ages millions of years ago that lasted for long periods of time. Many creation scientists believe that there was only one ice age and that it happened after the Flood.

A recent theory helps support the view of many creationists. According to this theory, three conditions were necessary for an ice age: a cold climate, warm oceans, and heavy snowfall.

Fig. 6-15 During the ice age much of North America was covered by glaciers.

First, northern parts of North America, Asia, and Europe became very cold. This could have been caused by the eruption of volcanoes at the time of the Flood. These eruptions would have blown millions of tons of ash into the air, blocking out much of the sun's warmth and causing a drop in temperature (fig. 6–16).

Fig. 6–16   Ash from the Mount St. Helens eruption covered thousands of square kilometers and reduced temperatures by blocking sunlight.

Second, the oceans warmed. The Bible talks about the "fountains of the deep" erupting during the Flood. This warm water from within Earth, along with volcanic activity under the sea, may have caused further warming of the ocean.

The third condition necessary for an ice age is heavy snowfall. Glaciers form from large amounts of snow. Lots of snow needs lots of moisture. A warm ocean would supply enough moisture to form large amounts of snow. Warm water would evaporate rapidly and create many clouds carrying large amounts of moisture. Once these moisture-laden clouds moved to an area of colder temperature, heavy snowfall would result.

The conditions described above may explain how glaciers could have built up and melted in only hundreds of years. This supports the view many creationists have concerning the ice age.

REVIEW IT

1. How do scientists know there was an ice age?
2. How is a creationist's understanding of the ice age different from that of an evolutionist?

CHAPTER 6 WRAP-UP
SKILLS DEVELOPMENT

THINKING SKILLS: CAUSE AND EFFECT

The chapter that you have just completed was about erosion caused by water, wind, gravity, and/or glaciers. Each of these has its own characteristics or features. The water, wind, gravity, and glaciers are known as the cause, and what they do is called their effect. In this case we have a cause-and-effect relationship.

Make up three statements for each category of erosion to show a cause-and-effect relationship.

Example: The U-shaped valley was formed by the glacier.
    cause—glacier movement
    effect—U-shaped valley

STATEMENT	CAUSE	EFFECT
1. EROSION BY WATER A. B. C.		
2. EROSION BY WIND A. B. C.		
3. EROSION BY GRAVITY A. B. C.		
4. EROSION BY GLACIER A. B. C.		

QUESTIONS AND PROBLEMS
1. How do sinkholes form?
2. What is the difference between a hot spring and a geyser?
3. Why does a delta form at the mouth of a river?
4. How do waves create beaches?
5. How are sand dunes evidence of wind erosion?
6. How are glaciers formed?
7. What is the difference between a moraine and an esker?
8. When do you think the ice age occurred? Why?
9. What is the difference between ground water and runoff water?
10. How does gravity cause landslides?
11. Why do glaciers near oceans move faster than those far from oceans?
12. How are valleys eroded by glaciers different from valleys eroded by water?
13. What is the ice age?
14. What conditions would be necessary for an ice age?

RESEARCH
1. Draw a series of color diagrams that explains how ground water and runoff water cause erosion.
2. Make a graph showing the top 10 rivers of the world that carry the most eroded material (sediment).
3. Make a poster that illustrates the features caused by glaciers. Provide a brief description of each feature you illustrate.
4. Draw a large map of the world indicating those areas still covered by continental glaciers. Also indicate areas where valley glaciers exist. Provide labels for each glacier.
5. Use a library to learn about the "dust bowl" of the 1930s. Prepare a written report that describes the cause, effects, and area affected. Also describe farming methods designed to prevent this from happening again.

REVIEW

HIGHLIGHTS
1. Features created by ground water include springs, aquifers, wells, sinkholes, and geysers.
2. Features caused by runoff water are sandbars, mudbars, alluvial fans, and deltas.
3. Wave erosion creates beaches, cliffs, caves, sea stacks, arches, and sandbars.
4. Features resulting from wind erosion are sand dunes, depressions in rock

DGC—8

surfaces, and "carved" rocks created when softer rock is carved away and the harder rock remains.

5. Gravity causes landslides as well as a buildup of material at the base of cliffs, hills, and mountains.
6. Continental glaciers almost cover entire continents; valley glaciers cover smaller regions and are located in mountain valleys.
7. Features caused by glaciers include moraines, eskers, kettle lakes, erratic boulders, glacial polish, and U-shaped valleys.
8. Evidence that supports the existence of an ice age includes fossil findings and the widespread distribution of glacial features.
9. Many creation scientists believe that there was only one ice age and that it occurred in the time since the Flood. A theory that supports this view suggests that three conditions would have been needed to bring on the ice age: a cold climate, warm oceans, and heavy snowfall. Noah's flood could account for these conditions.

VOCABULARY LIST

alluvial fan	geyser	landslide
aquifer	glacial polish	load
continental glacier	glacier	moraine
delta	ground water	runoff water
erratic boulder	hot spring	sinkhole
esker	ice age	U-shaped valley
flood plain	kettle lake	valley glacier

PRACTICE

Multiple Choice. Choose the best answer.

1. Which of these features would be associated with rivers?
   a. mudbar
   b. alluvial fan
   c. flood plain
   d. all of these
2. Which is not caused by glaciers?
   a. kettle lakes
   b. sinkholes
   c. glacial polish
   d. moraines
3. Which are features caused by waves?
   a. eskers
   b. deltas
   c. landslides
   d. sea stacks
4. Which is not necessary for an ice age?
   a. cold temperatures
   b. millions of years
   c. warm oceans
   d. heavy snowfall

5. Which kind of erosion produces sinkholes, aquifers, hot springs, and geysers?
   a. gravity
   b. waves
   c. runoff water
   d. ground water
6. What can waves do?
   a. deposit material
   b. carve material
   c. wash away material
   d. all of these
7. How many continental glaciers are there?
   a. 2
   b. 7
   c. 20,000
   d. 200,000
8. The conditions created during and after the Flood provide an explanation as to how the ice age may have occurred.
   a. true
   b. false
9. Which feature results from gravity?
   a. landslides
   b. earthquakes
   c. both a and b
   d. neither a nor b
10. In what area would wind cause the most erosion?
   a. in a forest
   b. in the mountains
   c. in a desert
   d. none of these

Matching. Match each word with its definition or description.
1. rain or snow that soaks into the ground
2. creates sand dunes
3. caused by the grinding of glaciers
4. small glaciers in high mountains
5. creates alluvial fans
6. piles of material pushed by glaciers
7. occur when caves collapse
8. the eroded material carried by a river
9. causes landslides
10. long, winding ridges caused by glaciers

a. sinkholes
b. valley glaciers
c. eskers
d. glacial polish
e. runoff water
f. load
g. gravity
h. moraine
i. ground water
j. wind

CHAPTER 7

THE FLOOD

INTRODUCTION

These fossils were found at the top of Mount Stevens in British Columbia. How these animals came to be at the top of a 2500–3000 m (9000–10,000 ft) mountain is a question that has puzzled scientists for many years. Although they have offered many theories, they have not agreed on any one answer. One suggestion is that the Flood, recorded in the book of Genesis, could explain how these animals got to the top of a mountain.

Was the Flood a fact? Is there any evidence that the Flood actually happened? As you study this chapter, you will investigate these and other questions.

SECTION TITLES

7–1 Interpreting Evidence
7–2 Evidences of the Flood
7–3 The Flood's Effects

Fossil trilobites found on the top of Mount Stevens, British Columbia.

7–1 INTERPRETING EVIDENCE

VOCABULARY
principle of uniformity

Fig. 7–1 People interpret evidence differently.

OBJECTIVES

- Identify the work of scientists.
- Explain how assumptions influence the interpretations of scientists.
- Distinguish between the assumptions of creationists and evolutionists.

A group of fifth and sixth graders was divided into several groups. Each group was given some of the pieces of a ceramic item and instructed to put the pieces together to make the original item. Within an hour the students came up with three different solutions (fig. 7–1). Each group of students had similar pieces but developed a different solution.

TRY THIS 7–1: WHATZIT?

Materials:
  irregularly shaped objects – 5
  shoe boxes – 5

Procedure:
  1. Examine each of the five boxes. DO NOT OPEN THEM.
  2. Decide what you think is in each box. To do this you may handle them and perform any test that does not ruin the boxes or remove the lids.
     - Write down what you think is in each box.
     - Write down a reason for each of your guesses or hypotheses.
  3. Now, without looking inside, remove the lids and carefully feel the contents of each box.
     - Write down any changes you want to make about what is in each box.
     - Did you make any changes? Why?
     - Did everyone come up with the same conclusions? Why?

RESEARCH IT
Find out what has been discovered at the La Brea Tar Pits in Los Angeles, California.

The work of scientists is quite similar to the task the students were given. Scientists study evidence and events to try to explain them. But, like the students, several scientists studying the same information may come up with different explanations or interpretations.

Many of the differences in explanations given by creationists and evolutionists are due to different interpretations of evidence. Scientists always interpret the things they observe based on assumptions they accept by faith.

Creationists accept several basic assumptions. They believe that God is active in nature and that He does intervene at times to change the outcome of natural events. These scientists believe that the Bible is God's Word and that it is a reliable history of Earth. The Bible, in Genesis, records that life on Earth was created in six 24-hour days (fig. 7–2). Genesis also records that a worldwide Flood destroyed most life on Earth.

Fig. 7–2   God created Earth in six 24-hour days.

DID YOU KNOW?

Radiometric dating is not always foolproof. A snail shell dated to be 50,000 years old came from a snail known to be less than two years old.

As a result of accepting these assumptions, most creationists look at the evidence in Earth's crust and interpret it according to the Bible record. They believe that many of the geological features of Earth's crust resulted from the Flood. These scientists do not accept the long ages suggested by evolutionists to explain the features of Earth's crust. Creationists believe that the Flood could have caused rapid changes that could have resulted in the many features of Earth's surface.

Similarly, evolutionists also make some basic assumptions. Most evolutionists believe that all nature can be explained by natural law and that God does not interfere in nature. Most evolutionists believe in the **principle of uniformity**, which states that events always happen at the same rate (fig. 7–3). Suppose Point A was at position 1 in 1970. Ten years later Point A had moved to position 2, a distance of 25 cm. It is assumed then that the crust is moving 2.5 cm each year. Based on these assumptions, evolutionists look at many of Earth's geological features and conclude that it has taken millions of years for them to form.

Fig. 7–3 According to the principle of uniformity, point A is moving 2.5 cm/year.

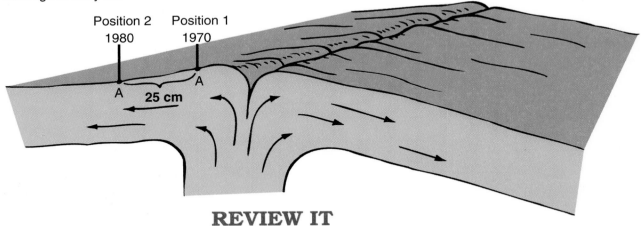

Position 2   Position 1
   1980   1970

A   25 cm   A

REVIEW IT

1. What is the work of a scientist?
2. How do the assumptions of scientists affect their work?
3. What is a basic difference between the assumptions of creationists and evolutionists?

7–2 EVIDENCES OF THE FLOOD

OBJECTIVES

- Identify the evidences of the Flood.
- Explain the importance of sedimentary deposits to the study of Earth's history.

VOCABULARY

coal
fossil
geologic column
guyot
sediment

Fig. 7–4 Noah's ark.

Did Noah's Flood really happen (fig. 7–4)? Some scientists don't believe it did. Others believe that if it happened, it was a gentle flood that affected only the Mesopotamian Valley where Noah lived. Some believe that there were several major floods, and one of them came to be called Noah's Flood. None of these views agrees with the story in the Bible.

According to Genesis, there was only one worldwide Flood. This Flood was violent and covered the whole Earth, not just a small area. God promised that never again would He destroy Earth by a flood, and He gave us the rainbow as a sign of this promise.

While finding the story of the Flood in the Bible is reason enough to believe that it happened, God provides us with more evidence to believe in the Flood. Several evidences in Earth point to a destructive worldwide flood, including sedimentary (sed ə men´ tər ē) deposits, geological features, and flood legends.

Fig. 7–5 Sedimentary rocks often have a layered appearance.

SEDIMENTARY DEPOSITS. Sedimentary deposits are layers of rock that make up 75 percent of Earth's surface (fig. 7–5). These layers are made up of **sediments**, small particles of rock, soil, dead plants, and animals. A worldwide flood could have spread these sediments over Earth's surface.

Some of the plant and animal remains became hardened to form **fossils** (fig. 7–6). For fossils to form, the remains must be buried quickly. If the remains are buried gradually, no fossils will form because the material decays before it can harden. The rapid burial

Fig. 7–6 Fossils come in many shapes and sizes.

The Geologic Column

Era	Period	Epoch
CENOZOIC	Quaternary	Pleistocene Pliocene Miocene Oligocene
CENOZOIC	Tertiary	Eocene Paleocene
MESOZOIC	Cretaceous	
MESOZOIC	Jurassic	
MESOZOIC	Triassic	
PALEOZOIC	Permian	
PALEOZOIC	Pennsylvanian Mississippian	
PALEOZOIC	Devonian	
PALEOZOIC	Silurian	
PALEOZOIC	Ordovician	
PALEOZOIC	Cambrian	
PRECAMBRIAN		

Fig. 7–7   The geologic column shows layers of fossils.

required for the formation of fossils could have happened during the Flood.

The distribution of fossils provides strong evidence of a worldwide flood. Fossils usually occur in layers arranged in the same order. This layered sequence of fossils is called the **geologic column** (fig. 7–7). Some scientists believe the order of the geologic column supports evolution. Others believe the geologic column provides evidence of the Genesis Flood (fig. 7–8).

A worldwide flood could explain how fossils became layered in the geologic column. The Flood probably

Ecological Zonation

Fig. 7–8   During the Flood animals near or in the water would have been buried first. Animals that could run from the rising waters would have been buried later.

destroyed and buried plants and animals as the water moved higher and higher.

Coal, a dark-colored rock found around the world, is made from the remains of plants and animals. Scientists have determined that it would take about 4 m (13 ft) of these remains to make a layer of coal 30 cm (1 ft) thick. A deposit of brown coal in the Latrobe (le trōb´) Valley of Australia is nearly 150 m (500 ft) thick (fig. 7–9). It would have taken a layer of plants 2000 m (6500 ft) deep to make a coal seam this thick!

Without the Flood it is difficult to explain how enough vegetation could have accumulated to make the huge deposits of coal we find today.

Fig. 7–9   Australian coal seams more than 150 m thick are being mined.

123

Fig. 7–10 Some mountains look as though their tops have been washed away.

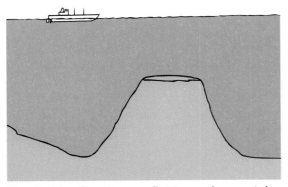

Fig. 7–11 Guyots are flat-topped mountains under the sea.

RESEARCH IT

Find legends of the Flood from cultures around the world.

GEOLOGICAL FEATURES. Evolutionists believe the Grand Canyon took millions of years to form because it is forming slowly today. On the other hand, many creationists believe that the Flood could have carved out the Grand Canyon in much less time.

Mountain ranges such as the Bighorn and Wind River mountains of Wyoming appear to have had their tops rapidly eroded away (fig. 7–10). This same evidence is demonstrated by flat-topped mountains called **guyots** (gē´ ōs) found in the Pacific Ocean (fig. 7–11). To many scientists, the tops of these mountains look as though they were washed away by a great flood.

FLOOD LEGENDS. Stories of a worldwide flood exist in almost every society around the world.

People on the island of Sumatra say that when Earth grew old and dirty, the Creator sent a flood to destroy every living thing. When the water reached the knees of the last pair of humans, who were standing on top of a high mountain, the Creator brought the flood to an end.

It is important to know that the story recorded in the Scriptures is supported by the record on Earth's surface. However, no interpretation can yet answer all of the questions or explain all of the geologic evidence found in Earth's crust. The interpretation is influenced by a person's faith, accepted assumptions, and personal experience.

REVIEW IT

1. List evidences that support the story of the Flood.
2. How does the study of sediments help scientists understand Earth's history?

CLASS ACTIVITY 7–2: Model Rocks

Question: How do sedimentary rocks form?

Materials:

graduated cylinder (100 ml)	water
gravel – 1 cup	wax paper
paper cups – 3	white glue
plastic spoon	

Procedure:
1. In cup A, mix 50 ml of white glue with about 25 ml of water.
2. Use the pencil to carefully punch 15–20 holes in the bottom of cup B.
3. Add the gravel to cup B.
4. Pour the glue-water mixture over the gravel while holding cup B over cup C so that the glue-water mixture can be collected as it runs out.
5. Pour the collected glue mixture back over the gravel, using the empty cup to collect any glue that leaks out.
6. Repeat steps 4 and 5 until no glue mixture leaks out.
7. Set the cup containing the gravel-and-glue mixture on a piece of wax paper and let it dry for a day.
8. The next day, tear away the paper cup and observe the contents.
9. Draw a detailed diagram of your "rock."

Data:

ROCK DIAGRAM

Questions:
1. What components make up the "rock"?
2. How is this rock like other sedimentary rocks? How is it different?
3. In the rock you made, what does the glue represent?

Conclusion: Write 3–5 sentences about what you learned from this activity.

7–3 THE FLOOD'S EFFECTS

OBJECTIVE

- Describe how the Flood affected Earth.

Dramatic changes have taken place on Earth since it was formed. Many people believe it took millions of years for all these changes to occur, but the Flood could have caused them quickly. The Bible and Spirit of Prophecy describe how the Flood may have changed Earth.

WATER. During the Flood, heavy rains fell to Earth. Fountains of water burst from within Earth, throwing rocks hundreds of feet into the air (fig. 7–12). The violent storm hurled trees, buildings, rocks, and water in every direction. The crust of Earth was broken up and changed. Mountains and hills were destroyed. Large amounts of rocks and soil, along with plants and animals, washed into layers. More layers of rocks and soil washed in on top of the lower layers. Some of these deposits covered hundreds of square kilometers. This all happened very quickly.

Fig. 7-12 The Flood violently changed the surface of Earth.

LAND MOVEMENT. After 40 days the rains stopped, but the Flood waters continued to alter Earth. During this time, Earth's plates may have moved due to the tremendous weight of the water. Earthquakes caused some plates to move vertically, forming high mountains in some areas and basins that became oceans and lakes in other places. Other plates may have moved horizontally, causing the continents to move to their present locations.

DID YOU KNOW?

The coal beds in the Appalachian Mountains of Pennsylvania and Ohio cover an area of more than 180 000 km² (70,000 mi²).

WIND. The Bible says that God caused "a wind to pass over the earth" (Genesis 8:1). This violent wind may have created gigantic waves. In *Patriarchs and Prophets*, Ellen G. White states that the wind blew off the tops of some mountains (see p. 108). This strong wind helped dry up the water and clean off the land. It covered the dead plants and animals with rocks and soil.

VOLCANOES. At the time of the Flood, volcanoes spewed out lava and ash. Ash filled the air and blocked out much of the sun's warmth. As Earth cooled, moisture in the air became snow. In a short time, continental glaciers started to form, bringing on the ice age.

For hundreds of years, glaciers reshaped Earth's surface. The great plains of central North America and central Europe were caused by the cutting effects of glaciers (fig. 7–13).

As volcanic activity slowed, the air gradually became clear again. Sunshine warmed Earth, causing the glaciers to melt rapidly. The water from the melting glaciers ran off in rivers, washing away some of the newly formed land. Erosion happened very quickly in some areas, more slowly in others. The melting of the glaciers ended the ice age.

Fig. 7–13 These lakes were carved as glaciers moved across much of North America.

Since the Flood, geological activity has occurred at a much slower pace. Volcanoes still erupt and earthquakes still shake the ground, but these events are not world-wide, nor are they as violent as they were during the Flood. Today earthquakes, volcanoes, and floods are small-scale examples of the worldwide destruction of the great Flood.

REVIEW IT

1. What were four ways the Flood affected Earth?

RESEARCH IT

Why are there so few mammal fossils found in comparison to the number of other animal fossils?

CHAPTER 7 WRAP-UP
SKILLS DEVELOPMENT

THINKING SKILLS: INTERPRETING EVIDENCE

One characteristic of a good scientist is having an open mind. A good scientist must be able to interpret the evidence correctly and come up with a conclusion that the evidence supports.

Some of the evidences for the Flood are mentioned in your textbook and are listed below. Think about each evidence listed and decide how a creation scientist might interpret the evidence and then how an evolution scientist might interpret the same evidence. Write your ideas in the area provided. You may find it helpful to work with a classmate on this activity.

CREATION	EVIDENCE	EVOLUTION
	Flood legends	
	Geological features (Grand Canyon, etc.)	
	Worldwide distribution of sediments	
	Fossils	
	Geologic column	

QUESTIONS AND PROBLEMS

1. What do evolutionists believe about the Flood?
2. Explain the principle of uniformity.
3. How many floods does the Bible mention?
4. Do all creationists believe in the Flood?
5. How are sediments usually moved?
6. What assumptions are accepted by most creationists?
7. How can two scientists examine the same evidence and come to different conclusions about the evidence?
8. How many meters of plant and animal remains would it take to make a seam of coal 3 m (10 ft) thick?
9. How do flood legends support the Flood story recorded in the Bible?
10. What part did underground water play in the Flood?
11. What effects did volcanic action after the Flood have on Earth's climate? Why did it have this effect?
12. How did the earthquakes that occurred during the Flood affect Earth's surface?
13. What is the geologic column?
14. How do fossils support the Flood story?

RESEARCH

1. Obtain a large piece of coal. Break the piece in two and draw a diagram of any plant or animal remains you find.
2. Survey 20–25 adults and find out whether they believe Noah's Flood really happened. Record the reasons for their beliefs. Make a graph of your findings and present it to your class.
3. Make a list of Bible references that provide information about the Flood. Provide a brief description for each reference listed.
4. Make a bulletin board display of the events of the Flood as recorded in the Bible and in the book *Patriarchs and Prophets*.
5. Read two or three actual flood legends from around the world. Compare these legends to the Bible record. What are the similarities and differences? Present an oral report on your findings.

REVIEW

HIGHLIGHTS
1. The work of scientists is to study evidence and events and try to explain them.
2. Assumptions accepted by faith determine the way a scientist interprets evidence.
3. Creationists assume that there is a great God who is able to create just by speaking. Evolutionists do not believe in such a God but assume things occur naturally over long periods of time.
4. Evidences of the Flood include sedimentary deposits, fossils, coal beds, geological features, and flood legends.
5. By studying layers of sedimentary deposits, scientists can determine the order of the layers and the conditions prevailing when they were deposited.
6. The Flood dramatically altered Earth's surface features through water erosion, land movement, wind erosion, and volcanic eruptions.

VOCABULARY LIST

coal	geologic column	principle of uniformity
fossil	guyot	sediment

PRACTICE
Multiple Choice. Choose the best answer.
1. Which supports the Flood?
   a. the Bible
   b. fossil distribution
   c. legends
   d. all of these
2. How much of Earth's crust is made of sediment?
   a. 10 percent
   b. 25 percent
   c. 50 percent
   d. 75 percent
3. Which of the following influences scientific interpretations?
   a. the facts
   b. the evidence
   c. assumptions
   d. all of these
4. Which did not happen during the Flood?
   a. formation of mountains
   b. earthquakes
   c. ice age
   d. burial of plants and animals
5. Why did God send a great wind to blow on Earth?
   a. to kill off the birds
   b. to bury dead animals
   c. to make big waves
   d. to move the ark

6. What ended the ice age?
   a. the Flood
   b. a lack of moisture
   c. a slowing in volcanic activity
   d. warm oceans
7. Where did the water of the Flood come from?
   a. the atmosphere
   b. the ground
   c. both a and b
   d. neither a nor b
8. All of the geologic evidence found on Earth's surface proves the story of the Flood recorded in the Bible.
   a. true
   b. false
9. The hardened remains of plants and animals are called
   a. sediments
   b. fossils
   c. guyots
   d. geologic column
10. Which is an assumption accepted by creationists?
   a. nature can be explained by natural law
   b. God is active in nature
   c. the principle of uniformity
   d. none of these

Matching. Match each word with its definition or description.
1. formed as Earth cooled
2. covered the whole Earth
3. hardened plant and animal remains
4. a dark-colored rock
5. makes up most of Earth's crust
6. may have removed the tops of mountains
7. a sequence of fossils
8. the theory that things always happen the same way
9. affect how people interpret facts
10. helped to form glaciers

a. assumptions
b. principle of uniformity
c. sediments
d. wind
e. geologic column
f. the Flood
g. coal
h. fossils
i. volcanoes
j. glaciers

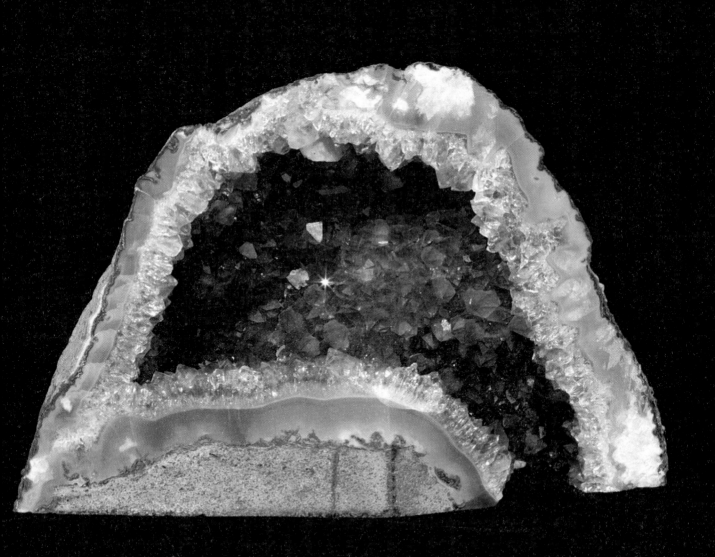

CHAPTER 8

MINERALS AND ROCKS

INTRODUCTION

For thousands of years, people have cherished crystals for their rare beauty. But who would know, just from looking at the outside of this geode found in Brazil, that its hollow core enclosed hundreds of precious amethyst crystals?

How do minerals form? Do all minerals have crystals? How do rocks differ from minerals? You will explore these and other questions as you study this chapter.

SECTION TITLES

Amethyst crystals found inside a Brazilian geode.

8–1 ELEMENTS AND MINERALS

VOCABULARY

compound
element
matter
mineral

OBJECTIVES

- Explain the relationship between elements, compounds, and minerals.
- Identify the features common to all minerals.
- Describe how mineral deposits form.

Fig. 8-1 A pencil, a glass of water, and steam are all examples of matter.

Fig. 8-2 There are three forms of matter: solid, liquid, and gas.

Fig. 8-3 Sulfur, gold, and carbon have properties that help identify them.

Fig. 8-4 Many common household products are compounds.

How do the pencil, the glass of water, and the steam from the kettle differ from each other (fig. 8–1)? What do they have in common? If you said that each is made of matter, you would be correct. **Matter** is anything— solid, liquid, or gas—that has mass and takes up space (fig. 8–2).

Matter on Earth is made up of one or more of the 92 kinds of naturally occurring atoms or **elements**, substances that normally do not change into other substances. Each element has special properties that identify it (fig. 8–3). While elements do not change, they can combine with others to form **compounds**. For example, water, a common compound, forms when hydrogen and oxygen combine. Fig. 8–4 shows other common compounds.

Minerals are elements or compounds that occur in Earth. Gold, silver, and copper are single-element minerals. Most minerals, however, are compounds made up of two or more elements. Table salt, for example, is made of sodium and chlorine (fig. 8–5).

All minerals share four features:

1. They occur naturally in the environment.
2. They do not come from living things.
3. Each has unique properties and composition.
4. Their atoms are arranged in an orderly pattern.

Minerals are often found in concentrated deposits. Some minerals, such as quartz and feldspar, form as magma cools in the cavities or cracks in the crust (fig. 8–6). Heavy minerals, such as gold, are deposited as water washes them into rivers and they settle to the bottom. Still other minerals, such as gypsum (jip´ səm) and halite (hāl´ it) (rock salt), form

Fig. 8-5 Salt is a compound made of sodium and chlorine.

Fig. 8-6 Minerals are sometimes deposited in cracks of rocks and form veins such as these.

RESEARCH IT

Find out what fool's gold is and what it is used for today.

135

The largest crystal ever found is a beryl crystal. This crystal measures 18 m (59 ft) long, 3.5 m (11.5 ft) in diameter, and weighs more than 170 000 kg (185 tons)!

as the water they are dissolved in evaporates from shallow lakes (fig. 8–7).

Fig. 8-7 Mineral formations such as these form as mineral-rich water evaporates.

TRY THIS 8–1: Hey, This Is Salty

Materials:

| magnifying lens | rock salt |
| plastic bag (reclosable) | table salt |

Procedure:
1. Shake a few grains of table salt into a reclosable plastic bag.
2. Use the magnifying lens to look closely at the grains of salt.
   - What is the shape of most of the grains?
   - Describe any grains that look different from the others.
   - Do all of the grains have flat surfaces?
3. Place a few pieces of rock salt in a plastic bag.
4. Use the magnifying lens to look closely at the pieces of rock salt.
   - What is the shape of most of the pieces?
   - Do the pieces have flat surfaces?
   - Do the surfaces appear to meet at right angles?
5. Look for some pieces of rock salt that do not appear to be cube-shaped. Remove these from the bag and crush them by rolling your pencil over them. (Note: You may need to press very hard to do this.)
6. Look at the crushed pieces with the magnifying lens.
   - Are any of these pieces shaped like a cube?
   - Do these pieces have flat surfaces?
   - Do the surfaces meet at right angles?
   - Can pieces of salt be classed as minerals? Why?

REVIEW IT

1. True or false. All minerals are elements. Explain.
2. What features do all minerals have in common?
3. What are three ways mineral deposits form?

8-2 IDENTIFYING MINERALS

OBJECTIVES

- Describe common tests used to identify minerals.
- Identify common minerals.

VOCABULARY
cleavage
fluorescent
fracture
luster
metal
Mohs' scale
streak

Figure 8-8 shows real gold and fool's gold. Which one is really gold? To know for sure, you would need to test them to determine their properties. Geologists use several tests to identify the properties of minerals, five of which are described below.

HARDNESS TEST

The **Mohs' scale** indicates the hardness of a mineral. It is based on 10 minerals (fig. 8-9). Number 10 is the hardest, and number 1 is the softest. A mineral is tested by seeing which other minerals it will scratch. If it scratches numbers 1, 2, and 3 but not 5, it has a hardness of 4. Diamond has a hardness of 10 and can scratch all other minerals.

Fig. 8-8   Gold (left) has different properties from fool's gold (right).

| Talc = 1 | Gypsum = 2 | Calcite = 3 | Fluorite = 4 | Apatite = 5 |
| Orthoclase = 6 | Quartz = 7 | Topaz = 8 | Corundum = 9 | Diamond = 10 |

Fig. 8-9   These ten minerals make up the Mohs' scale of hardness.

An easier way to test hardness uses only your fingernail, a penny, a knife blade, and a piece of glass (fig. 8-10).

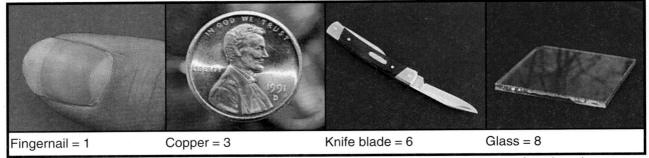

| Fingernail = 1 | Copper = 3 | Knife blade = 6 | Glass = 8 |

Fig. 8-10   These common items can be used to determine the approximate hardness of a mineral.

STREAK TEST

Some minerals are identified by their color. Sulfur, for example, is bright yellow. When the color of a mineral is hidden by dirt, you can do a **streak** test by rubbing the mineral across a rough piece of tile or a metal file. The color of the streak helps identify it. Fool's gold leaves a dark-green streak (fig. 8–11). Real gold leaves a golden streak.

Fig. 8-11   Iron pyrite leaves a green streak.

LUSTER TEST

Luster refers to how a mineral reflects light. A mineral can have a metallic or nonmetallic luster. Galena, which shines like a piece of metal, has a metallic luster (fig. 8–12). Quartz has a nonmetallic luster because it is glassy, waxy, or dull in appearance.

Fig. 8-12   Galena has a silvery luster.

138

CRYSTAL-SHAPE TEST

The crystals of each mineral have a specific shape. Salt crystals, for example, are always shaped like a cube (fig. 8–13). If you can see the shape of a crystal, you can identify the mineral. However, seeing the crystals is not always easy because many are very small.

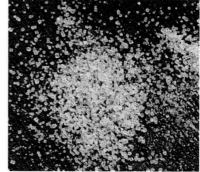

Fig. 8-13 Salt forms cube-shaped crystals

CLEAVAGE/FRACTURE TEST

If a mineral is hit hard enough, it will break or **fracture**. Some minerals, like fool's gold, break unevenly. Others, such as mica, split into thin sheets (fig. 8–14). This quality is called **cleavage** (klēv´ ij).

There are other ways of identifying minerals besides these five tests. A few minerals contain iron and are attracted by a magnet (fig. 8–15). Some minerals contain carbonates that bubble and fizz when acid touches them (fig. 8–16). **(YOU SHOULD NEVER TEST WITH ACID UNLESS YOU WORK CAREFULLY AND WITH THE SUPERVISION OF YOUR TEACHER.)** Rock salt or halite can be recognized by its salty taste. **(NEVER TASTE ANYTHING IN THE LAB UNLESS DIRECTED TO DO SO**

Fig. 8-14 Mica splits into thin sheets.

Fig. 8-15 Some minerals are magnetic.

Fig. 8-16 Some minerals react to acid.

Custom Design • Precious/Semi-Preciou
Wholesale Jewelry Sup   Certified Gemo

LAPI   IA

s

DAVID   RTON

obby

vd., Anaheim,
(714) 827-5680

Fig. 8-17   Calcite forms a double image

BY YOUR TEACHER.) Calcite (kal´ sīt) splits light into two beams that form a double image (fig. 8–17). Some minerals are **fluorescent**. They normally look dull, but are bright and colorful under ultraviolet light (fig. 8–18).

Fig. 8-18   Fluorescent minerals produce bright colors under ultraviolet light.

Fig. 8-19   Metals can be hammered into thin sheets or pulled into wire.

Other minerals, such as gold, copper, and aluminum, are **metals.** They have luster and can be hammered into flat sheets or drawn into a wire (fig. 8–19). Metals are also good conductors of heat and electricity. Because of these qualities, metals are widely used.

All minerals share some properties. To tell them apart you must test them in several ways. If enough properties of a mineral are known, it can easily be identified.

DID YOU KNOW?
Gold can be rolled so thin that 33 cc (2 cu in) of gold can be hammered into a thin sheet that would cover a tennis court.

REVIEW IT

1. What is the best test to distinguish between real gold and fool's gold?
2. What is the softest mineral?
3. What mineral fizzes when it contacts acid?
4. Why is the crystal-shape test difficult to use at times?

8–3 MINERALS AND ROCKS

OBJECTIVES

- Describe a mixture.
- Distinguish between rocks and minerals.

VOCABULARY
mixture

In figure 8–20, which examples are rocks and which are minerals? If you guessed that examples B, C, and D are rocks and the others are minerals, you are correct. But how are rocks and minerals different?

Fig. 8-20   Minerals are single elements or combinations of elements. Rocks are mixtures of various minerals.

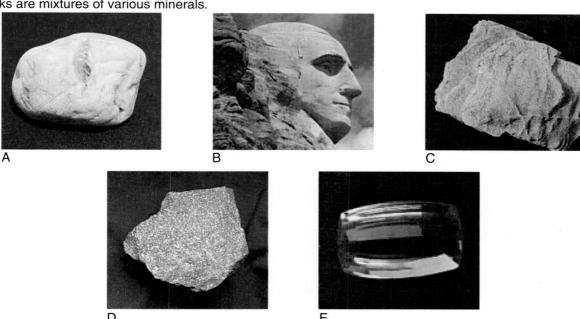

A   B   C

D   E

You learned in Section 8–1 that minerals are single elements or combinations of elements. Rocks, on the other hand, are mixtures of various minerals. In **mixtures**, the ingredients do not chemically combine and change; they simply stick together. Concrete and granite provide examples that demonstrate such mixtures. Rocks are often identified by the minerals that "stick together" to form them.

Fig. 8-21 Concrete is a mixture.

When construction workers make concrete, they mix cement with sand, then add water to make the mixture soupy (fig. 8–21). Gravel is added last. The electric cement mixer mixes the ingredients until they are thoroughly blended; then the concrete is poured into forms to make a sidewalk. In a day or two, the concrete hardens.

Fig. 8-22 Granite is a mixture of several minerals.

In a similar way, granite, a common rock used for monuments and buildings, is made of several minerals mixed together (fig. 8–22). Feldspar (feld´ spär) is the light-colored part of granite, quartz makes up the clear crystals, and biotite and mica are the dark-colored specks.

REVIEW IT

1. Are rocks mixtures or compounds? Explain.
2. How are rocks and minerals different?

142

8–4 TYPES OF ROCKS

OBJECTIVE

• Describe the three types of rock.

Rocks can be organized into three groups: igneous (ig´ nē əs), sedimentary, and metamorphic rock. The charts in this section describe the characteristics, uses, and examples of each group of rocks (fig. 8–23).

VOCABULARY
extrusive
igneous rock
intrusive
metamorphic rock
sedimentary rock

Igneous Rock

| Granite | Basalt | Pumice | Obsidian |

CHARACTERISTICS	USES
• Formed as magma cools. • **Intrusive** rocks cool slowly below ground and have a coarse texture. Example: granite. • **Extrusive** rocks cool above ground. Some are made up of small crystals (basalt), others lack crystals and have a smooth texture (obsidian), still others form as gas-filled lava cools (pumice).	• Used in construction. • Used to make monuments and statues. • Obsidian used by Native Americans for knives and arrowheads.

Fig. 8-23

143

Sedimentary Rock

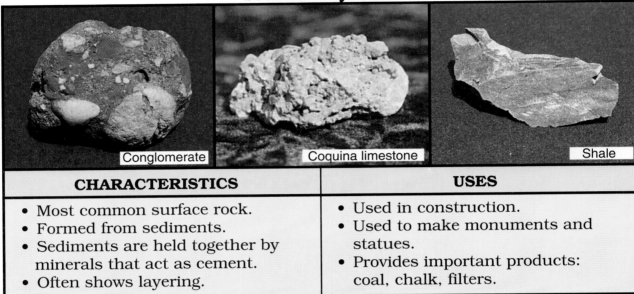

Conglomerate   Coquina limestone   Shale

CHARACTERISTICS	USES
• Most common surface rock. • Formed from sediments. • Sediments are held together by minerals that act as cement. • Often shows layering.	• Used in construction. • Used to make monuments and statues. • Provides important products: coal, chalk, filters.

Fig. 8-23

Metamorphic Rock

Marble   Schist   Slate

CHARACTERISTICS	USES
• Formed from other rocks that are changed by heat and pressure. • Banding or marbleized appearance.	• Used in construction. • Used to make monuments and statues.

Fig. 8-23

REVIEW IT

DID YOU KNOW?
Heat from campfires has changed sandstone into quartzite.

1. What are the three types of rocks?
2. What is the difference between intrusive and extrusive rocks?

8–5 THE ROCK CYCLE

OBJECTIVE

• Explain the rock cycle.

VOCABULARY
rock cycle

The rocks that make up Earth's crust are constantly forming, changing, and forming again in a process called the **rock cycle**. Usually the changes happen slowly. However, volcanoes and earthquakes change Earth's crust quickly.

Look at magma in the rock cycle diagram (fig. 8-24). Magma cools above or below ground to form igneous rock.

The Rock Cycle

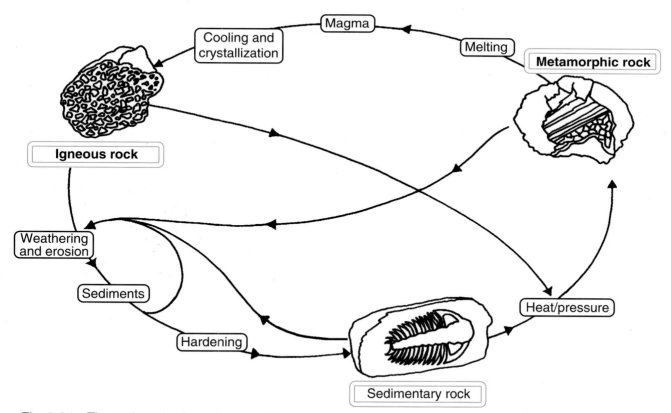

Fig. 8-24   The rock cycle shows how rock forms and changes.

Above ground, weathering and erosion slowly break off tiny bits of the rock. Wind, water, or gravity move these pieces around. The particles collect and form layers that harden into sedimentary rock. Sometimes the newly formed sedimentary rock remains on the surface. If this happens, it will weather again to form new rock. At other times, changes in the crust bury the sedimentary rock. When sedimentary rock is buried deep underground, heat and pressure change it into metamorphic rock.

Not all igneous rock comes to the surface. The igneous rock that remains buried below Earth's surface does not break into sediments. Often this buried rock changes into metamorphic rock because of pressure within the crust. At other times igneous rock comes in contact with the magma and melts back into the mantle.

The same processes that act on sedimentary and igneous rock also act on metamorphic rock. Metamorphic rock that is on Earth's surface is weathered slowly away, and new rock forms. Metamorphic rock that remains within the crust is changed again by heat and pressure.

RESEARCH IT
Find out how geodes are formed.

REVIEW IT

1. What is the rock cycle?
2. How are erosion and weathering involved in the rock cycle?

CLASS ACTIVITY 8–5: Crayon Rocks

Question: How does the rock cycle work?

Materials:

crayon pieces – 30–50	tin can (large)
hot water	transparent tape
tagboard strip (8 cm wide)	wax paper

Procedure:
1. Use the tagboard strip and tape to make a snug collar around the bottom of the tin can.
2. Cut a disk of wax paper the same size as the bottom of the can. Place another sheet of wax paper on your work surface.
3. Remove the collar from the tin can. Place the tagboard collar in the center of your work surface on top of the wax paper sheet.
4. Remove all of the paper from the crayon pieces and place the pieces inside the collar. Describe how the crayons are arranged in the Data section.
5. Place the disk of wax paper on top of the crayons. Place the can on top of the wax-paper disk.
6. Fill the can with hot water. When the can is cool, remove it. Observe and record.

Data:

CRAYONS BEFORE MELTING	CRAYONS AFTER MELTING

Questions:
1. How were the crayons changed?
2. How did the can of hot water cause a change in the crayons?
3. How are the changed crayons a model for what happens to rock underground?

Conclusion: Write 3–5 sentences about what you learned from this activity.

CHAPTER 8 WRAP-UP

SKILLS DEVELOPMENT

THINKING SKILLS: CLASSIFYING

Each of the three types of rocks has its own characteristics.
1. SEDIMENTARY ROCKS form from sediments, small particles laid down by wind or water. This type of rock shows layering.
2. IGNEOUS ROCKS form as magma cools. If this magma cools below ground, the rock has a coarse texture; if the magma cools above ground, the texture is smooth.
3. METAMORPHIC ROCKS form from other rocks that are changed by heat and pressure. These rocks often show banding or a marbleized appearance.

Examine the pictures of the 10 rocks below and classify them as one of the three types of rocks. Give a reason for your selection.

QUESTIONS AND PROBLEMS

1. How can gas be matter?
2. What is the difference between luster and streak?
3. How do mineral deposits form in lake beds?
4. What is the difference between intrusive and extrusive rock?
5. How is pumice unlike all other rock?
6. Limestone changes to what metamorphic rock?
7. What happens to magma in the rock cycle?
8. How are elements identified?
9. What is the difference between an element and a compound?
10. What are the properties of metals?
11. How are mixtures different from compounds?
12. How are rocks identified?
13. What holds the sediments in sedimentary rocks together?
14. Does metamorphic rock change? Explain.
15. How can sedimentary rock become new sedimentary rock?
16. How can sedimentary rock lying on the ground be changed into igneous rock?

RESEARCH

1. Collect 10–20 kinds of metals. Organize your samples into groups based on their properties. Label each group and describe its properties. Display your work on a poster.
2. Talk to a gem cutter or jeweler to investigate how gems are cut, displayed, and priced. Prepare an oral report that includes visual aids, and present your report to the class.
3. Find out which rocks or minerals are important in your state and how each is gathered. Make a bulletin board that displays your findings.
4. Make a model of the New Jerusalem showing the 12 stones that make up its foundation.
5. Construct paper models of as many crystal shapes as you can. Display your models with pictures of minerals that have each crystal shape.

REVIEW

HIGHLIGHTS

1. Elements are substances that do not usually change into other substances; compounds are made up of two or more elements chemically combined. Minerals are elements or compounds that occur in nature.
2. Certain features are common to all minerals. Each occurs naturally, each does not come from living things, each has unique properties and composition, and the atoms of each are arranged in an orderly manner.

3. Mineral deposits form when magma cools in cavities or cracks in rocks, water deposits minerals too heavy to carry, or dissolved minerals turn into a solid because the water evaporates.
4. Common tests used to identify minerals include hardness, streak, luster, crystal shape, and cleavage/fracture.
5. A mixture occurs when two or more elements or compounds stick together but do not chemically combine or change.
6. A rock is a mixture of several minerals; a mineral is a single element or a compound made of two or more elements or compounds.
7. Igneous rock is formed when magma cools. Sedimentary rock is formed from layers of sediments. Metamorphic rock is formed when heat and pressure act on igneous or sedimentary rock.
8. The rock cycle is the process rocks go through as they constantly form, change, and form again.

VOCABULARY LIST

cleavage	igneous rock	mineral
compound	intrusive	mixture
element	luster	Mohs' scale
extrusive	matter	rock cycle
fluorescent	metal	sedimentary rock
fracture	metamorphic rock	streak

PRACTICE

Multiple Choice. Choose the best answer.
1. Which test would not be helpful in identifying gold?
   a. streak
   b. magnetism
   c. luster
   d. hardness
2. Mineral deposits form because of . . .
   a. magma cooling
   b. settling
   c. evaporation
   d. all of these
3. Which is not a feature of all minerals?
   a. occur naturally
   b. have crystals
   c. come from nonliving things
   d. an orderly arrangement of atoms
4. Which are good conductors of heat and electricity?
   a. metals
   b. elements
   c. mixtures
   d. compounds
5. Which form of matter has a definite shape and a definite volume?
   a. solid
   b. liquid
   c. gas
   d. none of these

6. Which is not a single-element mineral?
   a. gold
   b. salt
   c. silver
   d. aluminum
7. Which is harder?
   a. knife blade
   b. corundum
   c. glass
   d. talc
8. Which mineral has a salty taste?
   a. quartz
   b. magnesium
   c. calcite
   d. halite
9. Which makes up rocks?
   a. elements
   b. compounds
   c. minerals
   d. all of these
10. Which rock type can form new igneous rock?
    a. metamorphic
    b. igneous
    c. sedimentary
    d. all of these

Matching. Match each word with its definition or description.
1. ability to split along flat surface
2. used to determine hardness
3. reflects light
4. formed as magma cools
5. change color under ultraviolet light
6. cool slowly below ground
7. most common surface rock
8. elements chemically combined
9. formed by heat and pressure
10. definite shape and volume

a. fluorescent rock
b. metamorphic rock
c. solid
d. compound
e. luster
f. cleavage
g. intrusive rock
h. igneous
i. sedimentary rock
j. Mohs' scale

CAREERS

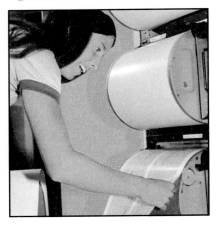

Seismologist

Description of Work
Seismologists are geologists who study earthquakes. They use various types of equipment to measure the strength and location of earthquakes. These scientists study faults and fault movement. Some seismologists are looking for ways to predict when earthquakes will occur.

Personal Qualifications
Seismologists must have good health and enjoy the outdoors. They must have inquiring minds and good problem-solving skills. They also need to be organized and to communicate well.

Requirements
A high-school diploma and at least six years of college.

Career Information
American Geological Institute
4220 King St.
Alexandria, VA 22302

Hydrologist

Description of Work
Hydrologists study water, both where it is and how it moves. They use various types of equipment to measure the amount of water underground, in the soil, and on the surface. They also study rainfall and snowfall levels and work with other scientists to determine the amount of water available for agriculture and other uses.

Personal Qualifications
Hydrologists need to have good health and enjoy the outdoors. They should be able to solve problems and to communicate well. Good organization is also important.

Requirements
A high-school diploma and at least six years of college.

Career Information
American Geological Institute
4220 King St.
Alexandria, VA 22302

Land Surveyor

Description of Work
Land surveyors establish official land and water boundaries and write descriptions of land for deeds and leases and other legal documents. Today's surveyors use satellites to locate exact locations being mapped. They must make sketches and compile notes.

Personal Qualifications
Land surveyors must have good health. They need to have good math, communication, and organization skills. Surveyors must also be able to get along well with other people.

Requirements
A high-school diploma and completion of an approved program in surveying.

Career Information
American Congress of Surveying
    and Mapping
5410 Grosvenor Lane
Bethesda, MD 20814

Soil Scientist

Description of Work
Soil scientists study soil, map its location, and determine the best use. They study farming and conservation practices and help people determine the best use of land. Soil scientists may help determine value of land or decide which fertilizers and soil enhancers should be used to improve the soil.

Personal Qualifications
Soil scientists spend lots of time outdoors, often alone. They need to be organized, to communicate well, and to have inquiring minds.

Requirements
A high-school diploma and a college degree.

Career Information
American Society of Agronomy
677 S. Segoe Rd.
Madison, WI 53711

Volcanologist

Description of Work
Volcanologists are scientists who study volcanoes and try to predict eruptions. They travel around the world to visit active volcanoes. Volcanologists collect samples of gas, ash, and lava and then use instruments to record any volcanic activity. Most volcanologists teach in colleges or work for the government.

Personal Qualifications
Volcanologists must have good health to hike long distances and enjoy the outdoors. They must ask questions, solve problems, and keep accurate records.

Requirements
A high-school diploma and at least six years of college.

Career Information
American Geological Institute
4220 King St.
Alexandria, VA 22302

Jeweler

Description of Work
Jewelers are artists who work with precious stones and metals to make, repair, and adjust jewelry, using a variety of tools. Their work requires a high degree of skill and attention to detail. Some jewelers own and manage stores; others work in manufacturing and usually specialize in a single operation.

Personal Qualifications
Jewelers must have good eyesight and steady hands. They must be honest and creative. Jewelers must also have good people skills when working with customers or employees.

Requirements
A high-school diploma and completion of an approved program in a technical school.

Career Information
Jewelers of America
1271 Ave. of the Americas
New York, NY 10020

UNIT II

THE HUMAN BODY

INTRODUCTION

Seen from the air, Washington, D.C., is an amazing pattern of squares, rectangles, and circles. The capital of the United States is one of the few cities in the world that was designed before it was built. The French engineer who planned the city wanted no crooked streets or winding avenues. Today, Washington's city dwellers, commuting government workers, and tourists are in almost constant motion on the city's streets, freeways, and underground rail system.

Your body is similar to Washington, D.C. Like it, you are operated by many different systems that support and control life, remove waste, and provide transportation and communication. Like the city, you were planned and designed before you came into existence. The Creator designed your body to perform in a trouble-free manner.

In this unit you will discover more about your body systems and how they work. As you learn more about your body, you will be better able to care for it.

CHAPTER TITLES

Washington, D.C., from the air.

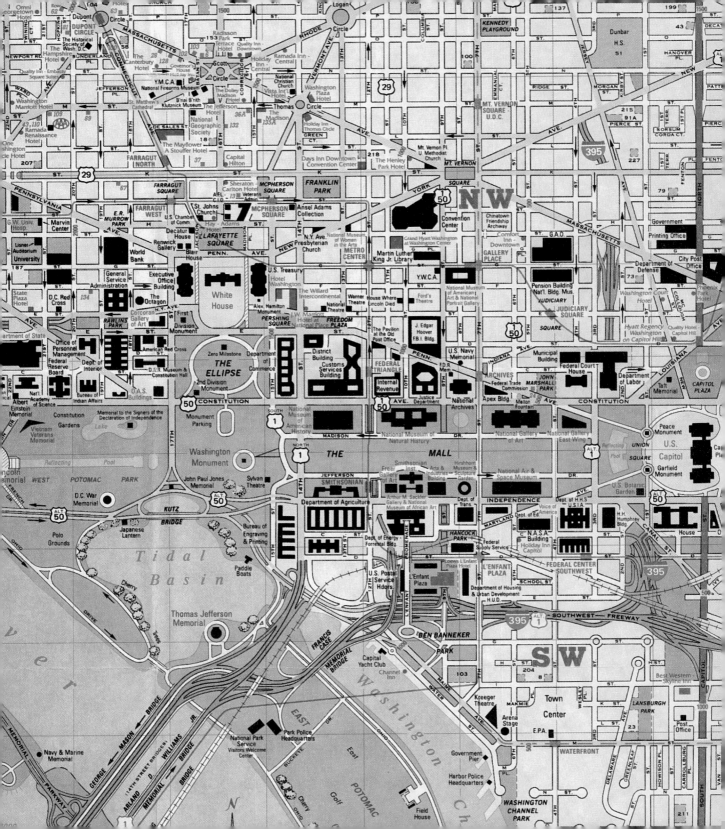

CHAPTER 9

THE BODY'S ORGANIZATION

INTRODUCTION

Imagine you have just moved to Washington, D.C. It is your first day there, and you are trying to find your way around. You need information because the city is very large and can be very confusing.

Your best resource would be a map of the city, such as the one shown on the opposite page. It gives an overall view of the city, helps you locate specific streets and landmarks, and even identifies subway and bus routes.

Use this chapter as a "map" to discover how your body is even more "fearfully and wonderfully" (Psalm 139:14) made than a well-planned city.

SECTION TITLES

9–1 Body Organization
9–2 Organ Systems

A map of downtown Washington, D.C.

9–1 BODY ORGANIZATION

connective tissue
epithelial tissue
mucous membrane
muscular tissue
nervous tissue
organ
tissue

OBJECTIVES

- Describe the organization of the human body.
- Identify the basic types of body tissues.

Your body is composed of more than 30 trillion cells of different shapes and sizes. These cells are the basic building blocks of your body. When similar cells are grouped together, they form **tissues** in much the same way that bricks are put together to build a wall. These tissues usually perform one specific job. The body contains four basic kinds of tissue: epithelial (ep i thē ́ lē əl), muscle, nerve, and connective (fig. 9–1).

Fig. 9–1

TYPES OF TISSUE

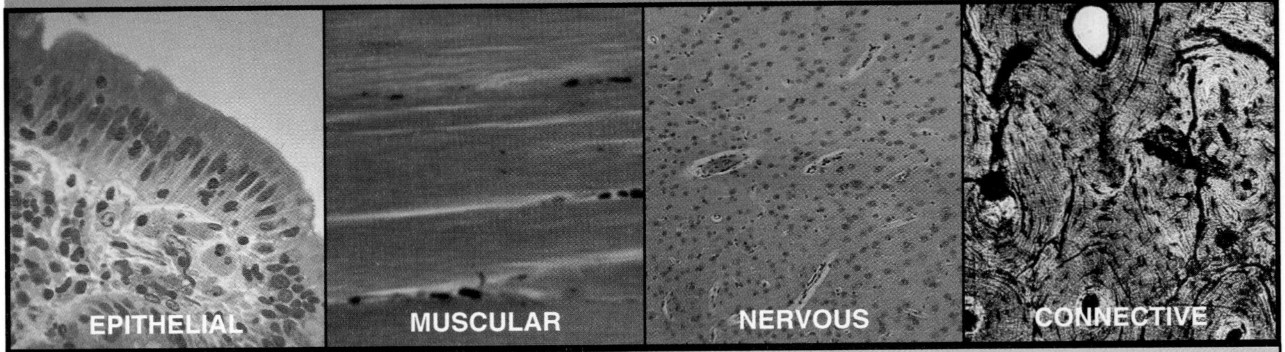

EPITHELIAL   MUSCULAR   NERVOUS   CONNECTIVE

TISSUE	FUNCTION
EPITHELIAL TISSUE	• Forms your skin. • Forms **mucous membrane** (the lining of the stomach, mouth, and intestines).
MUSCULAR TISSUE	• Forms the muscles of the heart, stomach, arms, and legs. • Is able to shorten or contract.
NERVOUS TISSUE	• Forms the brain, nerves, and spinal cord. • Carries electrical messages throughout the body.
CONNECTIVE TISSUE	• Forms bone, cartilage, fat, and blood. • Helps to hold other tissues together.

Cotton fibers are spun into thread, then woven into cloth. Cloth is sewn to make clothing, which makes up your wardrobe. In a similar way, cells form tissue that can be organized to form organs (fig. 9–2). An **organ** is a group of tissues that performs a certain task. For example, your eyes are organs composed of muscular,

DID YOU KNOW?
A stack of 1 trillion sheets of paper would make a tower almost 50,000 miles high! If you counted to 1 trillion, counting one number every second, it would take 93,000 years!

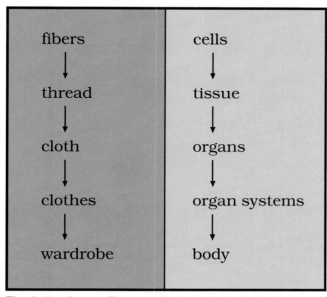

fibers	cells
↓	↓
thread	tissue
↓	↓
cloth	organs
↓	↓
clothes	organ systems
↓	↓
wardrobe	body

Fig. 9–2   Just as fibers make thread, cloth, clothes, and a wardrobe, cells form tissue, organs, organ systems, and the body.

nervous, connective, and epithelial tissue. All of these tissues work together to help you see.

Groups of organs work together to form organ systems. The nervous system is composed of the brain, nerves, and spinal cord. The heart and blood vessels make up the circulatory system.

REVIEW IT

1. What is the difference between cells and tissues?
2. List four tissues that make up your body.
3. How is an organ system different from an organ?

CLASS ACTIVITY 9–1: Things in a Wing

Question: What tissues form a chicken wing?

Materials:

chicken wing	paring knife
magnifying glass	toothpicks – 10
paper towels – 5	

Procedure:
1. Place the chicken wing on several layers of paper towel. Examine the outside of the wing.
2. Carefully remove all of the skin.
3. With a toothpick, pry the bundles of muscle apart. Locate the tubes that go to the muscle.
4. Break one of the large bones in two. Use a toothpick to remove some cells from inside the bone.
5. Find a tendon, white cords that connect muscles to bones. With a toothpick, free the tendon from the bone. Pull the tendon.
6. Find a ligament. They look similar to tendons except they connect bone to bone.
7. In the chart, list all of the tissues that make up the chicken wing and the organ system to which they belong.

Data:

CHART OF TISSUES

TISSUE	ORGAN SYSTEM	TISSUE	ORGAN SYSTEM

Questions:
1. What tissues make up the chicken wing?
2. The yellowish tissue is fat. What job does this tissue perform?
3. How is the wing designed to protect the blood vessels?
4. What does the tissue inside the bone look like?
5. What happens when you pull the tendon?
6. What would happen if there were no ligaments?

Conclusion: Write 3–5 sentences about what you learned from this activity.

9–2 ORGAN SYSTEMS

OBJECTIVES

- Identify the organ systems that make up the body.
- Describe what each of the body's organ systems do.
- Describe human beings' uniqueness in creation.
- Analyze how sin has affected the human body.

VOCABULARY
hormone
organ system

An **organ system** is two or more organs that work together to carry out a common task (fig. 9–3). Systems play an important role in handling all of the processes functioning in your body. In this section you will see how these organ systems have interconnected roles.

Your body is not organized by accident; God designed it to run smoothly. Every cell, tissue, and organ is part of you for a reason. Each system and every structure have a job to do, whether to build, repair, or give you the energy you need each day.

TRY THIS 9–2: How Many Can You Name?

Materials:
none needed

Procedure:

1. Without any resources other than your partner (do not open your book), list on your paper as many body systems as you can remember. Once you have made your list, rank the body systems in order of importance.
   - Which body system would you live the longest without?
   - Which body system would you live the shortest time without?
   - Which body system do you think is the most important? Why?

2. Next to each body system you have listed, list the organs that are part of the system.
   - Which organs can you live without?
   - Which organs can you not live without?

3. Describe the work each system does for the body.

YOUR BODY'S ORGAN SYSTEMS

Fig. 9–3

ORGAN SYSTEM	DESCRIPTION AND FUNCTION
	SKELETAL • Made of bones and connective tissue. • Shapes and supports your body. • Protects body parts (skull, ribs). • Makes blood cells. • Works with muscles to support movement.
	MUSCULAR • Made of muscles. • Shapes your body. • Pulls on bones to move your body. • Allows you to breathe, eat, talk, run, etc.
	INTEGUMENTARY • Made of skin, hair, and nails. • Covers and protects your body. • Cools and insulates your body. • Keeps bacteria and viruses out and moisture in. • Removes waste from the body through perspiration. • Allows you to feel pressure, pain, hot, and cold.

Fig. 9–3 continued

ORGAN SYSTEM	DESCRIPTION AND FUNCTION
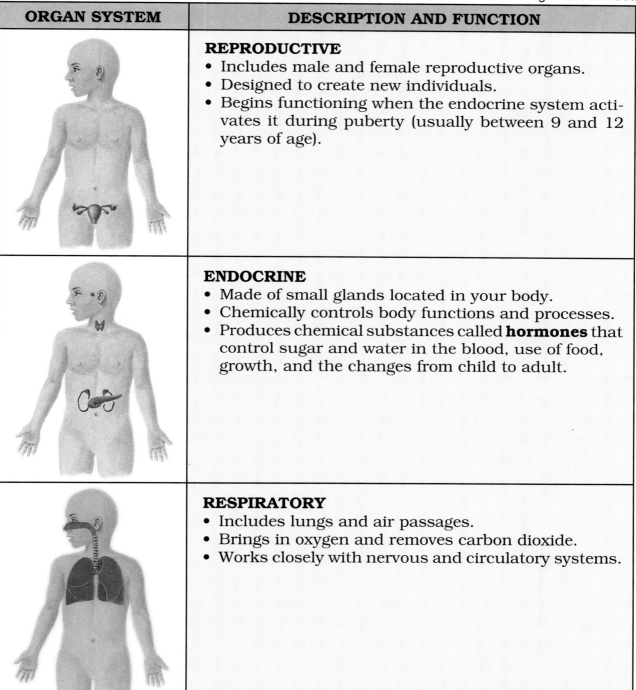	**REPRODUCTIVE** • Includes male and female reproductive organs. • Designed to create new individuals. • Begins functioning when the endocrine system activates it during puberty (usually between 9 and 12 years of age).
	ENDOCRINE • Made of small glands located in your body. • Chemically controls body functions and processes. • Produces chemical substances called **hormones** that control sugar and water in the blood, use of food, growth, and the changes from child to adult.
	RESPIRATORY • Includes lungs and air passages. • Brings in oxygen and removes carbon dioxide. • Works closely with nervous and circulatory systems.

Fig. 9–3 continued

ORGAN SYSTEM	DESCRIPTION AND FUNCTION
	NERVOUS • Made of nerves, the brain, and the spinal cord. • Carries messages to and from the brain. • Coordinates all body processes and functions. • Enables you to remember, experience emotion, and be aware of your surroundings. • Enables you to think, imagine, solve problems, and make decisions. These abilities make human beings unique in God's creation. • Is the system through which God communicates.
	EXCRETORY • Includes skin, lungs, large intestine, and kidneys. • Removes waste from the body, helps prevent disease and infection.
	CIRCULATORY • Includes heart, blood, and blood vessels. • Transports food and oxygen to cells, removes carbon dioxide and other wastes from cells. • Works closely with the nervous and respiratory systems.

Fig. 9–3 continued

ORGAN SYSTEM	DESCRIPTION AND FUNCTION
	DIGESTIVE • Includes mouth, esophagus (i säf´ ə gəs), stomach, small intestine, large intestine, liver, and pancreas (pan´ krē əs). • Digests the food you eat, making it ready to be picked up by the blood and transported to the cells.

We live in a sinful world where sin affects us in ways we do not even understand. One result is that some of the body systems God designed do not always work the way they were intended, whether because of injury, illness, pollution, or poor health habits. But even though sin is in the world, we can still see the beauty of God's design in the human body and how all of the systems work together for our good.

RESEARCH IT

Identify four birth defects or genetic disorders and the body system or systems they affect.

REVIEW IT

1. Which two systems help you move?
2. Name two systems, besides the excretory system, that remove waste.
3. Which system makes you different from other animals?
4. How does the body show God's design?

CHAPTER 9 WRAP-UP

SKILLS DEVELOPMENT

THINKING SKILLS: INTERPRETING A DIAGRAM

In science, it is not always possible to see things clearly or it may not be practical to examine something. Diagrams can be helpful in showing how things work or how something is arranged or the pathway followed. Being able to read a diagram accurately will help you understand important concepts in science.

When you look at a diagram, always read the information that tells you about the diagram. This information can be found in the text or near the diagram. Many times the important parts of the diagram are labeled, or arrows may show the pathway something follows. Some diagrams, like the one below, illustrate a view that cannot easily be seen.

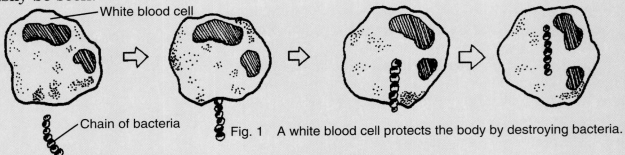

White blood cell

Chain of bacteria

Fig. 1   A white blood cell protects the body by destroying bacteria.

1. Look at the diagram in figure 2, and answer the following questions.
   A. What does the caption tell you about the diagram?
   B. List the labeled items.

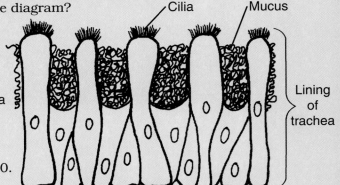

Cilia   Mucus

Lining of trachea

Fig. 2   The cilia and mucus in the trachea are part of the body's first line of defense.

2. Now look on page 219 and find figure 12–10.
   A. What is the title of this diagram?
   B. What are the important parts?
3. Make a diagram showing how to get to your home. Label important landmarks and the path you follow.

QUESTIONS AND PROBLEMS

1. What does connective tissue connect?
2. Do all animals have organ systems?
3. Why is the circulatory system so important?
4. Rank the systems of the body in order of their importance. Explain how you evaluated their importance.
5. How are the nervous and endocrine systems similar?
6. To what system of the body does the Bible refer when it says, "Love the Lord your God with all your heart" (Deuteronomy 13:3)?
7. Suppose you are a molecule of oxygen. What two systems must you travel through to get to the cells?
8. How are the four types of tissue used in the digestive system?
9. Identify the systems of the body that are used as you write the answer to this question. Explain how each is involved.
10. List things you have done today that have benefited your body.

RESEARCH

1. Find out what kind of doctor specializes in each body system.
2. Find several texts in the Bible that describe the importance of our bodies to God.
3. Compare the systems of your body to the systems that make up an automobile.
4. Research three different methods communities use to dispose of human waste. Write a report that includes an explanation of the advantages or disadvantages of each method.
5. A sheet of standard binder paper has an area of about 60 000 sq mm (93 sq in). Scientists estimate that your body is made up of about 30,000,000,000,000 (30 trillion) cells. If each cell were placed on 1 sq mm, how many sheets of paper would be needed? If it takes about 10,000 sheets of paper to make a stack 1 meter (3 ft) high, how tall will the stack of paper be?

REVIEW

HIGHLIGHTS

1. Cells make up tissue, tissue makes up an organ, and organs make up organ systems.
2. The four types of tissue are epithelial, muscular, nervous, and connective.
3. Your body is made up of ten organ systems: skeletal, muscular, nervous, integumentary, excretory, circulatory, respiratory, digestive, reproductive, and endocrine.

4. Each organ system has a job to do. These jobs are identified on pages 162–165.
5. The design of the nervous system and the ability to imagine, solve problems, make decisions, and think spiritually make human beings unique in God's creation.
6. The effects of sin—such as disease, injury, pollution, and poor health habits—all damage the bodies God created for us.

VOCABULARY LIST

connective tissue
epithelial tissue
hormone

mucous membrane
muscular tissue
nervous tissue

organ
organ system
tissue

PRACTICE

Multiple Choice. Choose the best answer.
1. Which shows the body's organization?
   a. cell, tissue, system, organ
   b. tissue, cell, system, organ
   c. organ, system, cell, tissue
   d. cell, tissue, organ, system
2. Which is *not* one of the four basic body tissues?
   a. connective tissue
   b. muscle tissue
   c. cartilage tissue
   d. nerve tissue
3. Which body system includes the skin, lungs, and kidneys?
   a. respiratory
   b. nervous
   c. excretory
   d. endocrine
4. Which two systems are involved in getting food to the cells?
   a. excretory/digestive
   b. digestive/circulatory
   c. circulatory/nervous
   d. respiratory/endocrine
5. Which body system makes us different from other animals?
   a. nervous
   b. integumentary
   c. reproductive
   d. endocrine
6. Which body system is responsible for producing hormones?
   a. excretory
   b. endocrine
   c. circulatory
   d. none of the above
7. What type of tissue makes up your heart?
   a. nervous
   b. epithelial
   c. muscular
   d. connective

8. Which body system helps you breathe?
   a. muscular
   b. endocrine
   c. digestive
   d. integumentary
9. Which of the following is a function of the skeletal system?
   a. makes blood cells
   b. cools the body
   c. forms fingernails
   d. produces hormones
10. What type of tissue lines the wall of the stomach?
    a. nervous tissue
    b. epithelial tissue
    c. muscular tissue
    d. connective tissue

Matching. Match each word with its definition or description.
1. tissue that surrounds and supports
2. group of organs that works together
3. body system that provides support
4. units that make up tissue
5. main part of integumentary system
6. tissue that carries electrical messages
7. groups of cells that work together
8. tissue that lines your mouth and stomach
9. group of tissues that performs a task
10. the only tissue that can contract

a. cells
b. connective
c. epithelial
d. muscular
e. nervous
f. organ
g. organ system
h. skeletal
i. skin
j. tissue

CHAPTER 10

THE SKELETAL AND MUSCULAR SYSTEMS

INTRODUCTION

Have you ever thought about how statues are made? Most small statues, like the ones sold in souvenir stores, are solid. Large statues—such as the Statue of Liberty, which is nearly 50 m (155 ft) tall—would use too much material and weigh too much if they were solid. So they are usually built around a framework strong enough to support the entire structure. If you look on the opposite page, you will see that you and the Statue of Liberty are supported by similar systems, except that your supporting framework is composed of bones and muscles, and it allows for movement.

What parts make up this framework of support? How does it help you move? How should you care for these systems? In this chapter you will explore answers to these and other questions.

SECTION TITLES

10–1 The Skeleton
10–2 Joints
10–3 Bones and Their Care
10–4 Muscles and Their Care

The Statue of Liberty has a supporting steel framework.

10–1 THE SKELETON

VOCABULARY
cranium
femur
pelvis
rib
spinal column
sternum
vertebra

OBJECTIVES

- Identify the major bones of the body.
- Describe the functions of the skeletal system.

Take a look at your wrist and hand. How many bones do you think are inside? 5? 10? 15? You may be surprised to learn that there are 27 individual bones in your wrist and hand. More than 200 bones make up your entire skeleton (fig. 10–1). The skull, or **cranium**, made up of

Fig. 10–1   Your skeleton is made up of more than 200 bones.

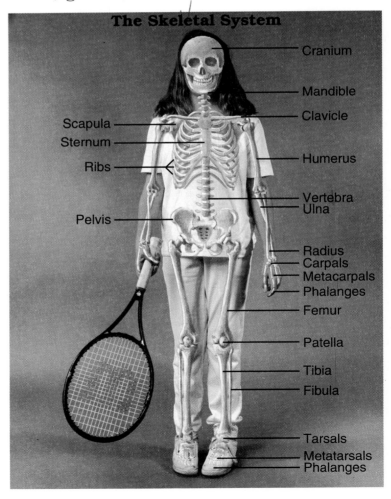

The Skeletal System

Cranium

Mandible

Clavicle

Scapula

Sternum

Humerus

Ribs

Vertebra
Ulna

Pelvis

Radius
Carpals
Metacarpals
Phalanges

Femur

Patella

Tibia

Fibula

Tarsals

Metatarsals
Phalanges

DID YOU KNOW?
The female's pelvis is wider and has a larger opening than the male's. This design allows for a baby to pass through the pelvis during birth.

RESEARCH IT
Locate the smallest bones in the body.

the bones of the head and face, protects the brain. The **spinal column**, or backbone, reaches from the top of the neck to the pelvis, provides vertical support for your body, and protects the spinal cord. It is composed of 33 bones called **vertebrae**. Each vertebra has an opening all the way through it (fig. 10–2). The delicate spinal cord runs through the openings of all these vertebrae.

In your chest are 12 pairs of **ribs** attached to the vertebrae of the spinal column. Your ribs attach in front to a narrow, flattened bone called the **sternum**, or breastbone. The ribs and sternum help protect the heart and lungs.

The **pelvis** is the bowl-shaped set of bones in the hip area that supports the body and protects several organs from damage. The pelvis also provides a place for the leg bones to attach at the hips.

The longest bones in your body are in your arms and legs. These bones support your weight, help you move, and determine how tall you are. The **femur**, or thighbone, is the longest bone of all. In addition to helping you move, these long bones also manufacture red blood cells.

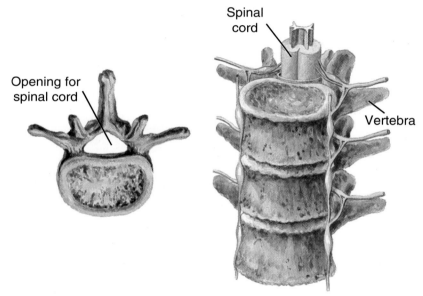

Fig. 10–2 Each vertebra has an opening through which the spinal cord runs.

REVIEW IT

1. Which bones protect the heart and lungs?
2. What are vertebrae?
3. Which bones have the greatest influence on your height?
4. List four functions of the skeletal system.

173

10–2 JOINTS

cartilage
fixed joint
joint
ligament
movable joint
sprain

OBJECTIVES

- Describe the types of joints.
- Explain the function of cartilage and ligaments.

Feel your ankle while you wiggle your foot. This place where bones come together is called a **joint**. Different kinds of joints allow bones to be connected in different ways (fig. 10–3). Many joints are flexible, allowing you to

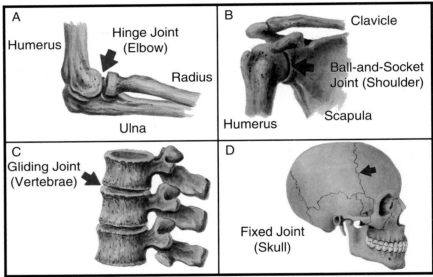

A Humerus — Hinge Joint (Elbow) — Radius — Ulna

B Clavicle — Ball-and-Socket Joint (Shoulder) — Humerus — Scapula

C Gliding Joint (Vertebrae)

D Fixed Joint (Skull)

Fig. 10–3   There are four basic types of joints: hinge (elbow) (A), ball-and-socket (shoulder) (B), gliding (vertebrae) (C), and fixed (skull) (D).

walk, talk, and move. Some of these **movable joints**, such as the knee, were designed to move in only one direction. Others, like your wrist, are able to move in almost any direction. **Fixed joints** are inflexible. If they did move, your body would not have the support and protection it needs.

The bones that make up joints are held in position by tough bands of tissue called **ligaments**. In fig. 10–4, you can see where ligaments hold the bones together. Normally ligaments stretch a little during movement, but extra stretching during a twist or fall may result in a **sprain**.

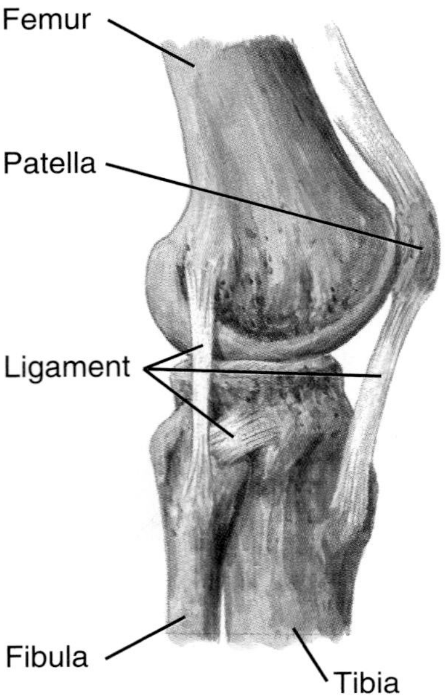

Femur

Patella

Ligament

Fibula

Tibia

Fig. 10–4   Ligaments hold the bones of the knee together.

Cartilage is connective tissue that forms part of your skeleton. It is found at the ends of bones and helps cushion them and reduce friction (fig. 10–5). Cartilage also makes up part of your nose and ears, which is why the tip of your nose is soft and flexible. Cartilage also gives the outer part of your ears shape and support. Imagine how easily your ears and nose would break if God had made them of thin bone instead of cartilage. Imagine how they would look if they were made only of skin.

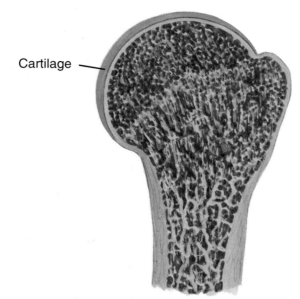

Cartilage

Fig. 10–5   Cartilage at the ends of bones reduces friction and provides a cushion.

TRY THIS 10–2: What a Joint

Materials:
none needed

Procedure:
1. There are many joints in the body. List eight of them on your paper.
2. Describe the type of motion allowed by each joint. (For example, the elbow works like a hinge.)
3. Organize the joints you have listed into categories based on the type of motion they allow. Give a name for each category.
   • Which of the eight joints you listed allow for the greatest degree of motion?
   • Which of the eight joints you listed allow for the least degree of motion?
   • Which joints can move like the elbow?
   • True or False. Every joint in the body allows some sort of motion.

REVIEW IT

1. Why are joints necessary?
2. What type of joint allows for the greatest amount of movement?
3. What are ligaments?
4. Why is cartilage important?

10–3 BONES AND THEIR CARE

VOCABULARY
marrow
osteoporosis

DID YOU KNOW?
Human bone is four times stronger than concrete. A piece of bone the size of a matchbox can support 9000 kg (10 tons)!

OBJECTIVES

- Describe the way bone develops.
- Identify how to care for the skeletal system.

Even though bones seem dead, they are very much alive. Fig. 10–6 is a diagram of a living bone. A membrane containing blood vessels and nerve cells covers each bone. The blood vessels carry food and oxygen to the bone and remove waste.

Because of their design, bones are both lightweight and strong. The outer layer of each bone is very hard and gives the bone its strength. Inside the bone is a hollow space, or cavity, that is filled with **marrow**. This soft tissue makes bone cells and many of the body's blood cells.

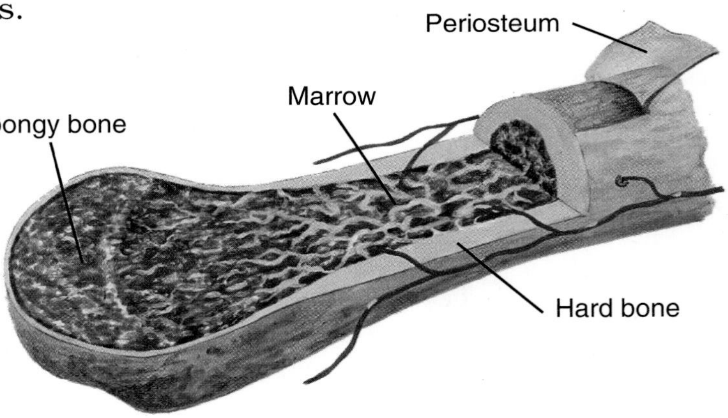

Fig. 10–6 Bone is not just the hard bone you are used to seeing. It is living tissue made up of several parts.

Like all living tissues, bones grow. First, bone cells create cartilage. After cartilage is formed, the bone cells release calcium and phosphorus (fäs´ fər əs) into it. As the calcium and phosphorus crystalize, the cartilage hardens into bone, a process that is not complete until you are 30 to 40 years old.

RESEARCH IT
What foods are highest in calcium and phosphorus?

To function properly, the skeleton must be cared for. Diet and exercise are the most important factors in caring

Fig. 10–7 These foods are rich in calcium and phosphorus, two minerals that maintain strong bones.

for the skeleton. A balanced diet supplies adequate amounts of calcium and phosphorus, two minerals necessary to maintain strong, healthy bones (fig. 10–7). Bones are also strengthened by exercise. As a muscle becomes stronger, the bone to which it is attached becomes stronger too.

Sometimes, if extra calcium is needed somewhere else in the body, bone cells may dissolve minerals out of the bone around them. If too many minerals dissolve out of the bone, the bones become weaker. This weakening of bones, called **osteoporosis** (äs tē ō pə rō´ sis), is most common in older people, especially women. Eating food rich in calcium while you are young ensures rich calcium deposits in your bones. This is one of the best protections against developing osteoporosis when you are older.

REVIEW IT

1. What is the function of the marrow?
2. How does good nutrition help the skeleton?
3. What happens to the skeleton as you exercise?

10–4 MUSCLES AND THEIR CARE

VOCABULARY

biceps
cardiac muscle
involuntary muscle
skeletal muscle
smooth muscle
triceps
voluntary muscle

DID YOU KNOW?

The smallest muscle in your body is located in your ear. This tiny muscle is less than 1 mm long.

Fig. 10–8   There are three types of muscle tissue: cardiac, smooth, and skeletal.

OBJECTIVES

- Identify the major muscles.
- Distinguish between voluntary and involuntary muscles.
- Describe the three types of muscle.
- Identify ways of caring for the muscular system.

Today you have walked, talked, and eaten. Your heart is beating, and your eyes are blinking. All this motion is possible because muscle cells are unique—they are the only cells that shorten, or contract. When a muscle contracts, its ends pull closer together, causing movement. Scientists identify three types of muscle tissue (fig. 10–8). There are more than 600 muscles in your body (fig. 10-9). These muscles are divided into two groups: ones that you control and ones that move automatically.

TYPES OF MUSCLE TISSUE		
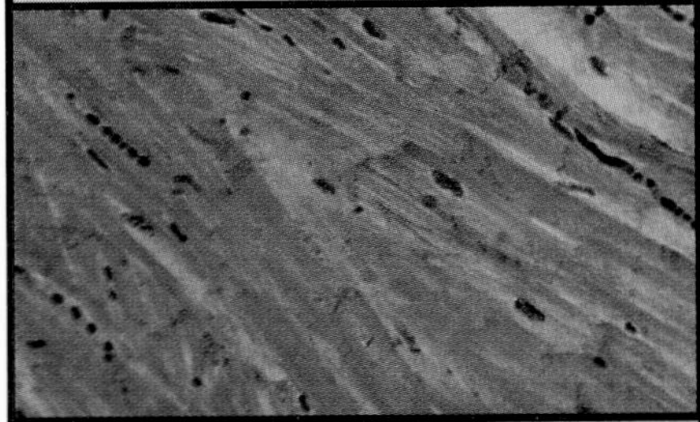 CARDIAC MUSCLE	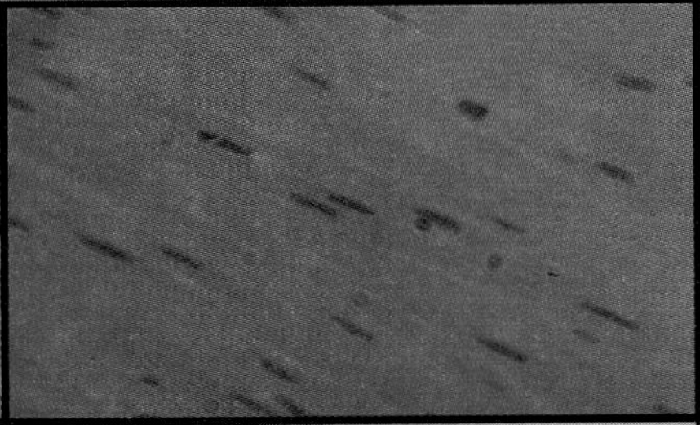 SMOOTH MUSCLE	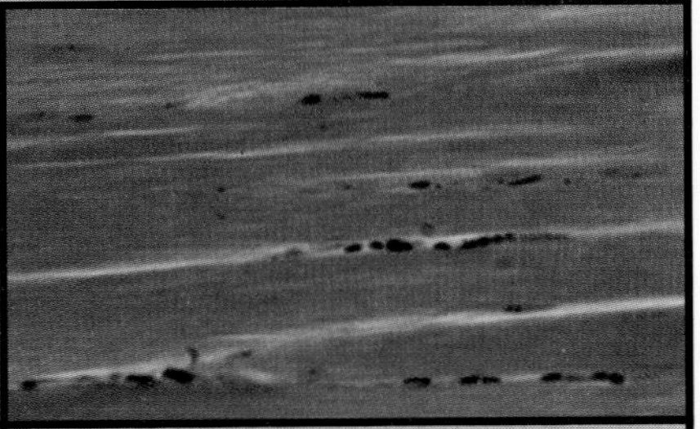 SKELETAL MUSCLE
• Forms the heart. • Involuntary muscle. • Tires less easily than other types of muscle.	• Forms the organs of the digestive system. • Involuntary muscle.	• Forms the muscles that move your skeleton. • Makes up about one-third of your total weight. • Attached to bones by tendons (fig. 10–10).

The Muscular System

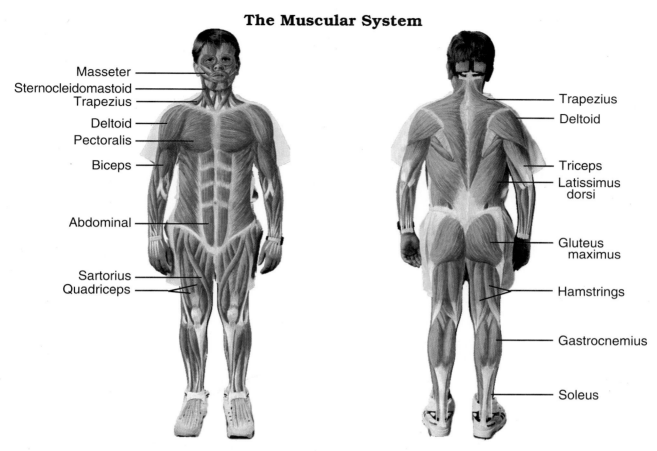

Fig. 10–9 Over 600 muscles make up your body.

Muscles you can control are called **voluntary muscles**. You use these to walk, talk, reach, grasp, etc. The **involuntary muscles** are automatically controlled by your brain. The heart and stomach are examples of involuntary muscles.

Some muscles are both involuntary and voluntary. While your eyelids blink automatically, you may also choose to blink any time you wish. You can also choose to control your breathing, even though breathing is normally automatic.

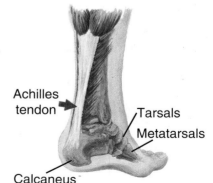

Fig. 10–10 The muscle of the lower leg is attached to the foot by a tendon.

CLASS ACTIVITY 10–4:   Are Ya Git'n Tired Yet?

Question: How long does it take for your muscles to get tired?

Materials:
   kite string (20–30 cm)
   stopwatch
   washers – 3

Procedure:
1. In one end of the string, make a loop that will easily fit over the end of your finger. Tie the three washers securely to the other end of the string.
2. Slip the loop over the end of your finger and place your forearm and hand on your desk as shown.
3. Have your partner record how many finger lifts you can do in one minute.
4. Repeat step 3 two more times.
5. Hold your arm out straight and have your partner count how many times you can open and shut your hand in 30 seconds. Record data.
6. Repeat step 5 two more times.
7. Hold your arm out straight and have your partner time how long you can hold your science textbook without lowering your arm. Record data.
8. Repeat step 7 two more times.

Data:

	TRIAL 1	TRIAL 2	TRIAL 3
FINGER LIFTS (number)			
HAND CLOSINGS (number)			
BOOK HOLDING (time)			

Questions:
1. Which trial for each activity was the best? Why?
2. Which trial for each activity was the worst? Why?
3. Was there much difference between the performance of boys and of girls?
4. What would have happened to the results of trial 3 in finger lifts and hand closing if you had increased the number in trials 1 and 2? What if the number had decreased in trials 1 and 2?

Conclusion: Write 3–5 sentences about what you learned from this activity.

Because muscles can only contract, skeletal muscles are designed to work in pairs. One muscle pulls one way while the second muscle pulls the other way. Make a "muscle" with your arm (fig. 10–11). The **biceps** muscle on top of your arm flexes your arm up. As you straighten your arm out, feel the lower muscle, or **triceps**, contract to pull your arm straight. Each movement is caused by a pull, never by a push.

Muscles stay in good working order only if they are cared for properly. Proper diet and exercise are the best ways to ensure muscle health. Without exercise, muscles become weak and tire more easily. A proper diet gives muscles the materials they need to work. Drinking plenty of water also ensures healthy muscles. Studies have shown that athletes who drink lots of water can exercise longer than those who don't drink enough water.

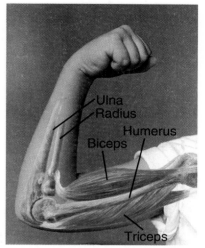

Fig. 10–11 The biceps and triceps move the lower arm.

TRY THIS 10–4: Blinking

Materials:
stopwatch

Procedure:
1. Your job in this activity is to answer this question: Are eye-blinking muscles voluntary or involuntary?
   • What is your hypothesis?
2. Blink your eyelids three times. Now, try not to blink. Have your partner time how long it is before you blink. Record the time.
3. Repeat step 2 two more times and record your results.
   • What is the average time you can go without blinking?
   • How does your average compare to the average of other classmates?
   • Was your hypothesis correct or incorrect?
   • Are eye-blinking muscles voluntary or involuntary?

REVIEW IT

1. What is the name of the muscle in your shoulder?
2. Explain the difference between voluntary and involuntary muscles.
3. What parts of the body are made of smooth muscle?
4. To what are the skeletal muscles attached?
5. Why is exercise important for healthy muscles?

RESEARCH IT
If a muscle never pushes, only pulls, how can you stick out your tongue? Find out.

CHAPTER 10 WRAP-UP
SKILLS DEVELOPMENT

THINKING SKILLS: MAKING OBSERVATIONS

Making observations is an important skill used in many aspects of life. A soccer coach observes a player kick a ball to help the player improve. Making observations is an important part of science. Learning to make careful observations will be of benefit to you in science.

In making observations you must first learn to look carefully at the object. Second, you must observe the object in a systematic way. Finally, you must accurately record your observations.

1. Look at the X-ray picture of the human hand. What observations can you make?

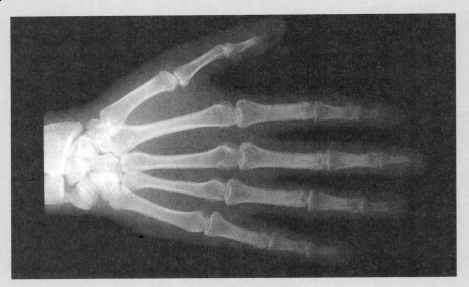

2. How can these observations be useful?
3. What observations can you make about your hands?

QUESTIONS AND PROBLEMS
1. What would happen if we didn't have bones?
2. List protective bones and the organs they protect.
3. What bones and joints are involved in throwing a baseball?
4. The ribs are connected to the sternum by cartilage. Why is this necessary?
5. What can you do to promote a healthy skeleton?
6. What is osteoporosis, and how can it be prevented or delayed?
7. Based on appearance, how are the three types of muscle tissue different?
8. What major pair of muscles allows you to kick a soccer ball?
9. How does cardiac muscle work differently from smooth and skeletal muscle?
10. Suppose you broke your upper arm and had to have it in a cast. Explain what would happen to your biceps.

RESEARCH
1. What provides support to an animal that lacks bones? List three examples.
2. Discover how human bones are different from bird bones. Draw a diagram to show contrasts.
3. Find out how arthritis affects joints. Report on methods of treatment.
4. Construct a model of a long bone that shows the internal and external structure.
5. Find out the symptoms and treatment of rickets.

REVIEW

HIGHLIGHTS
1. Two hundred six bones make up your skeleton. Twenty-one of these are identified on page 172.
2. The skeleton provides support, protection, and movement.
3. The two main classes of joints are fixed and movable. Movable joints include ball and socket, hinge, gliding, and pivot joints.
4. Cartilage is connective tissue in the skeleton that acts as a cushion and reduces friction between bones at a joint.
5. Bone develops as bone cells produce cartilage. The cartilage hardens into bone as minerals are added to it.
6. A balanced diet and adequate exercise are good ways of ensuring a healthy skeleton.
7. Over 600 muscles are contained in your body. Seventeen of these are identified on page 179.

8. Voluntary muscles are those that you control, such as those in your arms and legs. Involuntary muscles, such as the heart and stomach, are automatically controlled by your brain.
9. Three types of muscles are cardiac, smooth, and skeletal.

VOCABULARY LIST

biceps	ligament	smooth muscle
cardiac muscle	marrow	spinal column
cartilage	movable joint	sprain
cranium	osteoporosis	sternum
femur	pelvis	triceps
fixed joint	rib	vertebra
involuntary muscle	skeletal muscle	voluntary muscle
joint		

PRACTICE

Multiple Choice. Choose the best answer.

1. Which is not a function of the skeletal system?
    a. provide support
    b. aid in digestion
    c. produce blood cells
    d. protection
2. Which is a gliding joint?
    a. hip
    b. elbow
    c. wrist
    d. jaw
3. At what age is the skeleton completely hardened?
    a. 8–10 years
    b. 10–20 years
    c. 22–26 years
    d. 30–40 years
4. Which is a function of cartilage?
    a. reduce friction
    b. cushion the bone
    c. cover end of bone
    d. all of these
5. Which muscle allows you to lift a book?
    a. abdominal
    b. biceps
    c. triceps
    d. hamstrings
6. What attaches muscles to bones?
    a. tendons
    b. fibers
    c. cartilage
    d. hamstrings
7. Which two minerals are important for strong bones?
    a. zinc/silver
    b. sulfur/iron
    c. potassium/sodium
    d. calcium/phosphorus

8. What muscles are involved in throwing a baseball?
   a. voluntary
   b. involuntary
   c. both a and b
   d. neither a nor b
9. What muscle action allows you to raise your hand?
   a. muscles expand
   b. muscles contract
   c. muscles expand and contract
   d. muscles push
10. What one bone do most ribs connect to?
   a. femur
   b. sternum
   c. vertebra
   d. patella

Matching. Match each word below with its definition or description.
   1. the point at which two bones join
   2. part of the bone that makes blood cells
   3. a weakening of the bone
   4. muscle that makes up the heart
   5. muscle involved in body movement
   6. tissue that attaches bone to bone
   7. tissue that attaches muscle to bone
   8. the elbow is this type of joint
   9. type of joint located in the hip
   10. muscle that makes up stomach

   a. ball and socket
   b. cardiac
   c. hinge
   d. joint
   e. ligaments
   f. marrow
   g. osteoporosis
   h. skeletal
   i. smooth
   j. tendon

CHAPTER 11

THE NERVOUS SYSTEM

INTRODUCTION

Every time you use the telephone, you tap into a network that includes wires, receivers, transmitters, and translators, as well as satellite dishes and fiber optics. The calls that come in and go out are monitored and controlled by equipment in the switching room. Each hour up to 700,000 calls pass through this room. Some calls are sent to telephones nearby, while others are sent great distances. If this control room shut down completely, thousands of phone calls would be interrupted.

Your nervous system is the communications network of your body. But your nervous system is much more complicated than a telephone switching room and can handle more messages more quickly. Read this chapter to discover how the nervous system is designed and works.

SECTION TITLES

Large telephone switching rooms such as this one are found in most major cities.

11–1 THE NERVOUS SYSTEM

OBJECTIVES

- Describe the parts of the nervous system.
- Identify the body functions controlled automatically by the nervous system.

Have you ever wondered what keeps a millipede from tripping as it walks? What tells its legs how and when to move? A simple nervous system is the answer. Your nervous system, however, is more complex than a millipede's. God designed humans to have dominion over "all the earth" (Genesis 1:26). This does not mean people must control with physical strength. Rather, it means human beings hold the highest position among living creatures because of their ability to think.

Your nervous system is composed of the brain, spinal cord, nerves, and sense organs. This system controls your body as a computer controls all the telephones and telephone calls in a city. It controls your movement, the work of your organs, and your thought processes.

The nervous system is made of two parts that work together to keep your body running smoothly. The first part is called the central nervous system. Made up of the brain and spinal cord, it is involved in all the activities of the body (fig. 11–1).

The second part of the nervous system is made up of nerves and sense organs. Nerves carry messages back and forth through the body. Sense organs are your eyes, ears, nose, tongue, and skin. Without them you would not know about your surroundings. These organs help you read the words on this page or let you know that a large truck is driving directly toward you.

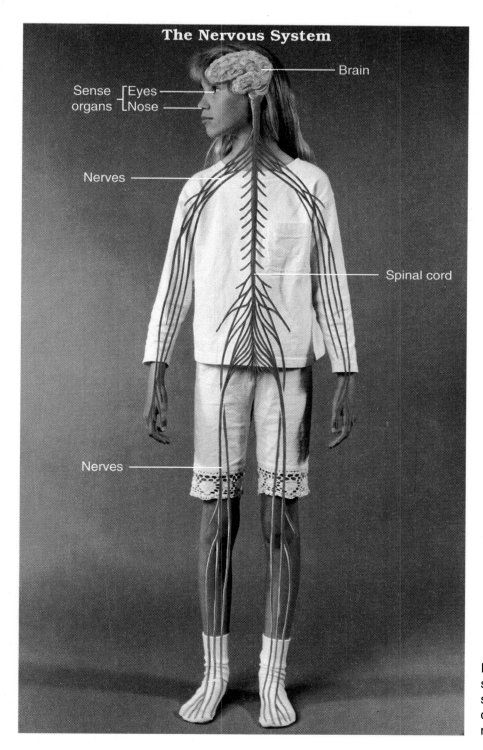

The Nervous System

Brain

Sense organs { Eyes
Nose

Nerves

Spinal cord

Nerves

Fig. 11–1 The nervous system is made up of the brain, spinal cord, nerves, and sense organs such as the eye and nose.

Certain parts of your nervous system are under automatic control—they work without your having to think. The automatic control system keeps your lungs breathing, heart beating, and food digesting. It also changes the size of the pupils in your eyes and makes goose bumps stand up on your skin.

TRY THIS 11–1: Faster, Faster

Materials:
stopwatch

Procedure:
1. Sit quietly. Determine your normal breathing rate for one minute. Record.
2. Determine your pulse rate for one minute. Record.
3. Stand and run in place as fast as possible for 30 seconds.
4. Determine your pulse rate again. Record.
5. Rest for 3–5 minutes. Repeat step 3.
6. Determine your breathing rate again. Record.
   - How do your two pulse rates compare?
   - How do your two breathing rates compare?
   - Why do pulse rate and breathing rate increase with exercise?
   - Does the change in pulse rate and breathing rate involve the voluntary or involuntary part of the nervous system?

REVIEW IT

1. What are the two main parts of the nervous system, and what do they do?
2. How many sense organs do you have?
3. What body processes are controlled automatically by the nervous system?

11–2 NERVE CELLS

OBJECTIVES

- Describe the parts of the neuron.
- Identify the different types of neurons.
- Explain how neurons relay messages.

VOCABULARY
axon
cell body
dendrite
impulse
motor neuron
neuron
sensory neuron
synapse

A Major League batter has only a fraction of a second to decide whether to swing at a fastball or let it pass. How does he make such a split-second decision? Electrical messages from the batter's eyes travel to his brain over nerve cells called **neurons**. The brain processes the messages and sends the appropriate instructions to the muscles. Billions of nerve cells make up the batter's nervous system. Each neuron has three parts: the dendrites (den´ drīt), the cell body, and the axon (fig. 11–2).

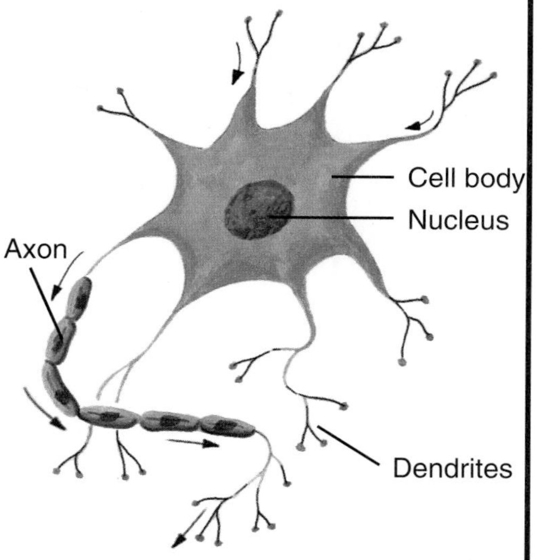

Fig. 11–2 A neuron is made up of a cell body, an axon, and dendrites.

THE NEURON		
PART	**FUNCTION**	
DENDRITES	• Short, branchlike fibers that spread out from the cell body. • Receive messages coming to the cell from other neurons. • Messages move from dendrite to cell body.	
CELL BODY	• Main part of the neuron. • Acts as a message center. • Usually lies within the spinal cord or brain. • Those not inside the brain or spinal cord are located in little clusters.	Cell body Nucleus Axon Dendrites
AXON	• Long fiber of the neuron opposite the dendrites. • Sends messages from the cell to other neurons.	

DID YOU KNOW?

The "funny bone" in your elbow is a nerve that is not well-protected. Hitting this nerve sends strong messages that cause a tingling sensation.

DID YOU KNOW?

The longest axon in the body extends from the lower spinal cord to the big toe, over 100 cm in a tall basketball player.

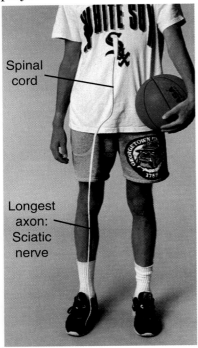

Spinal cord

Longest axon: Sciatic nerve

The longest axon

Although all neurons have the same basic structure, based on the job they perform, they can be separated into two basic types: sensory and motor. **Sensory neurons** take messages to the brain. They keep you in touch with events happening inside and outside your body. When you feel a sticker in your sock, a sensory neuron has taken a message from your skin to your brain. **Motor neurons** carry messages from the brain to your muscles and organs. A motor neuron enables you to reach down and remove the sticker from your sock.

Electrical messages, or nerve **impulses**, travel through neurons in much the same way electricity travels through electrical wire. The axon of a neuron carries the impulse to the next neuron. At the end of the axon is a small gap, called the **synapse** (sin´ aps), between it and the next neuron (fig. 11–3). When the message reaches the

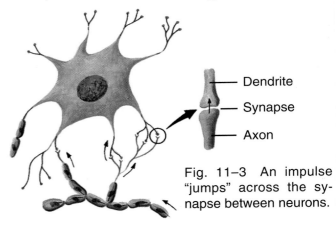

Dendrite

Synapse

Axon

Fig. 11–3 An impulse "jumps" across the synapse between neurons.

synapse, the signal "jumps" across the gap to the next nerve cell. In this way signals move from neuron to neuron throughout the body at a speed of 100 m (300 feet) per second.

REVIEW IT

1. Draw and label the parts of a neuron.
2. What type of neuron carries messages from the brain to the muscles?
3. How does a message get from one neuron to the next?

11–3 THE CENTRAL NERVOUS SYSTEM

OBJECTIVES

- Identify the areas of the brain.
- Describe the function of each area of the brain.
- Describe how a reflex works.

José Delgado walked into the bullring. At his nod, the raging bull was let out of the chute. The bull charged Delgado, who was armed with only a radio transmitter. As the bull closed in, Delgado pushed the button on the transmitter. The bull stopped dead in his tracks. The transmitter had sent a message to an electrode in the bull's brain. The message turned off the bull's aggressive behavior, and he walked calmly away. We have learned much about the brain as a result of the work done by scientists like Delgado.

The brain and the spinal cord make up the **central nervous system**. The **brain** is the master of the nervous system. It controls the entire body and is the body's most complex organ. Although it weighs only 1.4 kg (3 lbs), the brain has more than 10 billion nerve cells and uses 20 percent of the oxygen in the blood.

God provided several layers of protection for the brain. The bones of the skull protect it from most damage; liquid and fatty tissue surrounding the brain cushion it from harder blows.

VOCABULARY
brain
central nervous system
cerebellum
cerebral cortex
cerebrum
medulla
reflex
spinal cord

DID YOU KNOW?
The brain makes up only 2 percent of the body's total weight but uses 20 percent of the food and oxygen in the blood.

DID YOU KNOW?
The right half of the brain enables you to be creative and helps you recognize things. The left side of the brain enables you to understand things.

The brain has three parts: the cerebrum (ser´ ə brəm), cerebellum (ser ə bel´ əm), and medulla (fig. 11–4).

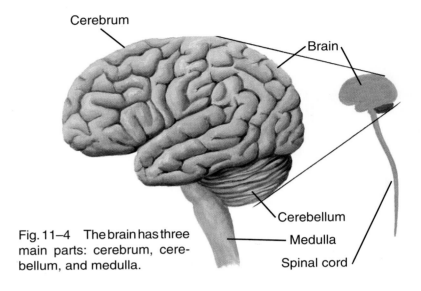

Cerebrum

Brain

Cerebellum

Medulla

Spinal cord

Fig. 11–4   The brain has three main parts: cerebrum, cerebellum, and medulla.

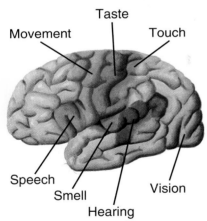

Taste

Movement

Touch

Speech

Smell

Vision

Hearing

Fig. 11–5   The cerebral cortex allows you to see, hear, taste, smell, and feel.

CEREBRUM. The **cerebrum** is the largest part of the brain. It is the center of intelligence and creativity and controls voluntary movements. It is also the part of the brain through which God communicates with you.

The cerebrum has a right and left half. The right half controls the left side of your body; the left half controls the right side. Nerves connect the two halves to coordinate both sides of your body.

The gray outer layer of the cerebrum is called the **cerebral cortex**. The cortex controls your movement and allows you to see, hear, taste, smell, and feel (fig. 11–5).

CEREBELLUM. The **cerebellum** is the balance center of your body. Located between the cerebrum and the spinal cord, it helps coordinate your muscles. This coordination is needed so that you can keep your balance and move around smoothly.

MEDULLA. The **medulla** is the connecting link between the brain and spinal cord. It is located below the cerebellum and controls involuntary activities, such as breathing, heartbeat, digestion, and eye movement.

The **spinal cord,** made completely of nerves, attaches to the medulla. This cord allows the brain and body to communicate. To save time in emergencies, the spinal cord handles some messages by itself. Such actions are called **reflexes**.

If your finger touches a burning match, you quickly jerk your finger back. The jerk happens because a signal from a sensory neuron in your finger arrives at the spinal cord. The spinal cord almost instantly sends a "jerk back" message by a motor neuron to the muscle. When the muscle receives the message, your finger jerks away from the match (fig. 11–6). A reflex takes place in a fraction of a second. No thinking is necessary; the process is all automatic. Only after you have pulled away do you begin to feel pain. Your finger would be damaged if the signal had to go to the brain instead of being handled by the spinal cord. A reflex saves time by decreasing the distance a message must travel. God designed such reflexes to protect you from many dangers.

RESEARCH IT
What part of the medulla controls breathing, heartbeat, and digestion?

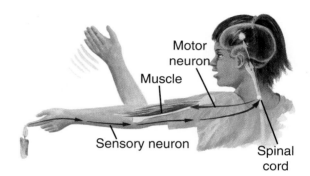

Fig. 11–6   Jerking your finger out of a flame is a reflex action.

TRY THIS 11–3: Oops!

Materials:
  meterstick
  stopwatch

Procedure:
  1. On the floor or sidewalk, mark a square 30 cm (12 in) on each side.
  2. Have your partner time how long you can stand inside the square while balancing on one foot. KEEP YOUR ARMS AT YOUR SIDES. Stop timing as soon as you lose your balance or part of your foot touches the line.
     • How long did you stay balanced?
  3. Repeat this activity using the following variations:
     (Record how long you balanced with each variation.)
     a. Stand tiptoe on your left foot.
     b. Repeat "a" with your eyes closed.
     c. Repeat "a" with your head resting on your left shoulder.
     d. Repeat "a" with your head resting on your right shoulder.
     • With which variation did you have the longest balancing time? Why?
     • With which variation did you have the shortest balancing time? Why?

Ivan Petrovich Pavlov

I am a Russian doctor. But something happened a few years ago that changed what I was studying.

I was studying human digestion. In my work I had found dogs good subjects to work with, and so there were always some around my laboratory. Now as everyone knows, dogs salivate, even slobber. One day I noticed that my dogs would begin to salivate when they saw one of my lab assistants bringing their food. I found this very curious because I had always believed that dogs would salivate only after they tasted their food.

Some people would have ignored this, but not me. Since I was studying digestion and salivating has to do with the digestive system, I decided to investigate this behavior of the dogs. To begin with, I got some new "untrained" dogs. For several days I rang a bell and then fed them. After several days of training, I decided to see if the bell by itself could trigger a response in the dogs. Much to my enjoyment, when I rang the bell they began salivating without any food being present. This proved that the dog's brain had been trained to respond to the bell, not the smell.

Being even more curious, I continued my experiment. I substituted two lights for the bell. One light was circular; the other was oval. The dogs were shown the circular light just before being fed. I never fed them when the oval light was turned on. In a few days, the dogs would salivate when they saw the circular light, but never responded to the oval light. Then I began to change the shape of the oval light to make it more circular. Eventually the oval light became so round that the dogs became confused because they couldn't tell the lights apart. The poor things became agitated and would howl and pace nervously. I believe that people often learn in a similar fashion.

REVIEW IT

1. What part of the brain connects to the spinal cord?
2. What area of the brain helps you keep your balance?
3. What is a reflex?
4. What two parts of the nervous system are involved in a reflex?

11–4 CARE OF THE NERVOUS SYSTEM

OBJECTIVE

- Analyze ways of protecting the nervous system.

Your nervous system needs special care (fig. 11–7). If it is damaged, your whole body suffers. One way you can

Fig. 11–7 A healthy nervous system needs protection (A), rest (B), exercise (C), and good nutrition (D).

protect your nervous system is to wear a seat belt every time you ride in a car. Using a helmet when bicycling or riding a motorcycle can also help reduce injuries. Do not dive where the water is shallow, where you can't see the bottom, or where there are rocks or logs. Eating a healthful diet and getting plenty of rest also benefit your nervous system.

Another way of protecting your nervous system is to make careful choices about the chemicals you take into your body. In your nervous system, chemical reactions

RESEARCH IT

Identify findings that result from human dream research.

197

Fig. 11–8 Drugs such as these damage your body.

constantly take place that control what is happening in your body. Using drugs can change these reactions and cause damage (fig. 11–8).

Alcohol slows down the nervous system and destroys brain cells. As the brain slows down, other body systems begin to slow down. If the brain slows too much, the person becomes unconscious and may die.

Caffeine is a stimulant found in coffee, tea, and many soft drinks. Although most people do not consider it dangerous, caffeine is not good for you. It makes the heart beat faster, affects the blood vessels in the brain, and irritates the stomach lining. It also makes many people sleepless and irritable.

Hallucinogens (hə lōō´ si nə jenz), like marijuana and LSD, alter brain functions and normal thinking patterns. This "high" can confuse sensory messages, increase fears, or remove inhibitions. Drug use can even erase memory. When people are not aware of what is around them, serious accidents may result. God did not intend the mind to work in such strange and confused ways.

REVIEW IT

1. What are some ways of protecting the nervous system?
2. How does caffeine damage the body?

11-5 THINKING

OBJECTIVES

- Identify the main kinds of thinking.
- Analyze how human beings' ability to think differs from animals'.

VOCABULARY
imagination
logic
memory
perception
spiritual thinking

When you think, your brain is handling ideas and facts. Scientists have identified five kinds of thinking: perception, memory, imagination, logical thinking, and spiritual thinking (fig. 11-9).

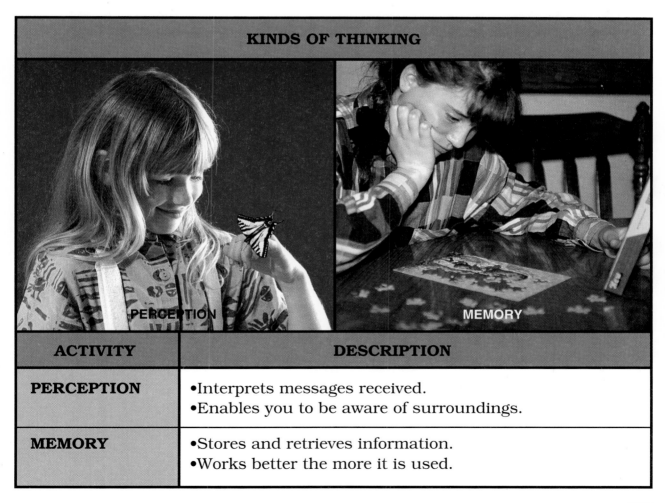

KINDS OF THINKING

PERCEPTION

MEMORY

ACTIVITY	DESCRIPTION
PERCEPTION	•Interprets messages received. •Enables you to be aware of surroundings.
MEMORY	•Stores and retrieves information. •Works better the more it is used.

Fig. 11–9 cont.

KINDS OF THINKING

IMAGINATION   LOGICAL THINKING   SPIRITUAL THINKING

IMAGINATION	• Creative thought—UNIQUE TO HUMAN BEINGS. • Enables you to think about things you can't see. • Enables you to think about things differently from the way they are.
LOGICAL THINKING	• Enables you to make decisions and solve problems.
SPIRITUAL THINKING	• Conscience—UNIQUE TO HUMAN BEINGS. • Enables you to tell right from wrong. • Enables you to experience emotion. • Involves love, faith, trust, courage, honor, and honesty.

A Christian should develop all five forms of thinking. God has given you unlimited potential. It is your responsibility to use what God has given you to become the best person you can be.

REVIEW IT

1. What are the five kinds of thinking?
2. What kinds of thinking are unique to human beings?

DID YOU KNOW?
Everything you have ever experienced is stored in your memory.

CLASS ACTIVITY 11–5: If I Could Only Remember

Question: What factors help you memorize?

Materials:
stopwatch

Procedure:
1. Look at List 1. Take 30 seconds to memorize the list.
2. After 30 seconds, cover the list and write the words in order. Record.
3. Repeat steps 1 and 2 using List 2.
4. Repeat steps 1 and 2 using List 3.

Data:

STUDENT 1		STUDENT 2	
LIST	NUMBER OF WORDS REMEMBERED	LIST	NUMBER OF WORDS REMEMBERED
1		1	
2		2	
3		3	

LIST 1: WAT, FIM, YIK, LAC, TUJ, MUR, DOK, KER, NOY, NAD

LIST 2: SILK, PUPPY, CABIN, FALL, TRAIN, LOTS, PLANET, MONEY, DRIVE, INK

LIST 3: WHEN, SCIENTISTS, STUDY, A, PROBLEM, THEY, USUALLY, FIND, A, SOLUTION

Questions:
1. Which list was the easiest to remember? Why?
2. Which list was the hardest to remember? Why?
3. What would have made it easier for you to memorize the lists?

Conclusion: Write 3–5 sentences about what you learned from this activity.

CHAPTER 11 WRAP-UP
SKILLS DEVELOPMENT

THINKING SKILLS: CLASSIFYING

Classifying is an important skill to develop. It is important to be able to organize items and/or activities into various categories so that the information can be stored or obtained easily. For example, shoes in a shoe store are organized several ways: type, style, sex, and size. When you want a pair of shoes, the clerk knows right where to find them.

The brain is also organized in much the same manner. The brain is the central control system of the nervous system of your body. It controls the entire body and is the most complex organ. Because the brain is so important to your well-being, God designed your body so that your brain is well protected. God also designed your brain into three parts, each part designed to carry out certain functions.

1. **Cerebrum**—center of intelligence; *controls voluntary movements.*
2. **Cerebellum**—balance center of your body; *helps coordinate your muscles.*
3. **Medulla**—connecting link between the brain and the spinal cord; *controls involuntary movements.*

Classify the following activities under the appropriate column below.
Keeps the heart beating, lets you reach out your hand, keeps your balance, keeps you breathing, lets you feel, digests your food, coordinates your muscles, lets you see, lets you move around smoothly, lets you hear, communicates with God, blinks your eyelids, lets you create ideas

CEREBRUM	CEREBELLUM	MEDULLA

QUESTIONS AND PROBLEMS
1. Why are the brain and spinal cord called the central nervous system?
2. Why are your eyes, ears, and nose located on your head?
3. What are two kinds of neurons, and what does each do?
4. Why are axons in your leg longer than the axons in your arm?
5. Why aren't all neurons motor neurons?
6. How is the brain protected from injury?
7. Why does the cerebral cortex have folds?
8. How is memory different from logic?
9. How do hallucinogens affect thinking?

RESEARCH
1. Make a poster that lists beverages and other products that contain caffeine. Find out why caffeine is added to these products.
2. Find out how messages pass from neuron to neuron. Write a report on your findings, including the chemicals and processes involved.
3. Make a list of "right brain" and "left brain" characteristics.
4. Find out the difference between "paraplegic" and "quadriplegic." Report on current treatments to help people with paralysis.
5. Draw and label a diagram of the central nervous system.

REVIEW

HIGHLIGHTS
1. The nervous system is made up of the brain, spinal cord, nerves, and sense organs.
2. Heartbeat, breathing, and digestion are body processes automatically controlled by your nervous system.
3. The neuron is made up of a cell body, dendrites, and an axon.
4. Two types of neurons are sensory neurons and motor neurons. Sensory neurons take messages from the body to the brain or spinal cord. The motor neurons take messages from the brain or spinal cord to the rest of the body.
5. In the neuron, the impulse travels from the dendrites to the cell body, then along the axon to the next neuron.
6. The three main areas of the brain are the cerebrum, cerebellum, and medulla.
7. The cerebrum is the thinking area of the brain. The cerebellum controls balance and coordination. The medulla controls breathing, heartbeat, digestion, and other involuntary functions.
8. In a reflex, the impulse travels only as far as the spinal cord. When the message is received, the spinal cord sends back the appropriate message to the body.

9. You can best protect the nervous system by wearing seat belts and helmets (when appropriate) and by not using harmful drugs.
10. The main types of thinking are perception, memory, imagination, logical thinking, and spiritual thinking.
11. Human beings' ability to imagine, think creatively, solve problems, make decisions, and tell right from wrong make them different from other animals.

VOCABULARY LIST

axon
brain
cell body
central nervous system
cerebellum
cerebral cortex
cerebrum

dendrite
imagination
impulse
logic
medulla
memory
motor neuron

neuron
perception
reflex
sensory neuron
spinal cord
spiritual thinking
synapse

PRACTICE

Multiple Choice. Choose the best answer.

1. Which is part of the neuron?
   a. cell body
   b. dendrite
   c. axon
   d. all of these
2. Which neurons carry messages from the brain to the muscles?
   a. sensory neurons
   b. motor neurons
3. Which part of the brain is involved in balance and coordination?
   a. cerebrum
   b. medulla
   c. cerebellum
   d. spinal cord
4. Which of the following functions is not automatic?
   a. breathing
   b. running
   c. digestion
   d. heartbeat
5. Which type of thinking allows you to "see" things in your mind?
   a. memory
   b. logical
   c. imagination
   d. spiritual
6. Which of the following would best protect your brain?
   a. getting plenty of calcium
   b. wearing a car seat belt
   c. getting adequate rest
   d. drinking plenty of water
7. Which of these is an effect of alcohol on the body?
   a. destroys brain cells
   b. impairs vision
   c. slows nervous system
   d. all of these

8. Which type of thinking makes human beings different from other animals?
    a. memory
    b. imagination
    c. perception
    d. none of these
9. Which is an example of a hallucinogen?
    a. cocaine
    b. chocolate
    c. caffeine
    d. marijuana
10. Which is the largest part of the brain?
    a. cerebrum
    b. medulla
    c. neuron
    d. cerebellum

Matching. Match each word with its definition or description.
1. attaches to the upper spinal cord
2. thinking area of the brain
3. carries messages to spinal cord
4. part of neuron that receives messages
5. links the brain and body
6. the brain's interpretation of messages it receives
7. controls balance
8. carries messages away from cell body
9. information stored in the brain
10. carries messages to muscles

a. axon
b. cerebellum
c. cerebrum
d. dendrite
e. motor neuron
f. medulla
g. memory
h. perception
i. sensory neuron
j. spinal cord

CHAPTER 12

THE SENSE ORGANS

INTRODUCTION

A parrot's tongue, an eagle's eye, a cat's whiskers, and a moth's antenna. What do they have in common? While all of these structures look different and have different jobs, they are all alike in one way. As strange as it may seem, these are all sense organs. What other sense organs can you find in the picture? What sense organs do you have?

The Creator designed your sense organs so that you can smell a pizza baking, hear your friend laughing, or feel a hug. In short, your sense organs allow you to enjoy life.

SECTION TITLES

Sense organs include tongues, eyes, whiskers, and antennae.

12–1 THE EYE

OBJECTIVES

- Identify the parts of the eye and their function.
- Explain how sight occurs.
- Distinguish between rod and cone cells.

God designed many different kinds of eyes for the animals He created. The compound eyes of insects are made up of hundreds of separate eyelets. Frogs have eyes equipped with a special membrane that allows them to see underwater. Eagles, hawks, and other birds of prey have eyes that can spot prey up to 4 km (2.25 mi) away. The eyes of owls are specially designed to see at night. Studies have shown that an owl can see prey nearly 800 m (.5 mi) away with the light of one candle.

Your eyes are perhaps the most marvelous of all your sense organs (fig. 12–1). They tell you many things about the world around you. They inform you about things that are close and things that are far away.

The eye is about the size of a ping-pong ball and is filled with liquid to keep its shape. Each eye sits inside a padded socket in the bones of your face. Inside the socket are muscles that move the eye. Nerves help control the eye, and blood vessels supply food and oxygen. Refer to fig. 12–2 as you read about the different structures of the eye.

Fig. 12–1 Your eye is an intricate sense organ.

TRY THIS 12–1: Now You See It; Now You Don't

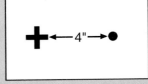

Materials:
marking pen (dark color)

Procedure:
1. On a sheet of paper draw a cross and a dot (fig A).
2. Hold the sheet about 25 cm (10 in) in front of your eyes so that the cross is directly in front of your right eye. While staring straight ahead, close your left eye. Now, without turning your head, look at the cross. Move the paper back and forth and up and down. Keep your right eye focused on the cross and your left eye closed.
   - What do you observe about the dot?
   - Why does this happen? Explain.
3. Repeat the procedure with your left eye open and your right eye closed.
   - What do you observe about the cross?

THE EYE

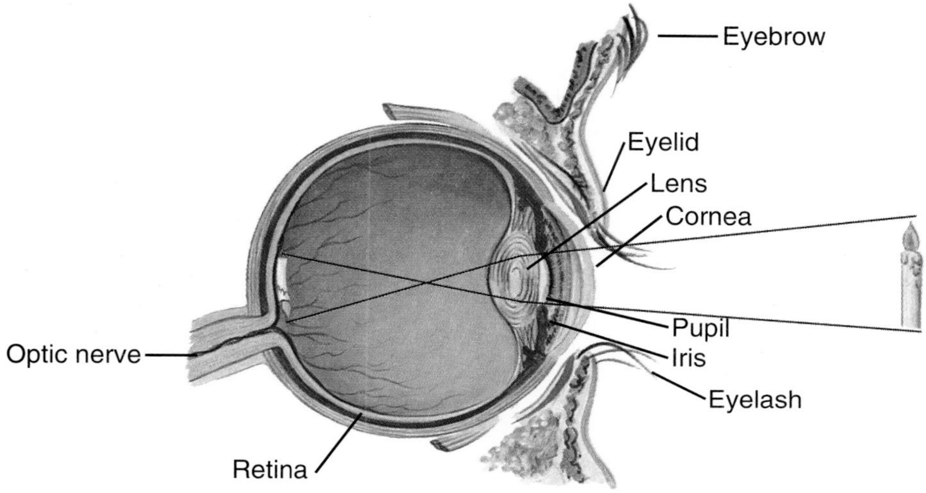

Fig. 12–2

STRUCTURE	FUNCTION AND DESCRIPTION
Eyebrow	• Shields and protects the eye.
Eyelid and eyelash	• Shields and protects the eye.
Tear gland	• Lubricates and keeps eye surface clean.
Tear duct	• Allows tears to drain away from the eye.
Cornea (kôr´ nē ə)	• Protective covering of the eye.
Iris	• The colored part of the eye. • Controls the amount of light that enters the eye.
Pupil	• Opening in iris through which light passes.
Lens	• Focuses light on the retina (ret´ n ə).
Retina	• Thin membrane that lines the back of the eye and works as the "film" to capture images you see. • Changes light energy to nerve impulses.
Optic nerve	• Takes the picture message from the retina to the brain for processing.

209

DID YOU KNOW?
The eyes of most animals contain rod cells, but only a few have cone cells. As a result, most animals see color differently than humans do.

The retina, which covers the back of your eye, contains two kinds of light receptor cells: rods and cones (fig. 12–3). About 125 million **rod cells** in each eye allow you to see movement and white and gray light. Because rod cells need little light to work, they help you see at night.

Seven million **cone cells** in each eye allow you to see color. Cones need bright light to work, so at night you do not see color as well as you do in the daytime.

The rods and cones send messages to the brain through the **optic nerve**. The brain puts the messages together and forms a picture of what you are looking at. You really see pictures in your brain, not in your eyes.

RESEARCH IT
Find out what causes near-sightedness and farsight-edness.

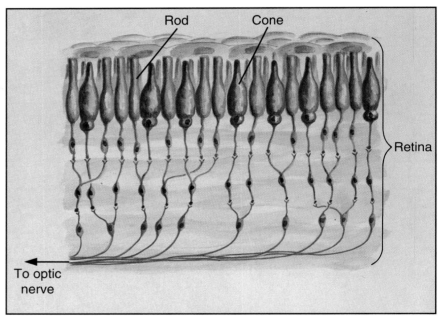

Fig. 12–3   Rod and cone cells make up the retina of the eye.

REVIEW IT

1. How does the lens help you see?
2. What structures protect the eye?
3. Why would damage to the retina make you unable to see?
4. What is the function of the rod cells?
5. Why is color more difficult to distinguish at night?

CLASS ACTIVITY 12–1: Don't Drop It

Question: Do you see as well with one eye as you do with two?

Materials:
- masking tape
- meterstick
- ping-pong ball

Procedure:
1. Use the meterstick to make two lines 3 meters apart.
2. Have your partner stand behind one line while you stand behind the other.
3. Keep both eyes open and have your partner toss the ping-pong ball to you 10 times. Record the number of times you catch the ball without dropping it.
4. Repeat step 3 two more times. Record data.
5. While closing your left eye and keeping your right eye open, have your partner repeat steps 3 and 4. Record data.
6. Repeat steps 3 and 4, but close the right eye and keep the left eye open. Record data.
7. Construct a bar graph of your data.

Data:

NUMBER OF TIMES CAUGHT

EYE(S) OPEN	TRIAL 1	TRIAL 2	TRIAL 3	AVERAGE
BOTH EYES				
RIGHT EYE				
LEFT EYE				

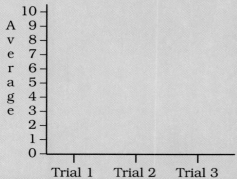

Questions:
1. Which trial had the highest average of catches? Why?
2. Which trial had the lowest average of catches? Why?
3. How does the average in trial 2 compare to the average in trial 3? Explain.
4. How do two eyes help in catching a ball?

Conclusion: Write 3–5 sentences about what you learned from this activity.

12-2 EYE CARE

VOCABULARY
pinkeye

RESEARCH IT
Find out how to protect your eyes if you wear contact lenses or use power tools.

OBJECTIVE

- Describe methods of preventing damage to the eye.

You can ensure the health of your eyes by protecting them from injury, being careful when playing, not looking at bright light, wearing UV-sunglasses, treating infections promptly, and eating a balanced diet. By properly caring for your eyes, you can ensure that they will continue to serve you as God intended.

Firearms, fireworks, slingshots, and sharp objects such as sticks, scissors, darts, and arrows cause thousands of eye injuries each year. Always use extreme caution when handling such things.

MINIBIOGRAPHYMINIBIOGRAPHYMINIBIOGRAPHYMINIBIOGRAPHYMINIBIOGRAPHY

Dr. Harold Ridley

Millions of people have worn eyeglasses and contact lenses to improve their eyesight. But for some people with cataracts, these devices do not help. As the lens in their eye becomes cloudy, they lose their sight and usually become blind.

During World War II, Dr. Harold Ridley noticed that some of the Air Force pilots got pieces of plastic plexiglass in their eyes.

The plexiglass came from airplane windows broken during fighting. He discovered that this plastic did not cause eye infections as he had expected. He decided later to use plexiglass to try to make artifical replacement lenses for people with cataracts.

In 1949 Dr. Ridley operated on a cataract patient in London, England. He removed the cataract and inserted the first intraocular lens. The plexiglass lens was placed behind the iris, exactly where the cloudy lens had been.

Today, artifical lenses have changed, and plexiglass is no longer used. But thousands of people receive new sight each year because of the pioneering work of Dr. Ridley.

MINIBIOGRAPHYMINIBIOGRAPHYMINIBIOGRAPHYMINIBIOGRAPHYMINIBIOGRAPHY

If a foreign body such as dirt, sawdust, or a small insect gets into your eye, don't rub the eye. Instead, rinse the eye with plenty of water. If the material doesn't wash out or if your eye becomes red or inflamed, see your doctor immediately.

Though light-colored eyes (blue) are more sensitive to light than are dark eyes (brown), any bright light can damage your eyes. A short glance at the sun or a very bright object can destroy an area of the retina, ruining your vision forever. Bright light reflected from water, sand, or snow can harm your eyes too. Wear dark glasses that block ultraviolet (UV) light to provide protection in bright light.

Eye problems can also be caused by bacteria that enter the eye. One infection, called **pinkeye,** causes red, irritated eyes and a sticky discharge (fig. 12–4). This infection is easily passed to other people. Eye infections should be treated by a doctor right away.

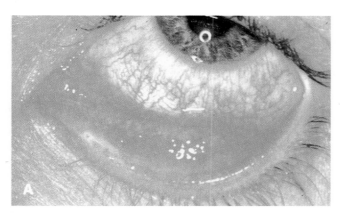

Fig. 12–4　Pinkeye is a common eye infection that is easily passed between people.

REVIEW IT

1. How does sunshine damage the eye?
2. What causes pinkeye?
3. What are some ways of protecting your eyes?

12–3 THE EAR AND ITS CARE

VOCABULARY
anvil
auditory nerve
auricle
cochlea
decibel
ear canal
eardrum
eustachian tube
hammer
semicircular canal
stirrup

OBJECTIVES

- Identify the parts of the ear and their function.
- Describe methods of preventing ear damage.

The Creator not only designed complex eyes for His creatures, He also designed sensitive ears for them. Elephants produce very low-frequency sounds that other elephants can hear up to five miles away. Bats use ultrahigh-frequency sounds to guide them as they fly and to find prey. Fortunately for them, moths have such sensitive hearing that they can hear a bat over 27 m (90 ft) away.

Although you may not be able to hear some sounds other animals hear, your ears allow you to hear and determine the direction of most sounds (fig. 12–5). You use your hearing to enjoy music and listen for warning sounds, such as sirens or the cry of a baby. Parts of your ears even help you keep your balance.

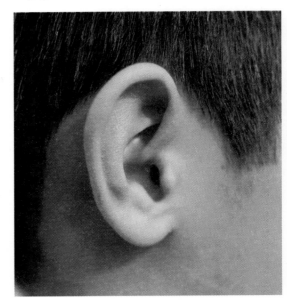

Fig. 12–5 The outer ear collects sound and helps the brain determine the direction of the sound.

214

Your ear is arranged into three parts: the outer ear, middle ear, and inner ear. Look at fig. 12–6 as you read about the structures of the ear.

The Ear

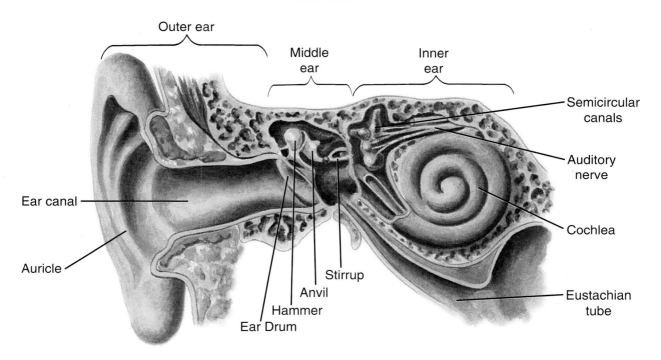

Fig. 12–6

THE EAR		
STRUCTURE		**FUNCTION AND DESCRIPTION**
O U T E R **E A R**	Auricle (ô´ ri kəl)	• Visible, outer part of the ear. • Collects sound waves.
	Ear canal	• Passageway that carries sound into the ear.
	Eardrum	• A thin membrane at the end of the ear canal. • Vibrates back and forth as sound waves hit it.

Fig. 12–6 cont.

M I D D L E E A R	Eustachian tube (yōō stā´ kē ən)	• Tube that connects middle ear with the throat. • Helps adjust air pressure in the ear.
	Hammer	• Small bone attached to the eardrum. • Moves when the eardrum vibrates.
	Anvil	• Small bone attached to the hammer.
	Stirrup	• Small bone attached to the anvil at one end and to the inner ear at the other. • Its movement causes the fluid of the inner ear to vibrate.
I N N E R E A R	Cochlea (käk´ lē ə)	• A coiled tube filled with fluid. • Contains tiny hairs that change vibrations into nerve impulses.
	Auditory nerve	• Takes nerve impulses from the cochlea to the brain for processing.
	Semicircular canals	• Small looped tubes. • Enable you to keep your balance and to determine your position and degree of motion.

DECIBEL LEVEL AND EAR DAMAGE	
Loudness	**Duration**
90 dB	8 hours
92 dB	6 hours
95 dB	4 hours
97 dB	3 hours
100 dB	2 hours
105 dB	1 hour
110 dB	30 minutes
115 dB	15 minutes
120 db (pain)	5 minutes

Fig. 12–7   The louder the sound, the less time it takes for ear damage to occur.

Injuries to the eardrum are common causes of hearing loss. Even though it is deep within the ear, the eardrum can be scraped or punctured. Pushing objects into your ear to clean it can easily damage the eardrum. The safest way to have excess wax removed is by a doctor.

Ear infections can cause hearing loss. An earache is often the first symptom of an ear infection. Such infections should be treated promptly by a doctor to prevent permanent damage.

A sudden push of air or water into the ear canal, caused by a slap on the ear or

TRY THIS 12–3: Hey, Where am I?

Materials:
blindfold

Procedure:
1. In a quiet area have your partner sit down. Blindfold your partner.
2. Stand about 3 m (15 ft) from your partner and clap your hands. Ask your partner to point to the direction the sound came from. Repeat this 10 times, standing in several different locations. Record the responses.
   • How many times was your partner correct out of the 10 tries?
3. Repeat the procedure, this time having your partner cup his hand tightly over his right ear.
   • How many times was your partner correct?
   • Did he do better or worse? Why?
4. Repeat the procedure, this time having your partner cup his hand tightly over his left ear.
   • How many times was your partner correct?
   • Was there a difference between the results in steps 3 and 4? Why?
   • Why do you think God designed us with two ears?

by diving or falling into water, can burst the eardrum.

The loudness of sound is measured in **decibels**. Loud sounds, those that exceed 90 decibels, can lead to hearing loss. Hearing loss may occur, depending on how loud or how long a sound is listened to (fig. 12–7). For example, listening to sound at 120 decibels for five minutes causes the same amount of ear damage that a 105-decibel sound can cause in one hour. Loud noises from fireworks, guns, lawn mowers, or airplanes can damage your eardrums. Listening to loud music through headphones can also damage your hearing (fig. 12–8). When necessary, protect your ears by wearing ear protectors, and avoid loud sounds and music.

Fig. 12–8   Listening to loud music through headphones can cause ear damage.

REVIEW IT

1. What are the three main parts of the ear?
2. What two structures in the inner ear send signals to the brain?
3. What part of the ear helps you keep your balance?
4. What are the main causes of ear damage?
5. How does listening to loud music damage the ear?

12–4 TASTE AND SMELL

VOCABULARY
nasal passage
olfactory nerve
taste bud

OBJECTIVES

- Explain how taste is perceived.
- Explain how smell is perceived.

Did you know that you can taste many more than 31 flavors of ice cream? Your tongue is responsible for this remarkable sense of taste. It also helps you chew, swallow, and speak.

On the tongue are about 10,000–15,000 tiny sense organs called **taste buds** that discern four main types of taste: sweet, salt, sour, and bitter (fig. 12–9). Taste buds send messages to the taste center of the brain, where they are translated into different tastes. Signals from all the taste buds result in the wide variety of tastes you experience.

To activate the taste buds, food must be moist or dissolved in saliva. Dry food is not usually tasted. When food is very hot or cold, the tasting process does not work well either.

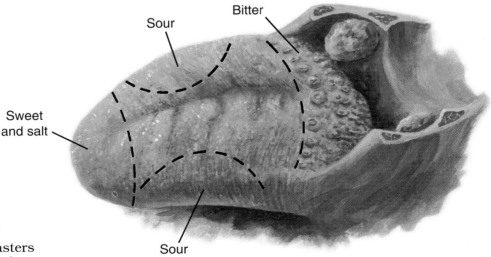

DID YOU KNOW?
Professional coffee tasters can distinguish more than 250 different tastes just in samples of coffee.

Fig. 12–9   Taste buds on the tongue detect four types of taste: sweet, salt, sour, and bitter.

The tongue does not do all the tasting by itself. Smell is very important in determining the flavor of food. Molecules of food floating in the air move up into the nose. These signals mix with those from the tongue to complete the flavor of the food you eat.

The Nose

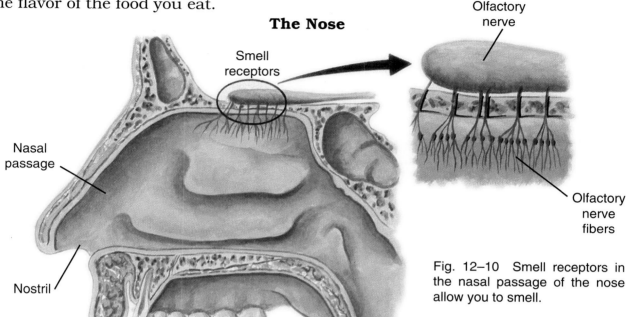

Fig. 12–10 Smell receptors in the nasal passage of the nose allow you to smell.

The nose is shown in fig. 12–10. Air moves through the nostrils and into the nasal passage and sinuses. Inside the **nasal passage** is an area the size of a dime that holds the smell receptors. As chemicals from the air contact these nerve endings, they send messages over the **olfactory** (äl fak´ te rē) **nerve** to the smell center of the brain. As these signals are put together, the brain interprets and recognizes the various smells. It is estimated that humans can identify up to 10,000 different smells.

DID YOU KNOW?
Dogs have between 125–300 million cells for smell, compared to a human's 15 million. With these extra receptors, a dog can detect very faint odors.

REVIEW IT

1. What kinds of taste buds are located on your tongue?
2. Why is saliva necessary to taste?
3. What is the olfactory nerve?

12-5 TOUCH

OBJECTIVE

- Explain how touch is detected.

Your skin detects touch, pressure, hot and cold, and pain. These sensations are detected by **receptor cells**, which send messages to the brain (fig. 12-11). The most sensitive parts of your body for touch are the tip of your tongue, your lips, and your fingertips. The backs of your shoulders are the least sensitive areas of your body.

Fig. 12-11

Types of Receptor Cells

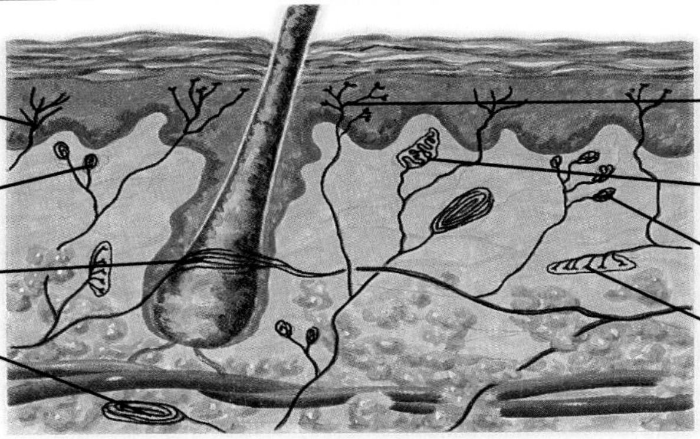

Pain/heat/cold/touch
Touch/intensity
Light touch/acceleration
Pressure/velocity

Light touch/acceleration
Touch/velocity
Touch/pressure
Pressure/intensity

RECEPTORS	FUNCTION AND DESCRIPTION
TOUCH	• Located on the fingertips and near hairs on the skin. • When the receptor is touched, an impulse is sent.
HOT AND COLD	• Activated by either hot or cold. • If cold receptors are stimulated, a cold sensation is felt. Hot sensations are created when a heat receptor is stimulated.
PRESSURE	• Located deep in the skin. • Tells you how strongly you are pushing against an object.
PAIN	• Located at the skin's surface and deep inside the body. • A small cut or scratch activates receptors on the skin. Major wounds activate deep pain receptors.

You depend on taste, touch, and smell more than you may have realized. Imagine what eating would be like without the ability to taste the food you eat. Imagine what you would miss if you could not smell. You would not feel a bee sting or a scraped knee if you lacked the sense of touch. Neither could you feel warm sunshine, soft puppies, or a hug.

REVIEW IT

1. Where in the body are touch receptors most concentrated?
2. What is the function of pressure receptors?

FRONTIERS: Fingerprints and Crime

Because everyone has his or her own unique set of fingerprints, they have been used by police for years to identify criminals. But it can take months or even years to compare fingerprints found at the site of a crime to thousands of police files.

Today police have a new crime fighter, AFIS. The Automated Fingerprint Identification System can rapidly sort through huge collections of fingerprints and do the work of many police officers. On its first job, AFIS compared fingerprints found on a stolen car with 380,000 sets of fingerprints and located a matching print in three minutes. Within two days the police arrested their suspect and charged him with fifteen serious crimes. Many police organizations have begun to use this powerful computer system.

Questions:
1. Why can fingerprints be used to identify people?
2. How is AFIS helpful?
3. Why do you think some police departments do not use AFIS?

CHAPTER 12 WRAP-UP
SKILLS DEVELOPMENT

THINKING SKILLS: COLLECTING DATA

Scientists collect data to support their ideas. This data is collected by using experiments and surveys. By observing what is happening, data can be collected by using some or all of the senses. These senses are tasting, seeing, hearing, smelling, and touching.

Imagine that you are deep in the mountains with trees spreading out over your head and a stream gently flowing over the rocks. A slight breeze presses against your face, carrying smells from far-off blossoms. Birds are singing, yet there is the quietness of the forest.

Using your imagination, list all the data that you can collect from your five senses. List the data under the headings shown below.

SIGHT	HEARING	TASTE	SMELL	TOUCH

QUESTIONS AND PROBLEMS
1. How are the eyes protected?
2. What design enables you to see things in three dimensions?
3. Why do you think you have more rod cells than cone cells?
4. How do sunglasses protect your eyes?
5. How does the outer ear help you hear?
6. How does sound get from the eardrum to the brain?
7. What causes motion sickness?
8. Why can't you taste food as well when you have a stuffy nose?
9. How do the receptors in your skin benefit you?

RESEARCH
1. Discover which animals see color. Write a report on your findings.
2. Discuss cataract surgery with an ophthalmologist. Write a report on your findings.
3. Discover why optical illusions occur. Present an oral report on your findings. Include pictures of optical illusions in your presentation.
4. Make a three-dimensional model of your tongue. Label your model to show the areas of taste.
5. Discover causes of hearing loss in young people. Write a report on your findings.

REVIEW

HIGHLIGHTS
1. The eye is made up of many structures; some protect the eye, others allow you to see. These structures and their functions are identified on page 209.
2. Sight occurs when the retina changes light energy into nerve impulses and passes them to the brain through the optic nerve.
3. Rod cells respond to dim light and help you to detect motion and to see when it is dark. Cone cells respond to bright light and enable you to see color.
4. You can protect your eyes by being careful when playing, not looking at bright light, wearing UV sunglasses, treating eye infections promptly, and eating a balanced diet.
5. The ear is divided into the outer ear, the middle ear, and the inner ear. Each part contains structures designed to help you hear. These structures and their functions are identified on page 215.
6. You can protect you ears by not sticking anything into them, treating ear infections promptly, and avoiding loud sounds and music.

7. Taste occurs as taste buds are stimulated by dissolved chemicals. The taste buds send impulses to the brain.
8. Smell occurs when scent receptors are stimulated by scents in the air. These receptors send impulses to the brain via the olfactory nerve.
9. Touch occurs as various touch receptors in the skin and body organs are stimulated. These receptors send messages to the brain.

VOCABULARY LIST

anvil	eardrum	pinkeye
auditory nerve	eustachian tube	pupil
auricle	hammer	receptor cell
cochlea	iris	retina
cone cell	lens	rod cell
cornea	nasal passage	semicircular canal
decibel	olfactory nerve	stirrup
ear canal	optic nerve	taste bud

PRACTICE

Multiple Choice. Choose the best answer.

1. Which is not a touch receptor?
   a. hot
   b. slippery
   c. pain
   d. pressure
2. Which area is most sensitive to touch?
   a. shoulders
   b. neck
   c. tongue
   d. nose
3. About how many taste buds cover your tongue?
   a. 70,000–80,000
   b. 45,000–50,000
   c. 10,000–15,000
   d. it is not known
4. Where in the nose are the smell receptors located?
   a. nasal passage
   b. nostril
   c. sinus
   d. olfactory nerve
5. Which is not located in the middle ear?
   a. saddle
   b. stirrup
   c. hammer
   d. anvil
6. Which is the best way of removing wax from your ear?
   a. use a cotton swab
   b. use a washcloth
   c. wash your finger and use it
   d. have it removed by a doctor
7. In what order does light pass into the eye?
   a. lens, cornea, pupil
   b. cornea, pupil, lens
   c. pupil, lens, cornea
   d. none of these

8. What fills the eyeball?
   a. air
   b. fluid
   c. blood
   d. none of these
9. Where does "seeing" take place?
   a. cornea
   b. pupil
   c. brain
   d. lens
10. Which of the following is found in the middle ear?
    a. cochlea
    b. anvil
    c. eardrum
    d. semicircular canal

Matching. Match each word with its definition or description.
1. vibrates as sound waves hit it
2. sense organs on the tongue
3. skin receptor
4. moved by vibration of eardrum
5. works as the "film" of the eye
6. eye receptors sensitive in dim light
7. the outer part of the ear
8. located in the inner ear
9. nerve involved in smelling
10. perceive color

a. auricle
b. cochlea
c. cone cells
d. eardrum
e. hammer
f. olfactory
g. pain
h. retina
i. rod cells
j. taste buds

CHAPTER 13

INTEGUMENTARY SYSTEM

INTRODUCTION

The architect who designed this old Victorian house gave as much attention to the outside as to the inside. Many elaborate details add to the beauty and structural safety of this house—shingles on the roof and sides, fancy woodwork around the doors and windows, bricks over the foundation, and wrought iron on the roof peaks.

Your Creator also made sure your body would be housed in a beautiful, functional covering. In this chapter you will discover how your skin is important to your body. You will also learn about the excretory system and its importance.

SECTION TITLES

The Carson House, Eureka, California.

13–1 INTEGUMENTARY SYSTEM

dermis
epidermis
follicle
integument
integumentary
   system
oil gland
sweat gland

OBJECTIVES

- Describe the structure of the skin.
- Identify the function of skin.

In the pictures below you see a fish, a watermelon, a tree, and a person (fig. 13–1). While the outer covering, or **integument** (in teg´ yōō mənt) in each picture is different, each covering performs a similar job. Your **integumentary system** is made up of skin, hair, and nails.

Fig. 13–1   Fish scales (A), watermelon rind (B), tree bark (C), and human skin (D) are types of integuments or coverings.

Although most people don't think of skin as an organ, it is actually the largest organ of your body. It covers about 1.5 square meters (15 square feet) and weighs approximately 2 kilograms (5 pounds). Your skin is a waterproof covering that has two cell layers: epidermis and dermis (fig. 13–2).

EPIDERMIS is the outer layer of cells that helps protect the body from infection and loss of fluid. It is made of dead cells that are constantly rubbed off and replaced.

DERMIS is the second layer of skin. It lies underneath the epidermis and contains blood vessels, nerve cells, sweat and oil glands. **Sweat glands** secrete perspiration that helps to cool the body. **Oil glands** secrete oil that keeps the skin soft and moisturized. By removing water, salts, and other materials, the skin helps rid the body of waste.

DID YOU KNOW?
You will shed more than 40 kg (100 lbs) of skin during your lifetime. During this time you will use more than 1000 complete layers of skin.

228

Hair grows from a **follicle**, a small sac-shaped structure in your skin, when cells are added at the base of each hair. Hair on your head grows about 1.1 cm (0.5 in) per month. When a tiny muscle attached to each hair contracts, the hair stands up, giving you "goose bumps."

The Skin

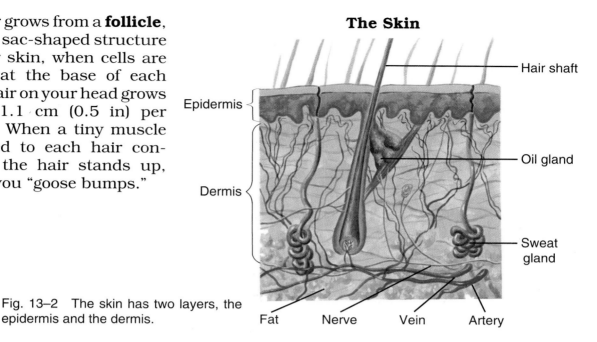

Fig. 13–2 The skin has two layers, the epidermis and the dermis.

TRY THIS 13–1: Brown Apples

Materials:

apple
paper towels – 5
paring knife

plastic cup (clear)
water

Procedure:
1. Carefully use the knife to cut three slices of apple. Try to make the slices about the same size.
2. Carefully remove the skin from two of the apple slices.
3. Place the unpeeled slice, cut side down, on the paper towel.
4. Place one of the peeled slices, cut side down, on the paper towel.
5. Place the other peeled slice under the water in the glass.
6. Leave the three slices for about 20 minutes. Then observe each slice.
   • Which slice has browned the least? Why?
   • Which slice has browned the most? Why?
   • How does the amount of browning of the unpeeled slice compare to the browning of the slice in the glass of water?
   • How does the skin of the apple protect it? How does your skin protect you?

REVIEW IT

1. What are the two layers of the skin?
2. What are three functions of the skin?

Class Activity 13–1: Can You Feel It?

Question: How well can different areas of skin distinguish between various textures?

Materials:
   blindfold
   scissors
   texture samples: (aluminum foil, binder paper, carpet, cotton ball, dish towel, plastic wrap,
                    sandpaper, wood)

Procedure:
1. Cut each of the test materials into 5 cm (2 in) squares.
2. Blindfold your partner. Tell him or her that you will lightly touch a test sample to seven different areas of skin. He or she is to identify the sample by its texture. Record data.
3. Repeat step 2 for each sample. Record whether the sample is identified correctly or incorrectly.

Data:

SAMPLE	CHIN	NOSE	ELBOW	FINGER	BACK OF HAND	PALM OF HAND	NECK
Wood							
Carpet							
Foil							
Sandpaper							
Cotton ball							
Cloth towel							
Plastic wrap							

Questions:
1. Which skin area is the most sensitive? The least sensitive?
2. Which sample was identified correctly the most times? The fewest times?
3. Why are some skin areas more sensitive than others?
4. What specific structures in the skin help to identify texture?
5. What function of skin does this lab demonstrate?

Conclusion: Write 3–5 sentences about what you learned from this activity.

13–2 CARE OF THE SKIN, NAILS, AND HAIR

OBJECTIVES

- Describe the proper care of the skin.
- Describe the proper care of nails and hair.

VOCABULARY
athlete's foot
dandruff

Plenty of rest, exercise, and a balanced diet help your skin stay healthy. Good hygiene is also essential because your skin works best when it is clean. Bathing regularly with soap and water removes dead skin and bacteria that can cause body odor. Using deodorants and drinking plenty of water also help to control body odor.

Athlete's foot and foot odor are common problems. **Athlete's foot** is an infection that causes itchiness of the foot, especially the toes (fig. 13–3). It is caused by a fungus that grows best where it is warm and moist. To prevent both athlete's foot and foot odor in general, keep your feet clean and dry and change your socks daily. If athlete's foot becomes severe, use medication available at a pharmacy or see your doctor.

Proper hair care begins with regular shampooing. Daily combing or brushing of your hair helps to remove loose hair, dirt, and dead cells. Bleaching, coloring, blow-drying, and hot curlers, when used improperly, can damage your hair. Chlorine in swimming pools or too much sun can also harm your hair.

DID YOU KNOW?
You can get athlete's foot by wearing socks or shoes of someone with athlete's foot. You can also become infected by walking barefoot in public showers.

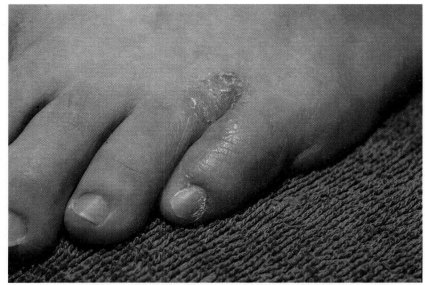

Fig. 13–3   Athlete's foot causes redness, itchiness, and foot odor.

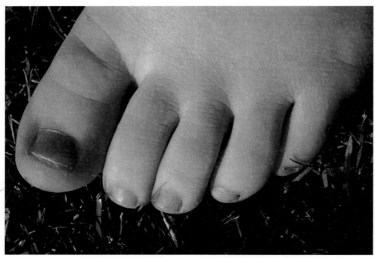

Fig. 13–4   Cutting toenails properly can prevent ingrown toenails.

Dandruff occurs when too many skin cells drop off your scalp at one time. Regular brushing and shampooing can prevent this condition. Severe dandruff may require a special shampoo or a doctor's treatment.

Caring for your fingernails and toenails is fairly simple. Keep them clean and reasonably short. Trim torn or jagged nails. Ingrown toenails occur when the nail edges grow under the skin. You can prevent this by cutting your toenails properly (fig. 13–4).

TRY THIS 13–2: Where's the Hair?

Materials:
   index card (3" x 5")
   magnifying lens

Procedure:
1. In the index card cut a square hole 1 cm (.5 in) on each side.
2. Place the hole on the back of your hand and count how many hairs are showing inside the hole.
   • How many hairs per square centimeter are there on the back of your hand?
3. Repeat step 2 using your forearm.
   • How many hairs per square centimeter are there on your forearm?
4. Have a friend help and repeat step 2 using your cheek.
   • How many hairs per square centimeter are there on your cheek?
5. Repeat step 4 using your scalp.
   • How many hairs per square centimeter are there on your scalp?
   • Which region had the most hairs per square centimeter? Which had the fewest?
   • Why do you think the amount of hair varies on the body?

REVIEW IT

RESEARCH IT
Study to discover the types of materials used as artificial skin and the advantages of each.

1. Why is bathing important to healthy skin?
2. Why are deodorants important?
3. What is the proper way of cutting your toenails?
4. What is dandruff?

13–3 ACNE

OBJECTIVE

- Identify the causes of acne.

Acne is a common skin disorder that starts during adolescence and usually appears on the face, back, and upper chest (fig. 13–5). In severe cases the skin may become pitted or scarred. Scientists believe that heredity determines whether or not you will have acne.

Acne occurs when oil, dirt, and bacteria get trapped in the skin (fig. 13–6). The bacteria cause an infection that forms a pimple. The longer the **pimple** goes untreated, the worse it becomes. Some cosmetics make acne worse by plugging the skin's pores.

Acne lotions are often helpful in treating mild cases of acne. Severe cases should be treated by a doctor who specializes in skin care. Modern treatments can prevent scarring and can remove scars already formed by acne.

Fig. 13–5 Acne causes pitting and scarring of the skin.

VOCABULARY
acne
pimple

RESEARCH IT
Find out what products are available for the treatment of acne.

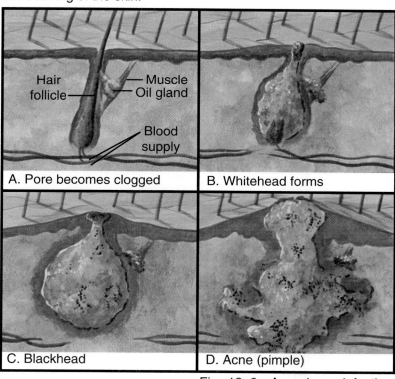

A. Pore becomes clogged

Hair follicle
Muscle
Oil gland
Blood supply

B. Whitehead forms

C. Blackhead

D. Acne (pimple)

Fig. 13–6 Acne is an infection that occurs when bacteria gets trapped in the skin.

REVIEW IT

1. What determines whether or not someone will have acne?
2. How does a pimple form?

13–4 SUN AND SKIN

carotene
melanin
sunscreen

OBJECTIVE

- Describe ways of protecting the skin from the effects of the sun.

God provided your body with built-in protection against sun damage. The skin's outer layer can thicken to protect the deeper layers. And two skin pigments, **melanin** (mel´ ə nin) and **carotene** (kar´ ə tēn), help block the damaging rays of the sun. The more of these pigments in the skin, the greater the protection.

The risk of skin damage increases with exposure to the sun. If skin is repeatedly damaged by sunburn or extreme tanning, skin cancer may occur, though it may not develop until you are older. Every year more than 8000 people in North America die from skin cancer.

You can reduce your chances of getting skin cancer by taking simple precautions.

- Avoid direct sunlight whenever possible.
- Wear a hat and clothing that covers your arms and legs.
- When you are outside, use **sunscreens**, lotions containing chemicals that block out harmful sun rays (fig. 13–7).

Fig. 13–7 Sunscreens block harmful sun rays.

REVIEW IT

1. How does skin protect itself from sunlight?
2. What problem can come from repeated sunburn?
3. How does a sunscreen help to protect your skin?

13–5 THE EXCRETORY SYSTEM

OBJECTIVES

- Explain the importance of the excretory system.
- Identify the parts of the excretory system and their function.

Imagine that the garbage collectors in a large city went on strike (fig. 13–8). Suppose that at the same time the sewage system broke down. Garbage and sewage would be everywhere. Just as a city needs a waste-removal system, your body must be able to remove the waste it creates every day. If wastes are not removed, your body's systems cannot do their jobs.

VOCABULARY
bladder
dialysis machine
excretory system
feces
kidney
urea
urethra
urine

DID YOU KNOW?
Your kidneys filter 190 L (47 gal) of blood each day.

Fig. 13–8 Just as garbage removal keeps your community clean, the excretory system keeps your body clean.

TRY THIS 13–5: Bad Breath?

Materials:

drinking straws – 2	stopwatch
limewater (50 ml)	test tubes – 2

Procedure:
1. Label one test tube A and the other test tube B.
2. Fill test tube A about one-fourth full of limewater and place a straw in it (fig A).
3. Rest for one minute. Gently blow through the straw and record the number of breaths it takes for the limewater to turn cloudy. **INHALE THROUGH YOUR NOSE AND EXHALE THROUGH YOUR MOUTH. DO NOT INHALE THROUGH THE STRAW!**
   - How many breaths did it take to turn the limewater cloudy?
4. Run in place vigorously for three minutes.
5. Repeat step 3 using test tube B.
   - How many breaths did it take this time to turn the limewater cloudy?
   - Why did it take fewer breaths to turn the limewater cloudy after exercising than before exercising?

The **excretory system** is the body's waste-removal system. It includes your skin, lungs, large intestine, kidneys, and bladder (fig. 13–9).

The Excretory System

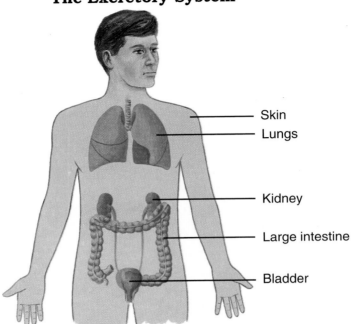

- Skin
- Lungs
- Kidney
- Large intestine
- Bladder

Fig. 13–9

THE EXCRETORY SYSTEM	
STRUCTURE	**FUNCTION**
SKIN	• Rids the body of extra heat as sweat evaporates from the skin. • Excretes excess salt, water, and other wastes through sweat. Bathing removes these wastes.
LUNGS	• Remove water and carbon dioxide.
LARGE INTESTINE	• Removes the solid waste, or **feces**, from the body.
KIDNEYS	• Filter excess salt, water, and **urea**, or liquid waste, from the blood. • These filtered wastes, called **urine**, are collected and passed to the bladder.
BLADDER	• Stores urine until it is released through the **urethra** during urination.

Because kidneys are vital in filtering waste from the body, any kidney disorder is serious and should be treated by a doctor. If kidneys fail completely, a **dialysis** (dī al´ ə sis) **machine** may be used to filter the blood and remove wastes (fig. 13–10). At other times, a kidney transplant may be necessary. This involves replacing the damaged kidney with a working one.

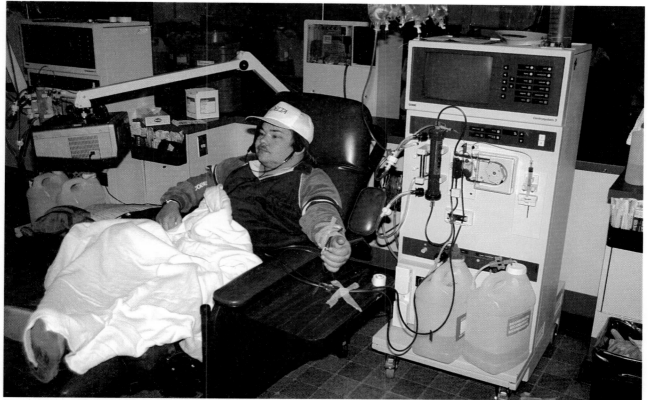

Fig. 13–10   People whose kidneys have failed rely on dialysis machines to filter wastes from the blood.

REVIEW IT

1. What would happen if you were not designed with an excretory system?
2. What are the main parts of the excretory system?
3. Why are the lungs important to the excretory system?
4. What is the job of the kidneys?

CHAPTER 13 WRAP-UP

SKILLS DEVELOPMENT

THINKING SKILLS: MAKING A MODEL

Models are often used to represent something. Models can be representations of events, objects, or ideas. They can be drawings, three-dimensional models, or models that have moving parts. The advantage of using a model is that something can be seen more clearly, it is more practical, relationships can be seen, or a movement can be repeated.

In the picture shown you can see a model of the skin. This model was purchased from a scientific supply house.

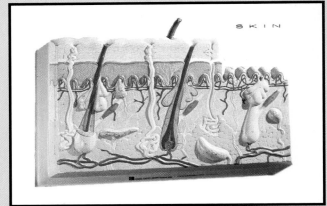

1. Make a model of the kidneys showing their structure and relation to the bladder using one of the methods described above.

QUESTIONS AND PROBLEMS

1. How is your integumentary system similar to tree bark?
2. During which season do people produce the most melanin?
3. What is the purpose of sweat?
4. Which is more important, bathing regularly or using deodorants? Why?
5. Explain how a pimple forms.
6. List three ways you can protect your skin from sun damage.
7. List, in order of importance, the parts of the excretory system. Explain the order of your list.
8. Where are the wastes from the cells removed from the blood? (Hint: more than one)
9. What are some possible causes of kidney stones?
10. Why aren't kidney transplants always used in treating people with failed kidneys?

RESEARCH

1. Draw a diagram comparing the human and bird excretory systems. Explain how they are different.
2. What makes up house dust? Make a graph that shows the most common components.
3. Gather literature on acne. Make an oral report to the class that summarizes your findings. Include visual aids in your presentation.
4. Compare deodorant and antiperspirant products as to cost and effectiveness. Make a poster that displays your findings.
5. Draw and label a diagram of a kidney-dialysis machine. Write a brief report that explains how it works.

REVIEW

HIGHLIGHTS

1. Skin makes up your outer covering. It has two layers, the epidermis and dermis. The epidermis is the outermost layer and consists of dead skin cells. The dermis is the inner layer and is made of living skin cells.
2. The skin is a waterproof covering that protects the body, regulates temperature, and removes waste.
3. Proper care of your skin, nails, and hair includes eating a balanced diet, drinking plenty of water, and bathing regularly.
4. Heredity is believed to be the main cause of acne.
5. You can protect your skin from the sun by avoiding exposure to direct sunlight, by wearing hats and clothing that cover you, and by using sunscreens.

6. The excretory system removes waste from the body.
7. The excretory system includes the skin, lungs, large intestine, kidneys, and bladder. The function of each of these parts is identified on page 236.

VOCABULARY LIST

acne	excretory system	pimple
athlete's foot	feces	sunscreen
bladder	follicle	sweat gland
carotene	integument	urea
dandruff	integumentary system	urethra
dermis	kidney	urine
dialysis machine	melanin	
epidermis	oil gland	

PRACTICE
Multiple Choice. Choose the best answer.
1. Which is not a function of the skin?
   a. cool the body
   b. help with breathing
   c. protect against infection
   d. excrete waste
2. Which of the following do you exhale?
   a. water
   b. air sacs
   c. calories
   d. plasma
3. What causes dandruff?
   a. dirt and unclean skin
   b. dry skin
   c. both a and b
   d. neither a nor b
4. Which of these are located in the skin?
   a. oil glands
   b. hair follicle
   c. sweat glands
   d. all of these
5. Which of the following are included in the excretory system?
   a. skin and kidneys
   b. kidneys and lungs
   c. lungs and large intestine
   d. all of these
6. What causes athlete's foot?
   a. a virus
   b. a bacteria
   c. a fungus
   d. none of these
7. What causes "goose bumps"?
   a. a muscle contraction
   b. a plugged oil gland
   c. an illness
   d. an allergy
8. Which is not filtered out by the kidneys?
   a. blood
   b. urea
   c. water
   d. salt

9. Where is urine stored?
   a. urethra
   b. bladder
   c. kidneys
   d. large intestine
10. Which of the following make up the integumentary system?
   a. skin, hair, and nails
   b. kidneys and bladder
   c. heart and blood vessels
   d. brain and spinal cord

Matching. Match each word with its definition or description.
1. filters out liquid waste
2. the outer layer of skin
3. a hereditary skin disorder
4. a product that blocks out harmful sun rays
5. dead skin cells on your scalp
6. removes solid waste
7. covers, cools, and protects your body
8. removes carbon dioxide gas
9. pigment in the skin
10. caused by a plugged hair follicle

a. acne
b. dandruff
c. epidermis
d. kidneys
e. large intestine
f. lungs
g. melanin
h. sunscreen
i. skin
j. pimple

DGC—16

THE CIRCULATORY SYSTEM

INTRODUCTION

Freeways and turnpikes, city streets and country roads crisscross the continent. These roadways make it possible to transport food, building material, merchandise, waste products—all the products of everyday life.

In a similar way, your circulatory system provides a means of transporting food, oxygen, and waste throughout your body. It includes the heart, blood vessels, and blood. The interstate highway system is simple compared to the complex circulatory system designed for you by the Creator.

SECTION TITLES

Freeway systems such as this allow many kinds of materials to be transported.

14–1 THE HEART AND BLOOD VESSELS

OBJECTIVES

- Describe the flow of blood through the heart.
- Compare the three types of blood vessels.

The **circulatory system** is the transportation system of your body (fig. 14–1). The heart is the power center, working continuously to keep you alive. It contracts about 100,000 times each day—that's more than two billion heartbeats during your lifetime!

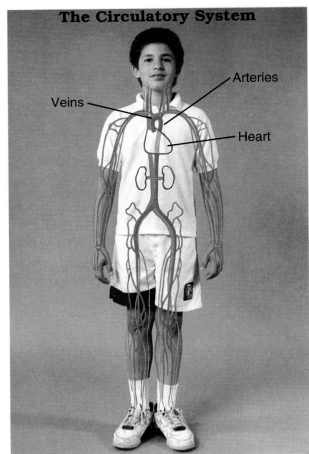

The Circulatory System

Veins

Arteries

Heart

RESEARCH IT
Find out what coronary by-pass surgery involves and why it is performed.

Fig. 14–1   The circulatory system, made up of the heart, blood vessels, and blood, transports materials through your body.

244

Your heart is a specially designed pump that is divided into four chambers: the right and left atrium (ā´ trē əm) and the right and left ventricle (ven´ tri kəl). Study fig. 14–2 to see how blood flows through each of these chambers.

Fig. 14–2

THE HEART	
STRUCTURE	**DESCRIPTION AND FUNCTION**
ATRIUM	• The upper chamber of the heart. • The right atrium receives oxygen-poor blood from the body. • The left atrium receives oxygen-rich blood from the lungs.
VENTRICLE	• The lower chamber of the heart. • The right ventricle pumps oxygen-poor blood to the lungs. • The left ventricle pumps oxygen-rich blood to the body.

The Heart

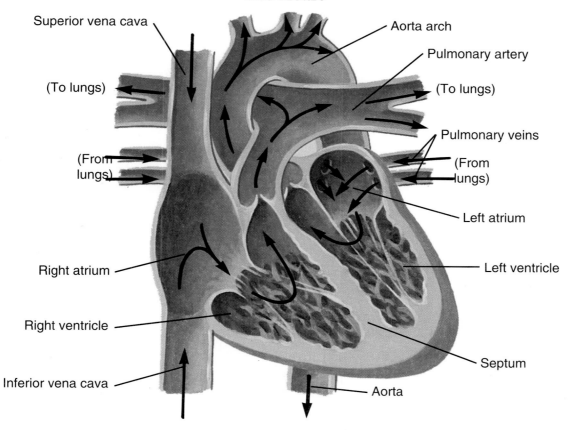

Superior vena cava

Aorta arch

(To lungs)

Pulmonary artery

(To lungs)

(From lungs)

Pulmonary veins

(From lungs)

Left atrium

Right atrium

Left ventricle

Right ventricle

Septum

Inferior vena cava

Aorta

Fig. 14–3 Your heart needs regular exercise to stay healthy.

The heart beats in response to messages sent through the automatic nervous system. It is made of cardiac muscle, and just as the muscles of your arms and legs need exercise, your heart needs regular exercise. To properly exercise your heart, your pulse must be increased for 20 or more minutes, three or four times a week (fig. 14–3).

In 1628, William Harvey, an English doctor, showed that blood flows through blood vessels as it is pumped by the heart (fig. 14–4). Before this discovery, it was believed that the blood simply oozed around inside the body.

DID YOU KNOW?
Each time your heart contracts, blood is squeezed into your blood vessels. This causes your pulse.

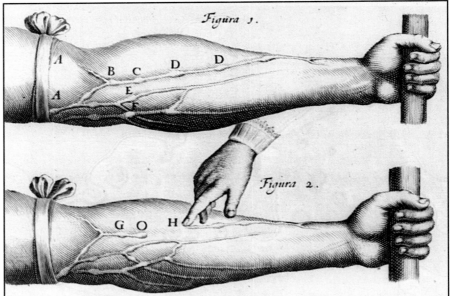

Fig. 14–4 Harvey found that a tourniquet stops the flow of blood and causes it to back up in the veins.

246

FRONTIERS: Infant Heart Transplants

Newborn Robbie was dying from kidney failure. He had been born with an under-developed heart and a rare blood type. The baby needed a heart transplant to survive. A donor heart with matching size and blood type might be impossible to locate in time to save his life. As days passed and the baby's condition worsened, Robbie's parents were devastated. They shared their concern with friends and co-workers. Fellow officers with Robbie's dad, a police officer, began a campaign to find a donor heart in hopes of saving the baby. They began wearing baby-blue ribbons under their badges, next to their hearts, in an effort to draw the public's attention. The story received widespread publicity in the media.

Finally, on Robbie's eleventh day, word was received that an acceptable donor had been found. Robbie's parents were overwhelmed with gratitude, relief, and anticipation. The donor was a baby who had died of Sudden Infant Death Syndrome. The heart was donated by parents who were able to see briefly through their grief, trying to turn their personal tragedy into something good. Robbie was flown by helicopter to Loma Linda University Medical Center, where he became the 142nd infant under six months of age to receive a heart transplant there. The surgery, using a heart weighing about one ounce, took four and a half hours.

Leonard L. Bailey, M.D., with a dream in his heart, pioneered the infant-heart-transplant program at Loma Linda University Medical Center. As of January 1, 1993, 148 babies under six months of age have received heart transplants at Loma Linda. Approximately 80 percent of them are still alive. All would have died without the surgery.

Questions:
1. Why are infant heart transplants so difficult?
2. What is the name of the doctor who pioneered the infant heart transplant?
3. How do you think the parents whose infant died felt about the success of Robbie's transplant? Explain.

Eventually, three types of vessels were discovered: arteries, veins, and capillaries (kap´ ə ler ēz) (fig. 14–5).

Fig. 14–5

TYPES OF BLOOD VESSELS	
BLOOD VESSEL	**DESCRIPTION AND FUNCTION**
ARTERIES	• Thick-walled blood vessels. • Carry blood rich in food and oxygen away from the heart. • The largest artery is the **aorta**, which comes directly out of the heart.
VEINS	• Thin-walled blood vessels. • Carry blood laden with waste and carbon dioxide back to the heart. • The largest vein is the **vena cava**, which comes into the heart.
CAPILLARIES	• The smallest blood vessels in the body. • Connect the arteries to the veins.

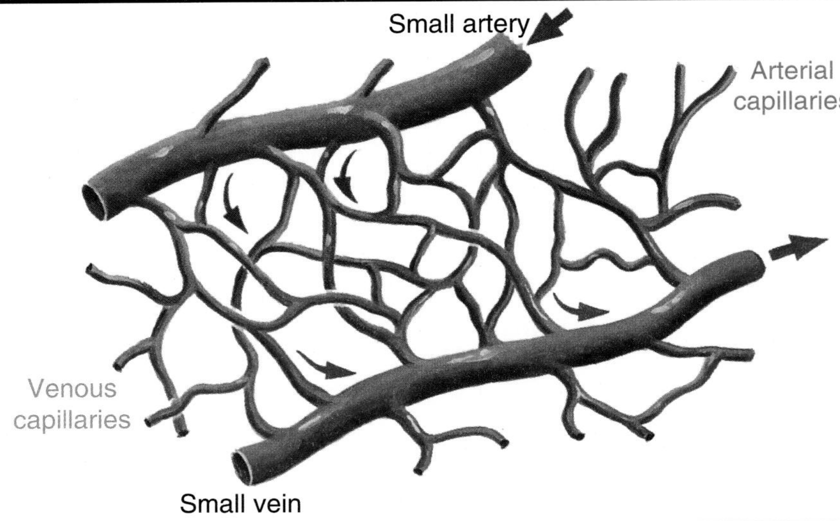

Small artery

Arterial capillaries

Venous capillaries

Small vein

DID YOU KNOW?

When you become frightened, special glands release chemicals that speed up your heartbeat. This causes more blood to be pumped to your muscles. The increased blood supply gives you extra strength. This response is called the **fright-fight-flight** reaction.

TRY THIS 14–1: Jump'n Matchsticks!

Materials:
thumbtack   wooden match

Procedure:
1. Push the thumbtack into the bottom of the matchstick.
2. Rest your arm on your desk. Place the thumbtack with the matchstick on your wrist as shown in A.
3. Watch the matchstick closely.
   • What happens to the matchstick? Why?
4. Repeat step 2 after running in place for one minute.
   • What happens to the matchstick? Why?

The **lymph** (limf) system is an important part of the circulatory system (fig. 14–6). As the blood moves through the capillaries, some of the liquid portion of the blood passes through the walls of the capillaries and into the surrounding tissue. This liquid moves in the spaces between the cells and is collected in tubes, where it becomes lymph. The lymph is important because it helps nutrients to be absorbed and rids the body of wastes. In addition, the lymph system produces **lymphocytes** (lim´ fō sītz), special white blood cells that help defend against infection.

The Lymph System

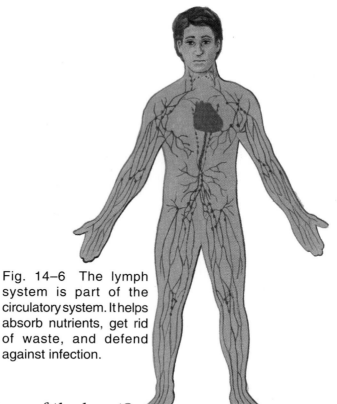

Fig. 14–6 The lymph system is part of the circulatory system. It helps absorb nutrients, get rid of waste, and defend against infection.

REVIEW IT

1. What are the four chambers of the heart?
2. What type of muscle makes up the heart?
3. Why must the blood travel through the lungs?
4. What are the three kinds of blood vessels?

14–2 BLOOD CELLS AND BLOOD TYPES

OBJECTIVES

- Identify the components of blood and their functions.
- Identify the main blood types.

The average body contains 3–5 L (3–5 qts) of blood that carries oxygen from the lungs and food from the digestive system to the cells. From the cells, blood carries carbon dioxide to the lungs and other wastes to the kidneys.

Blood is composed mostly of a clear liquid called **plasma** (55 percent). The plasma contains red blood cells, white blood cells, and platelets (fig. 14–7).

Fig. 14–7   Red blood cells, white blood cells, and platelets make up the solid part of the blood.

BLOOD COMPONENTS	

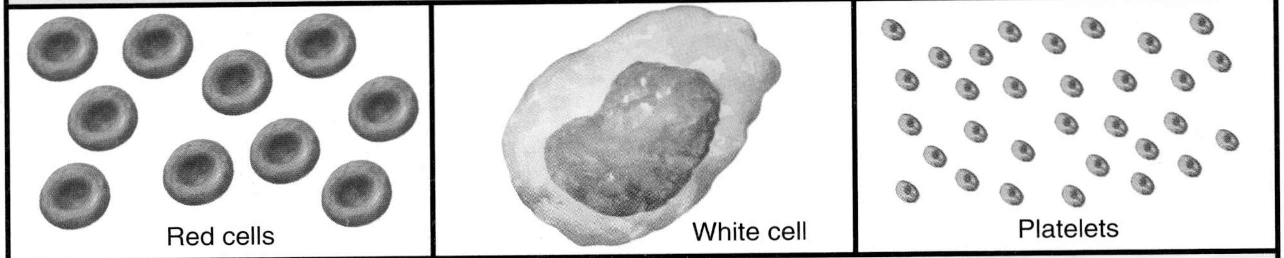

Red cells

White cell

Platelets

COMPONENT	DESCRIPTION AND FUNCTION
RED BLOOD CELLS	• The most common blood cells. • Red color is caused by **hemoglobin**, an iron–rich protein. • Carry oxygen to other body cells. • Produced by the bone marrow.
WHITE BLOOD CELLS	• The second most common blood cells fight infection by killing harmful bacteria or by producing chemicals called **antibodies** that kill harmful microorganisms. • Produced in the bone marrow.
PLATELETS	• Very small particles in the blood. • Help to form clots and scabs.

While everyone's blood looks the same, there are differences. Human blood is grouped into four main **blood types** (fig. 14–8): Type A, Type B, Type AB, and Type O. Type O blood can be given to anyone and is called the **universal donor**. People with Type AB blood can receive any type of blood. For this reason Type AB blood is called the **universal recipient**.

DID YOU KNOW?
Sickle cell anemia is an inherited disease that causes red blood cells to be mis-shaped. Instead of being round, the cells are shaped like a crescent moon. These smaller cells cannot carry enough oxygen throughout the body.

BLOOD TYPES		
TYPE	**CAN RECEIVE FROM**	**CAN DONATE TO**
A	O and A	A and AB
B	O and B	B and AB
AB	A, B, AB, and O	AB
O	O	A, B, AB, and O

Fig. 14–8   There are four types of human blood.

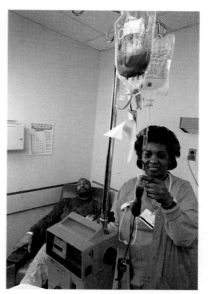

Fig. 14–9   Blood transfusions save many lives.

The process of giving blood from one person to another is called **transfusion** (fig. 14–9). Transfusing the wrong blood type causes the red blood cells to stick together in clumps, resulting in serious illness or death.

REVIEW IT

1. What is the job of red blood cells?
2. How do white blood cells fight infection?
3. What are the four main types of blood?
4. What happens if different types of blood are mixed?

CLASS ACTIVITY 14–2: Are You the Right Type?

Question: Which types of blood can be safely transfused?

Materials:

blue water	test-tube rack
drinking straws – 2	test tubes – 4
green water	yellow water
paper cups – 4	water

Procedure:
1. Label one cup Type A; fill it about half full with blue water. Label another cup Type B; fill it half full with yellow water. Label the third cup Type AB; fill it half full of green water. Label the last cup Type O; fill it half full of clear water. Each of the four cups represents a donor's blood.
2. Cut the two straws in half, and place a half piece of straw in each cup.
3. Label the test tubes 1, 2, 3, and 4.
4. Fill each of the four test tubes half full of Type A (blue) water. This is the recipient's blood.
5. Use the straw in cup A to add some colored water to test tube 1. Add B to tube 2, C to tube 3, and D to tube 4. Record what happens in the chart. Write "CHANGE" if the color changes or "NO CHANGE" if the color does not change. Clean and dry test tubes.
6. Repeat steps 4 and 5 using Type B (yellow) in each test tube.
7. Repeat steps 4 and 5 using Type AB (green) in each test tube.
8. Repeat steps 4 and 5 using Type O (clear) in each test tube.

Data:

		DONOR			
R E C I P I E N T		A	B	AB	O
	A				
	B				
	AB				
	O				

Questions:
1. What blood types can someone with type A blood receive safely?
2. What blood types can someone with type AB blood receive safely?
3. What blood types can someone with type O blood receive safely?
4. What type of blood can be given safely to anyone?
5. What type of blood can safely receive any other type of blood?

Conclusion: Write 3–5 sentences about what you learned from this activity.

14–3 CARE OF THE CIRCULATORY SYSTEM

OBJECTIVE

• Analyze ways of protecting the circulatory system.

Diseases of the circulatory system are the leading cause of death in North America and Europe. Many of these diseases can be prevented. One common disorder, **arteriosclerosis** (är tir ē ō sklə rō´ sis), occurs when fatty materials, such as **cholesterol** (kə les´ tər ôl), stick to the inner walls of the arteries, slowing blood flow through the vessels (fig. 14–10). The heart must pump harder to move blood through partially blocked vessels. As the heart works harder, the pressure increases. Increased blood pressure is called **hypertension**, a condition that can lead to many serious problems, such as heart disease or stroke.

VOCABULARY
arteriosclerosis
cholesterol
hypertension

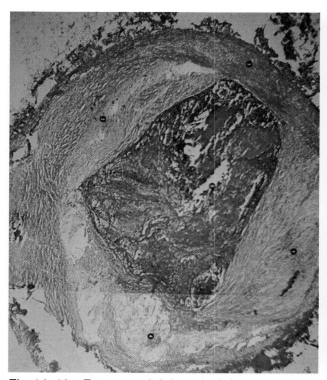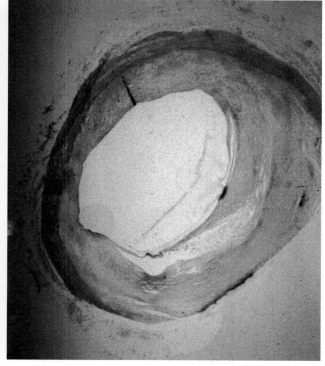

Fig. 14–10 Fatty material clogs the left artery, but blood moves easily through the unclogged artery on the right.

Materials:
  none needed
Procedure:
  1. On a sheet of notebook paper, list 20 prepared and prepackaged foods that your family eats. These may include canned foods, frozen foods, baked goods, etc.
  2. Predict which of the foods you listed contain added salt.
  3. Go to a grocery store and look at the ingredient labels of each food you listed. If salt is listed as an ingredient, it is added. Record the results of your survey.
     • How accurate were your predictions?
     • Which foods contained added salt?
     • Which foods did not contain added salt?
     • Based on the results of your survey, would it be easy to have a low-salt diet if you eat the foods in your list? Why?

The best way of caring for the circulatory system is to eat a balanced diet and get regular exercise. Avoiding excess salt and fatty foods and avoiding alcohol and other drugs will further protect this important body system (fig. 14–11).

Fig. 14–11 Eating a diet of low-fat foods helps the circulatory system.

REVIEW IT

  1. Name several ways of protecting the circulatory system.

14–4 THE IMMUNE SYSTEM

OBJECTIVES

- Describe the immune system.
- Explain how the immune system protects your body.
- Analyze the impact of AIDS on the immune system.

VOCABULARY
AIDS
immune system
immunity
interferon
vaccination

Your **immune system** protects your body from disease through three lines of defense against infection (fig. 14–12).

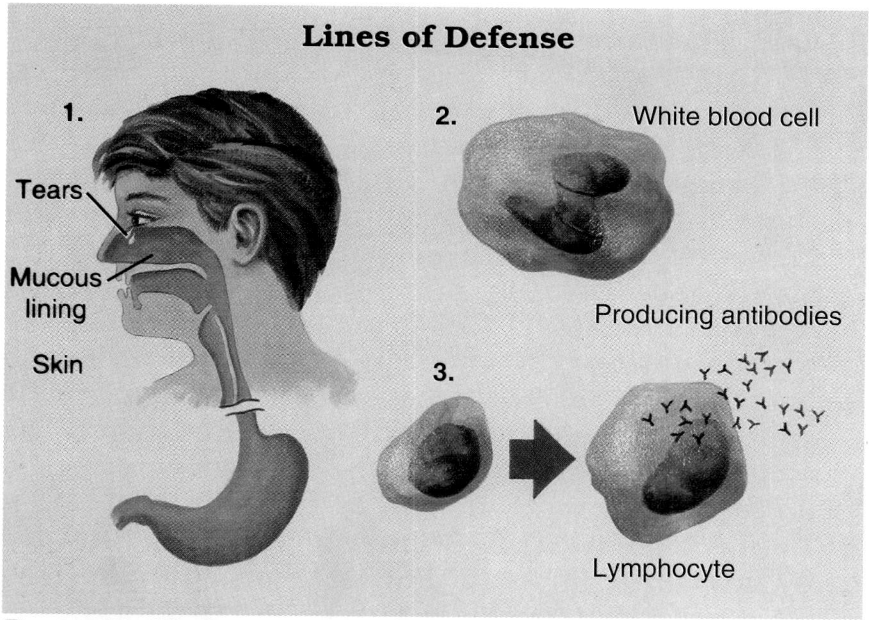

Lines of Defense

1. Tears, Mucous lining, Skin

2. White blood cell — Producing antibodies

3. Lymphocyte

Fig. 14–12 The immune system has three lines of defense.

THE FIRST LINE OF DEFENSE includes the skin, tears, and mucous linings of the nose and mouth. These protect you by keeping most bacteria and other micro-organisms from ever getting inside your body. If bacteria do become trapped in the moist linings of your nose and mouth, they are usually swallowed. Once swallowed, the bacteria are destroyed by the acids of your stomach and intestines.

THE SECOND LINE OF DEFENSE is comprised of white blood cells. When bacteria and viruses enter through a cut or break in the skin, they release chemicals that attract white blood cells. These cells invade the area and destroy the intruders.

THE THIRD LINE OF DEFENSE is lymphocytes, special white blood cells produced by the lymph glands. These special cells produce antibodies, chemical substances that recognize and attack invaders in your body. Each antibody attacks a specific organism, forming a system of immunity.

Immunity is your body's ability to defend itself against disease. There are three ways immunity develops.

NATURAL IMMUNITY. This type of immunity develops as a result of diseases you have already had, such as chickenpox. As your body fights a disease, antibodies are produced to destroy the bacteria or virus. Some of these antibodies stay in your body after the infection is over to provide a ready defense against the disease should it occur again.

ARTIFICIAL IMMUNITY. This immunity develops from a **vaccination**, an injection of dead or weakened bacteria or virus. The injection usually doesn't make you sick but causes your body to make antibodies. The next time the bacteria or virus enters your body, antibodies are ready to fight it.

CELLULAR IMMUNITY. Cellular immunity is provided by **interferon** (in tər fir´ ən), a chemical produced by your cells that prevents viruses from multiplying. When viruses are not able to multiply, they die out.

AIDS, or **Acquired Immune Deficiency Syndrome**, is a disease of the immune system. It destroys lymphocytes, which help to make antibodies (fig. 14–13). Without antibodies the body cannot fight disease. Because the body cannot fight disease, people who have the AIDS virus may get many serious diseases.

Fig. 14–13 The virus that causes AIDS destroys lymphocytes, making it dificult for the body to fight disease.

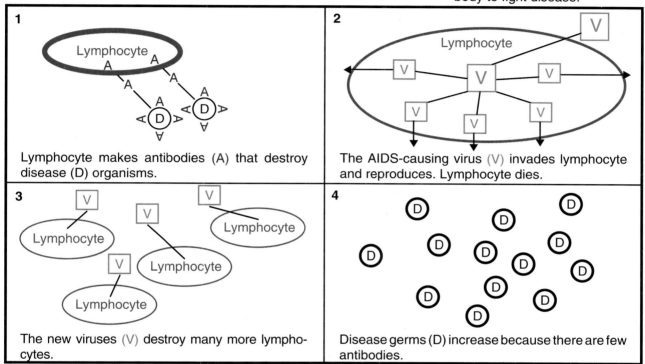

1 Lymphocyte makes antibodies (A) that destroy disease (D) organisms.

2 The AIDS-causing virus (V) invades lymphocyte and reproduces. Lymphocyte dies.

3 The new viruses (V) destroy many more lymphocytes.

4 Disease germs (D) increase because there are few antibodies.

The AIDS virus can be passed from one individual to another through sharing infected hypodermic needles or during sexual contact. Now, the AIDS virus eventually results in death for the person carrying it, but much research is being done to find ways of curing AIDS.

REVIEW IT

1. What are your body's three lines of defense against infection?
2. What are antibodies?
3. What is interferon?

CHAPTER 14 WRAP-UP

SKILLS DEVELOPMENT

THINKING SKILLS: MAKING A GRAPH

When making a graph of data, one must make sure that:
1. The graph has a title.
2. Each axis is named.
3. Each unit is identified.
4. If the units are numerical, each division must be equal.
5. Time must be placed on a horizontal axis.

The following table shows the effects of exercise on the heartbeat of a certain animal. This information is plotted on the bar graph and line graph below.

Amount of Exercise (in minutes)	Heartbeat Rate (beats/minute)
1	40
2	50
3	70
4	60

A. *Bar Graph*   B. *Line Graph*

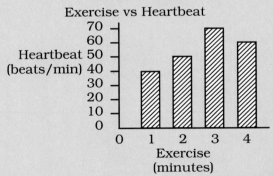

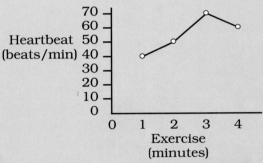

Using the graphs above as an example, draw a bar graph or a line graph of the following data, making sure you label your graph properly.

Age of Animal (months)	Length of Fur (millimeters)
1	5
2	10
3	20
4	35
5	45
6	50

QUESTIONS AND PROBLEMS

1. The brain cells have first priority for blood. Why might standing at attention for long periods of time cause a person to faint?
2. Name ten foods that are not good for the circulatory system.
3. What are the three main functions of the blood?
4. Why would it be helpful for you to know your blood type?
5. How are pulse and heartbeat related?
6. Why are the walls of arteries thicker than the walls of veins?
7. How are the atria different from the ventricles?
8. Why is salt added to so many prepared and prepackaged foods?
9. What is the advantage of long-lasting antibodies?
10. Why does your heartbeat speed up when you are frightened?
11. What is the role of the lymph nodes in the fight against infection?

RESEARCH

1. Construct a chart showing the blood types of your family. Indicate who can donate blood to whom.
2. Learn how different types of anemia can be treated. Write a report on your findings.
3. Discover how the body recycles red blood cells. Prepare an oral report that includes visual aids.
4. Draw diagrams of three different kinds of artificial hearts. Write a brief report on the advantages and disadvantages of each.
5. Investigate three genetic blood disorders. Make a set of posters that illustrates the effect of each.

REVIEW

HIGHLIGHTS

1. The vena cava brings blood from the body into the right atrium. From here the blood flows into the right ventricle, which pumps it into the lungs via the pulmonary artery. From the lungs the blood reenters the heart through the pulmonary vein into the left atrium. The blood next passes into the left ventricle and is pumped out the aorta to the body.
2. Arteries are thick-walled vessels that carry oxygen-rich blood from the heart to the body. Veins are thin-walled vessels that carry blood from the body back to the heart. The capillaries are the smallest vessels and link the arteries with the veins.

3. The blood is made of a liquid part called plasma and a solid part that includes red blood cells, white blood cells, and platelets. The functions of these components are identified on page 250.
4. The main blood types are A, B, AB, and O. Type O is the universal donor, and type AB is the universal recipient.
5. Eating a balanced diet, exercising regularly, and avoiding salty or fatty foods all help to protect the circulatory system.
6. The immune system protects your body from disease and infection. It includes your skin, tears, mucous membranes, white blood cells, and lymphocytes.
7. The immune system has three lines of defense against infection. The first is designed to keep disease and infection from getting into the body. The second attacks and destroys bacteria and viruses that get into the body. The third produces antibodies that attack specific invaders.
8. AIDS destroys the lymphocytes that produce antibodies. Without these antibodies the body is unable to adequately fight disease.

VOCABULARY LIST

AIDS	hemoglobin	transfusion
antibody	hypertension	universal donor
aorta	immune system	universal recipient
artery	immunity	vaccination
arteriosclerosis	interferon	vein
atrium	lymph	vena cava
blood type	lymphocyte	ventricle
capillary	plasma	white blood cell
cholesterol	platelet	
circulatory system	red blood cell	

PRACTICE

Multiple Choice. Choose the best answer.
1. What is the main job of hemoglobin?
   a. carry carbon dioxide
   b. carry oxygen
   c. both a and b
   d. neither a nor b
2. Which cavity of the heart pumps blood throughout the body?
   a. right atrium
   b. left atrium
   c. right ventricle
   d. left ventricle
3. Who first correctly identified how blood circulates?
   a. Louis Pasteur
   b. William Harvey
   c. Anne Campbell
   d. Aristotle

4. To whom can a person with Type O blood donate blood safely?
   a. Type A   c. Type AB
   b. Type B   d. all of these
5. Which blood vessels carry oxygen-rich blood?
   a. arteries   c. capillaries
   b. veins   d. both a and c
6. Which part of the blood fights infection?
   a. red blood cells   c. platelets
   b. white blood cells   d. plasma
7. What blood vessel returns blood from the body to the heart?
   a. capillary   c. interferon
   b. vena cava   d. aorta
8. Where are antibodies produced?
   a. liver   c. heart
   b. lymph glands   d. capillaries
9. Where does blood flow when it leaves the right atrium?
   a. left atrium   c. left ventricle
   b. right ventricle   d. lungs
10. What is the body's first line of defense?
   a. skin   c. white blood cells
   b. antibodies   d. lymphocytes

Matching. Match each word with its definition or description.
   1. needed by the heart to stay healthy   a. antibodies
   2. the liquid part of the blood   b. arteries
   3. carries blood away from the heart   c. capillaries
   4. a rhythmic bulging of an artery   d. cardiac
   5. protein that gives blood its color   e. exercise
   6. type of muscle that makes up the heart   f. hemoglobin
   7. carries blood to the heart   g. lymphocytes
   8. produced by the lymphatic system   h. plasma
   9. smallest blood vessels   i. pulse
   10. infection-fighting substances   j. veins

CHAPTER 15

THE RESPIRATORY SYSTEM

INTRODUCTION

High above the ground, atop a 50-story building, sits a huge heating/air-conditioning unit. Each hour it pumps thousands of liters of air into the building, through passageways to all the building's rooms and offices. This equipment warms or cools the air as needed, filters particles out of the air, and replaces stale air inside the building with fresh air from outside.

How is your respiratory system similar to the heating/air-conditioning unit? Does your respiratory system work alone? In this chapter, discover how your respiratory system is designed to heat, cool, and filter air for your body.

SECTION TITLES

Heating/air conditioning systems keep the air inside large buildings comfortable.

15–1 THE RESPIRATORY SYSTEM

VOCABULARY

mucus
mucous membrane
nasal passage
nostril
respiratory system
septum

OBJECTIVES

- Identify the parts of the respiratory system.
- Describe the function of mucus.

Ever since God breathed the breath of life into Adam, people have needed air to stay alive. You can live a few weeks without food, a few days without water, but only a few minutes without air. Your body must have oxygen, and your **respiratory system** is responsible for getting oxygen from the air into the blood. The main parts of the respiratory system are the nose, mouth, pharynx (far´ ingks), trachea (trā´ kē ə), bronchi, lungs, and diaphragm (fig. 15–1).

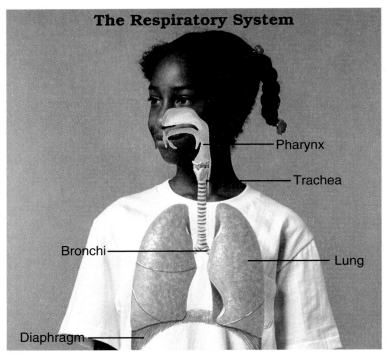

Fig. 15–1   The respiratory system includes the nose, mouth, pharynx, trachea, bronchi, lungs, and diaphragm.

TRY THIS 15–1: Hold It!

Materials:
   stopwatch
Procedure:
1. Take a deep breath and time how long you can hold it.
   • How long did you hold your breath?
2. Rest for a couple of minutes. Take 10 deep breaths and hold your breath. Time how long you can hold your breath.
   • How long did you hold your breath this time?
   • Did you hold it for a longer or shorter time than you did the first time? Why?
3. Rest for a couple of minutes. Again take 10 deep breaths and hold your breath while running in place. Time how long you can hold your breath.
   • How long did you hold your breath this time?
   • How does the length of time you held your breath while running in place compare to the two other times you held your breath? Explain.

The most obvious part of the respiratory system is the nose (fig. 15–2). Air enters the body through the two **nostrils**, or openings in the nose, which are divided by a wall, or **septum**. As air passes through the nose, hairs screen out dust and other particles.

The sides of the **nasal passages** are lined with **mucous membrane**. Warm blood flowing in capillaries of the nose warms the air as it passes through. The mucous membrane secretes a wet, sticky substance called **mucus**. It is the job of mucus to moisten the air and trap microorganisms and small particles that enter your body. When you have a cold or allergies, extra mucus is produced, giving you a "runny nose" and making you blow your nose often.

The Nose

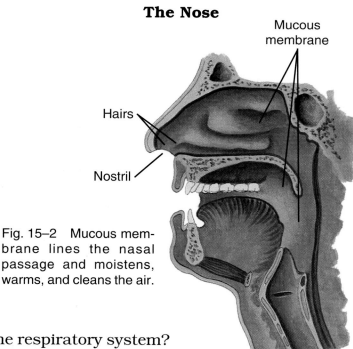

Fig. 15–2 Mucous membrane lines the nasal passage and moistens, warms, and cleans the air.

REVIEW IT

1. What structures make up the respiratory system?
2. What is the purpose of the hairs in the nose?
3. Why is mucus important?

15–2 PHARYNX, LARYNX, AND TRACHEA

bronchi
cilia
larynx
pharynx
trachea
vocal cord

OBJECTIVES

- Describe the pathway air travels as it moves in and out of the body.
- Explain the function of the larynx.

The nose, pharynx, trachea, and bronchi form a pathway for air to get in and out of the lungs. Study fig. 15–3 as you read about the movement of air in your body.

Fig. 15–3

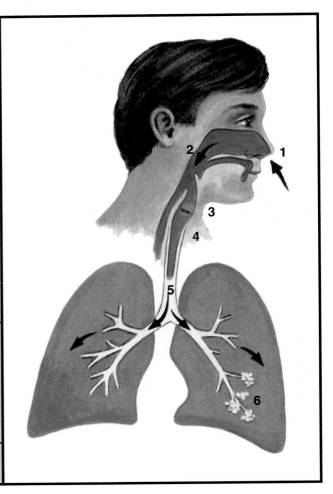

MOVEMENT OF AIR THROUGH THE RESPIRATORY SYSTEM
1. Air enters the body through the nose and mouth.
2. The air next passes through the **pharynx**, or throat.
3. Once through the pharynx, the air moves through the **larynx** (lar´ ingks), or voice box.
4. Next the air moves into the **trachea**, a muscular tube with rings of cartilage. These rings hold the sides in place and keep them from collapsing.
5. Before the trachea reaches the lungs, it branches into two tubes called **bronchi**. Each tube leads to one of the lungs. The air moves through the bronchi into smaller and still smaller tubes.
6. Eventually these tiny air tubes end in a cluster of air sacs.

When you talk, air from your lungs moves through your larynx, which contains your vocal cords. The **vocal cords** vibrate when air passes between them (fig. 15–4).

RESEARCH IT
Find out how people who have had a laryngectomy live a normal life.

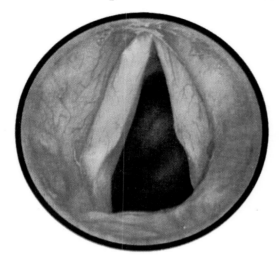

Fig. 15–4 Vocal cords vibrate when air passes between them.

These vibrations make sounds and allow you to speak. You can feel a portion of your larynx, called the Adam's apple, move by touching your throat when you swallow (fig. 15–5).

Fig. 15–5 The Adam's apple is another name for the larynx.

Like the nose and mouth, the rest of your respiratory system is also lined with mucous membrane. In the trachea and bronchi, this membrane is covered by tiny hairs called **cilia** (fig. 15–6). There may be as many as 200 cilia on a single cell, waving back and forth about 1200–

Cilia of the Trachea

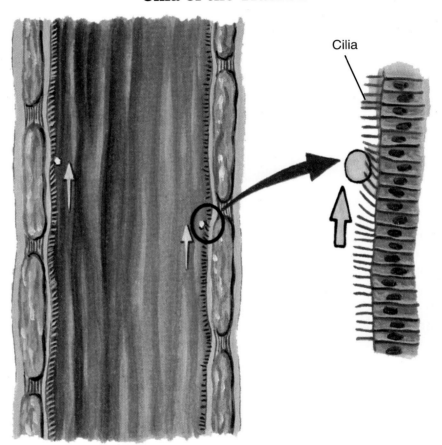

Trachea

Fig. 15–6   Cilia line the trachea and bronchi and help keep the respiratory system clean.

1300 times per minute. As they move, a film of mucus is pushed toward the top of the trachea. Dust, dirt, and other material are trapped and carried away from the lungs in the mucus.

The Epiglottis

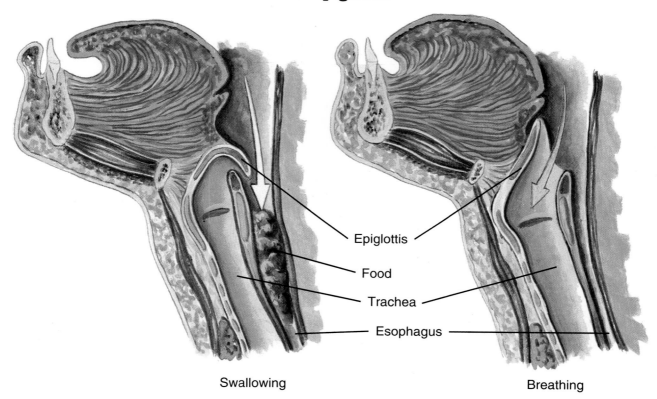

Swallowing   Breathing

Fig. 15–7   When you swallow, the epiglottis covers the trachea to prevent food from entering your lungs (left). Otherwise, the epiglottis stays "open" to allow air to enter the lungs (right).

When you swallow, two flaps close, one over your trachea and one over the nasal passageway (fig. 15–7). This allows you to swallow when lying down or standing on your head. Your brain coordinates this very complicated process. However, if you laugh when swallowing, food may get into your larynx, making you cough or even choke.

REVIEW IT

1. Through what structure does the air pass as it moves from the pharynx to the trachea?
2. Why are there two bronchi?
3. How does the larynx enable you to speak?

DID YOU KNOW?

The trachea is designed with rings similar to the way a vacuum cleaner hose is designed. This design prevents the trachea from collapsing.

269

15–3 THE LUNGS AND BREATHING

air sac
diaphragm
exhalation
inhalation
lung

OBJECTIVES

- Describe the lungs.
- Explain the process of breathing.
- Describe the effects of tobacco on the lungs.
- Identify ways of keeping your lungs healthy.

Your **lungs** are two lobe-shaped organs that look like a soft, moist sponge (fig. 15–8). The tissue that makes up the lungs contains millions of **air sacs** arranged in clusters. Each cluster of air sacs has a network of capillaries covering it.

Oxygen enters the lungs when you breathe in, and carbon dioxide leaves when you breathe out. Here's how it works. When cells use energy, carbon dioxide, a waste product, is produced. The carbon dioxide is carried to the lungs by the blood. As the blood passes into the capillaries surrounding each air sac, the carbon dioxide is exchanged for oxygen from fresh air. Once oxygen is taken into the blood, the capillaries carry it back to the heart and out to all the cells of the body. The exchange of carbon dioxide and oxygen happens quickly because of the many air sacs present in the lungs.

Lungs

Air sacs

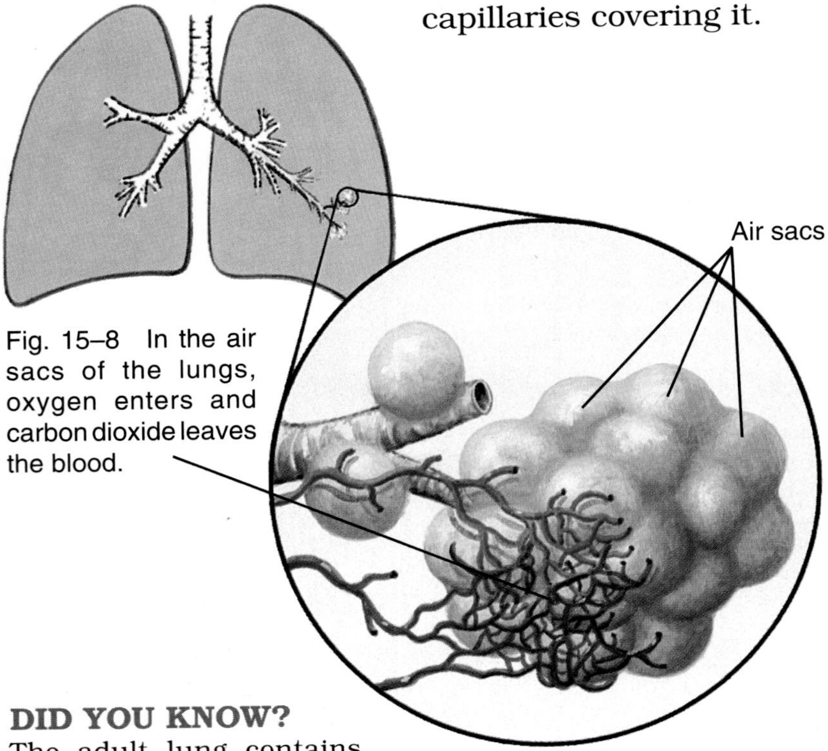

Fig. 15–8 In the air sacs of the lungs, oxygen enters and carbon dioxide leaves the blood.

DID YOU KNOW?

The adult lung contains more than three hundred million air sacs. If these were spread out, they would cover half of a tennis court.

As you can see, the purpose of breathing is to get oxygen into the blood. All of the cells must have oxygen in order to work. You can live only a few minutes without it. Because the lungs perform such a vital function, they are protected by the ribs. The ribs are attached to the skeleton in such a way that they can move every time you take a breath. Muscles between the ribs help to control this movement.

Each time you breathe, muscles work together to draw in the fresh air. Most of the work is done by the **diaphragm**, a shelflike muscle that separates your chest from your abdomen (fig. 15–9). When this powerful muscle contracts, it moves downward, sucking air into the lungs. This is called **inhalation**. When the diaphragm relaxes, the air is forced out of the lungs in a process called **exhalation**. Normally, this process of inhalation/exhalation occurs 12–15 times per minute.

DID YOU KNOW?
Each time you inhale, you breathe in at least one or more of the same air molecules you breathed in with your first breath as a baby.

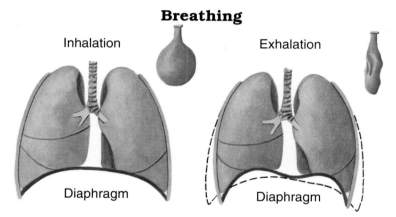

Breathing

Inhalation

Exhalation

Diaphragm

Diaphragm

Fig. 15–9 When the diaphragm contracts, it moves down, and air is pulled into the lungs (left). When the diaphragm relaxes, it moves up, and air moves out (right).

Your lungs can be damaged by breathing polluted air. However, the most common way of damaging your lungs is by smoking tobacco. Tobacco contains many poisons, some very harmful to your lungs. Smoking damages the air sacs, the air passages, and the cilia that line them (fig. 15–10). Even being in a room where a person is smoking can damage your lungs. Research shows that children raised in homes where people smoke have more respiratory problems than children who live in smoke-free homes.

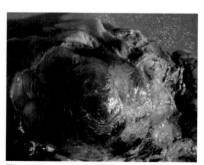

Fig. 15–10 This lung was damaged by cigarette smoke.

TRY THIS 15-3: Watch Out. It's Gonna Pop!

Materials:
balloon

Procedure:
1. Blow up a balloon. Count how many breaths it takes to make it pop.
   - How many breaths did it take?
   - How do your results compare to the results of other classmates?
   - Did everyone get the same results? Why?
   - Why were some able to blow up the balloon in fewer breaths than others?
   - What does the number of breaths it takes to blow up a balloon have to do with lung capacity?

RESEARCH IT

Identify four major poisons present in tobacco smoke and how each affects the respiratory system.

You can keep your lungs healthy by being careful about the air you breathe. The man in fig. 15–11 is wearing a device that protects his lungs while he is painting. You can help your lungs by exercising vigorously for 20 minutes at least three times a week. Good posture also will make it easier for your lungs to do their job (fig. 15–12).

Fig. 15–11 Masks protect the lungs by keeping harmful particles out.

Fig. 15–12 Correct posture allows for better breathing (left). Improper posture interferes with breathing (right).

REVIEW IT

1. Name two structures found in the lung.
2. Where does the carbon dioxide in the lungs come from?
3. What muscle allows you to breathe?
4. How does smoking damage the lungs?
5. What can you do to help your lungs stay healthy?

CLASS ACTIVITY 15–3: Blow Out

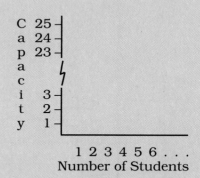

A   C

B   D

Question: How much air can your lungs hold?

Materials:
    dishpan (10–15 cm deep)
    drinking straw (flexible)
    plastic bottle (2L)
    water

Procedure:
1. Make measuring marks on the bottle (fig A).
2. Fill the bottle completely full of water.
3. Fill the dishpan with about 1–2 inches of water.
4. Cover the top of the bottle with the palm of your hand and tip it upside down. Be careful that no water leaks out (fig B).
5. Place the bottle in the dishpan (fig C).
6. Carefully place the straw in the bottle (fig D). (Steady the bottle so that it does not tip.)
7. Take a normal breath and blow into the straw. With one breath, try to fill the bottle as full of air as possible. Record data.
8. Repeat steps 2–7 two more times. Record data.
9. Repeat steps 2–7 after taking a deep breath. Record data.
10. Repeat step 9 two more times. Record data.
11. Construct a bar graph showing the lung capacities and the number of students having each capacity.

Data:

	NORMAL BREATHS	DEEP BREATHS
TRIAL 1		
TRIAL 2		
TRIAL 3		
AVERAGE		

Capacity

25 –
24 –
23 –

3 –
2 –
1 –

1 2 3 4 5 6 . . .
Number of Students

Questions:
1. What was your lung capacity?
2. Did everyone have the same capacity? Why?
3. What was the largest lung capacity? The smallest? What was the class average?

Conclusion: Write 3–5 sentences about what you learned from this activity.

CHAPTER 15 WRAP-UP

SKILLS DEVELOPMENT

THINKING SKILLS: CAUSE AND EFFECT

With air and water pollution increasing each day and the pollution in our cities and countryside becoming more severe, many people are wanting to find the cause. For each result or effect that happens around us, there is a cause. If we control the cause, then we determine the effect. If we control what goes into the atmosphere (cause), then we determine the amount of air pollution (effect).

Examine the following statements. The cause is underlined once, and the effect is underlined twice.

1. The man's weight was determined by the food he ate. (E—C)
2. The sun was so bright that my eyes hurt. (C—E)

Write the **cause** and **effect** of each sentence under the appropriate heading below.
1. The man's respiratory problems were due to the polluted air.
2. Food got caught in the boy's larynx and caused the boy to cough.
3. Your vocal cords vibrate when air passes between them.
4. When you swallow, two flaps close.
5. Carbon dioxide is produced when a cell uses energy.
6. Each time the diaphragm contracts, air is drawn into the lungs.
7. Air is moistened as it passes over the mucous membrane.
8. Your tongue gets a sour taste when you bite into a lemon.
9. The health of your respiratory system depends on how much you smoke.
10. God is always ready to help if you ask Him.

	CAUSE	EFFECT
1.		
2.		
3.		
4.		
5.		
6.		
7.		
8.		
9.		
10.		

QUESTIONS AND PROBLEMS

1. Do all animals have a respiratory system like humans? Explain.
2. Why is it necessary for oxygen to get into the blood?
3. Why should breathing take place through the nose rather than the mouth?
4. Why is excess mucus produced when you have a cold or allergy?
5. How can a cold affect your ability to taste food?
6. Describe the path a molecule of carbon dioxide travels from a cell to outside the body.
7. Why are there rings of cartilage in the trachea?
8. What other structures of the respiratory system, in addition to the larynx, are involved in speech?
9. What are the cilia, and how do they help the respiratory system?
10. Under normal conditions, through what parts of the respiratory system do both food and air pass? What parts allow only air to pass?
11. What happens when food gets into the air passages?
12. How is the structure of the lung different from other organs such as the liver?
13. Why is it necessary for the ribs to be able to move?
14. Is breathing always controlled automatically? Explain.
15. How does good posture benefit the respiratory system?

RESEARCH

1. Research how the following organisms breathe: a *Paramecium*, a grasshopper, a fish, a maple tree, a clam, and a tadpole. Report on your findings. Include a diagram of each organism that explains where and how respiration takes place.
2. Research one of the following respiratory diseases.
   a. asthma   b. emphysema   c. bronchitis
   Prepare an oral report that discusses the causes, symptoms, treatment, and preventive measures.
3. Find out what SCUBA divers do to prepare for dives of 15 m (50 ft), 30 m (100 ft), 60 m (200 ft), and 100 m (300 ft). Write a report on your findings.
4. Construct a bulletin-board display that illustrates the relationship between the respiratory system and the heart.
5. Find out the effects of side-stream smoke on public health and any steps that have been taken to protect the public from this hazard. Prepare a written presentation of your findings.

REVIEW

HIGHLIGHTS

1. The respiratory system includes the nose, mouth, pharynx, trachea, bronchi, lungs, and diaphragm.
2. Mucus moistens air and traps dirt, dust, and microorganisms.
3. Air enters the nose or mouth, passes into the pharynx and through the larynx. The air then moves into the trachea and the bronchi. Finally, the air enters the air sacs of the lungs.
4. The larynx contains the vocal cords, which allow you to speak.
5. The lungs are two lobe-shaped organs that look like a soft, moist sponge.
6. When you inhale, your diaphragm contracts and sucks air into the air sacs of the lungs. In the air sacs, oxygen moves into the blood while carbon dioxide and water move out. When you exhale, these waste products leave the body.
7. Poisons present in tobacco smoke damage the air sacs of the lungs and the cilia that line the air passages.
8. You can help your lungs by being careful about the air you breathe, practicing good posture, and exercising regularly.

VOCABULARY

air sac
bronchi
cilia
diaphragm
exhalation
inhalation

larynx
lung
mucus
mucous membrane
nasal passage
nostril

pharynx
respiratory system
septum
trachea
vocal cord

PRACTICE

Multiple Choice. Choose the best answer.

1. What separates the two nostrils?
   - a. nasal passage
   - b. septum
   - c. larynx
   - d. mucous membrane
2. Which is not a function of the nose?
   - a. warm the air
   - b. moisten the air
   - c. oxygenate the air
   - d. trap dust particles
3. What enables you to taste?
   - a. tongue and nose
   - b. mouth and pharynx
   - c. pharynx and tongue
   - d. cilia and nose

4. Where does incoming air go when it leaves the nose?
   a. the pharynx
   b. the mouth
   c. the bronchi
   d. the trachea
5. Where is carbon dioxide exchanged for oxygen?
   a. the cilia
   b. the heart
   c. the cell
   d. the air sacs
6. Between which two structures is the larynx located?
   a. pharynx and bronchi
   b. air sac and lung
   c. trachea and bronchi
   d. pharynx and trachea
7. Through what do food and air both normally pass?
   a. trachea
   b. bronchi
   c. pharynx
   d. larynx
8. What surrounds each air sac?
   a. arteries
   b. veins
   c. capillaries
   d. cilia
9. How often do people normally breathe in a minute?
   a. 3–4 times
   b. 6–8 times
   c. 12–15 times
   d. 18–20 times
10. What is another name for the voice box?
   a. mouth
   b. bronchi
   c. trachea
   d. larynx

Matching. Match each word with its definition or description.
1. forms the lining of the nose and throat
2. rids the body of carbon dioxide
3. gets oxygen into the blood
4. moves mucus in the trachea
5. the main air passage
6. the throat
7. traps dust and moistens the air
8. happens when the diaphragm contracts
9. tubes that bring air into the lungs
10. muscle that causes breathing

a. bronchi
b. cilia
c. diaphragm
d. exhalation
e. inhalation
f. mucous membrane
g. mucus
h. pharynx
i. respiratory system
j. trachea

CAREERS

Physical Therapist

Description of Work
Physical therapists promote health by applying scientific principles to help patients who have difficulty in movement. These health-care workers test and measure the function of nervous, skeletal, and muscular systems and determine the treatment programs. They often provide instruction to the patients' families.

Personal Qualifications
Physical therapists must be intelligent and be in good physical condition. They must also be patient, considerate, and willing to work with others.

Requirements
A high-school diploma and four years of college.

Career Information
American Physical Therapy Assn.
1111 N. Fairfax St.
Alexandria, VA 22314

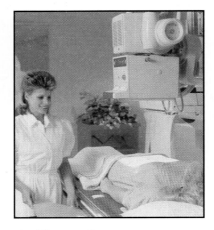

Radiographer

Description of Work
Radiographers help doctors by taking X-rays of patients. They adjust the X-ray equipment, position the patient, and make the correct number of X-rays. Sometimes the radiographer gives patients chemical mixtures so certain organs can be seen in the X-rays.

Personal Qualifications
Radiographers must be sympathetic, patient, and friendly—yet be aggressive and firm.

Requirements
A high-school diploma and completion of an approved program in radiologic technology.

Career Information
American Society of Radiologic Technologists
15000 Central Ave., S.E.
Albuquerque, NM 87123

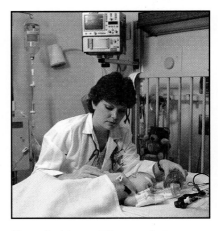

Respiratory Therapist

Description of Work
Respiratory therapists treat patients who have problems with their respiratory or circulatory systems. They use special equipment and gases to treat breathing problems and test their patients' progress. They must keep the equipment clean and sterile, and they must keep records of treatment.

Personal Qualifications
Respiratory therapists must have mechanical abilities, be sensitive to others, and be able to work well with people.

Requirements
A high-school diploma and completion of an approved program in respiratory therapy.

Career Information
American Assn. for Respiratory Care
11030 Ables Lane
Dallas, TX 75229

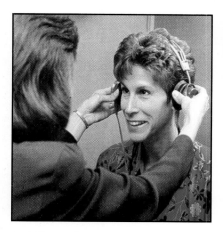

Audiologist

Description of Work
Audiologists identify and treat hearing problems. They use various machines to determine the type and severity of the problem. They help patients select hearing aids that provide improved hearing. They also instruct patients how to use amplifiers on telephones, TVs, and other audio devices.

Personal Qualifications
Audiologists must have good organizational skills and be able to keep accurate records. They must be patient and have pleasant personalities and good communication skills.

Requirements
A high-school diploma and a college degree.

Career Information
American Speech-Language-
  Hearing Assn.
10801 Rockville Pike
Rockville, MD 20852

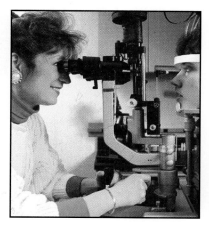

Optician

Description of Work
Opticians provide their customers with a selection of styles and frames for eyeglasses. They help people select frames, fit the lenses, and make adjustments in the frames to make sure the glasses fit properly and comfortably. Some opticians also make the lenses for the glasses. Opticians also assist customers with contact lenses and instruct the customers how to insert, remove, and care for the lenses.

Personal Qualifications
Opticians should be pleasant and have good social skills. They also need good communication skills.

Requirements
A high-school diploma and completion of at least a two-year apprenticeship program.

Career Information
Opticians Assn. of America
10341 Democracy Lane
Fairfax, VA 22030

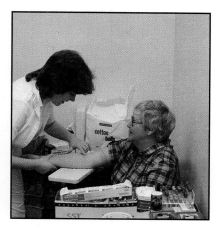

Phlebotomist

Description of Work
Phlebotomists are health-care workers who take blood samples from patients. In addition to taking blood, they also sort and process samples and keep accurate records.

Personal Qualifications
Phlebotomists must be well organized, keep accurate records, be patient, have pleasant personalities, and be good communicators.

Requirements
A high-school diploma and the completion of an approved program in phlebotomy. A license is often required.

Career Information
Board of Registry
2100 W. Harrison St.
Chicago, IL 60612

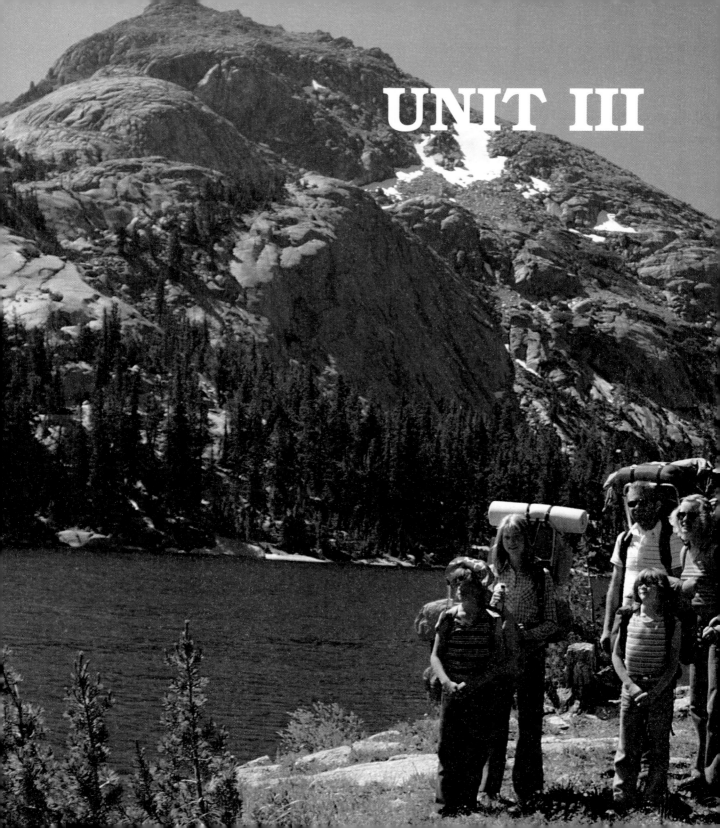

UNIT III

TAKE CARE

INTRODUCTION

The family in this picture is backpacking in the high country of the Rocky Mountains. They enjoy hiking and camping together, seeing the majestic mountains, and learning outdoor skills.

They are able to do these things because they have chosen a healthful lifestyle that keeps them fit. This unit discusses how you can take good care of your body by eating the right kinds of food and avoiding harmful substances. Remember, good health is the most valuable gift you can give yourself.

CHAPTER TITLES

Backpacking in the Colorado Rockies.

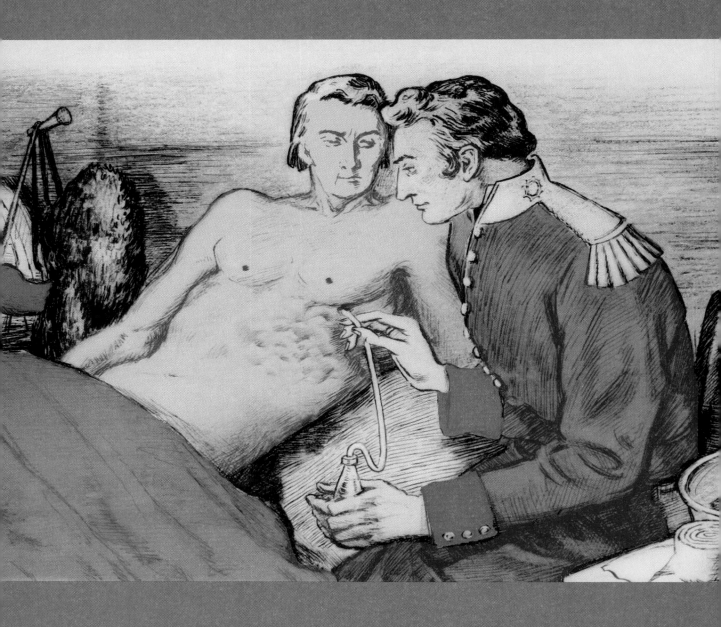

CHAPTER 16

DIGESTION

INTRODUCTION

If you could lift a flap of skin and peek inside your stomach, would you want to look? Much of what we now know about the digestive system was first discovered by a doctor who did just that. The doctor's name was William Beaumont, and his patient was a French Canadian trapper named Alexis St. Martin.

The year was 1822. St. Martin had been shot accidentally in his left side. Dr. Beaumont was able to save St. Martin's life, but the wound left a flap that did not completely heal shut. This opening allowed the doctor to look inside St. Martin's stomach and study the digestive process closely. Beaumont discovered many things about the stomach, including the fact that small pieces of food digest faster than larger pieces, carbohydrates digest faster than protein, and excitement interferes with digestion.

SECTION TITLES

Dr. Beaumont learned much about digestion by studying his patient, Alexis St. Martin.

16–1 THE DIGESTIVE SYSTEM

VOCABULARY
digestive system
molecule
mucus

OBJECTIVES

- Identify the parts of the digestive system.
- Describe the basic function of the digestive system.

Remember your last meal? It looks different now than it did when you ate it. In fact, your body has already started using the food you ate. Your meal has been broken down into particles called **molecules** that your body can use to move, think, and do your schoolwork.

Various groups of molecules make up the food you eat. Usually, the molecules are so large that your body cannot use them as they are. God designed your **digestive system** to break down these large molecules into smaller molecules. These small molecules pass through the wall of your small intestine and into your blood, which then carries them to your cells.

Figure 16–1 shows the digestive system. When you eat, food passes through your mouth and esophagus (i säf´ ə gəs), and on to your stomach. From your stomach the food moves through the small intestine and large intestine. Your digestive tract is about 6 m long and similar to a tube. Its inside surface is coated with **mucus**, which lubricates and protects the digestive tract.

DID YOU KNOW?
Your food's trip through your digestive system usually takes more than 24 hours.

REVIEW IT

1. What is the function of the digestive system?
2. Trace the path that food follows on its way to the large intestine.

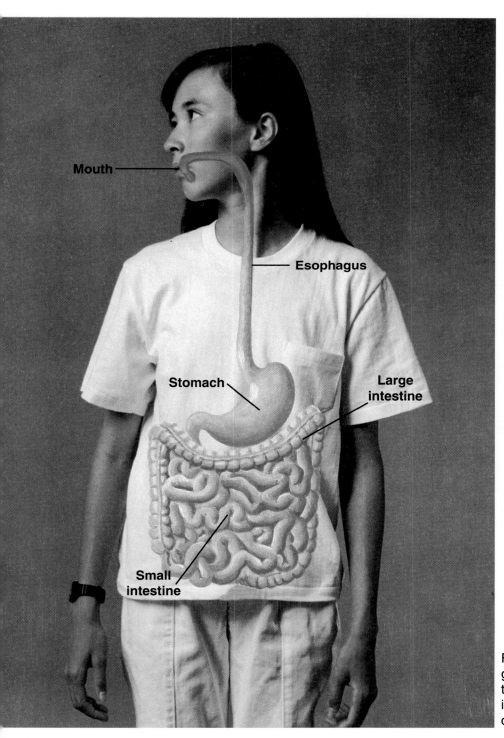

Mouth

Esophagus

Stomach

Large intestine

Small intestine

Fig. 16–1 The mouth, esophagus, stomach, small intestine, and large intestine are important organs of your digestive system.

16–2 THE MOUTH, TONGUE, AND ESOPHAGUS

VOCABULARY
esophagus
peristalsis
saliva

OBJECTIVES

- Describe the role of the mouth in digestion.
- Explain the function of saliva.
- Explain peristalsis.

Fig. 16–2 Chewing your food mixes it with saliva and starts the digestive process.

Digestion begins in your mouth (fig. 16–2). As you chew, your teeth break and grind large pieces of food into smaller pieces, which mix with saliva. Your tongue helps keep the food between your teeth when you chew.

Saliva is secreted by the salivary glands. It keeps your tongue and mouth moist and makes swallowing easier by lubricating your food. Saliva also begins the digestive process. Through chemical action it breaks down long starch molecules into sugar molecules.

After your food is thoroughly chewed and moistened, your tongue pushes it to the back of your mouth. When you swallow, the food is forced down into your **esophagus**, a tube about 20 cm (8 in) long that connects the mouth with the stomach. As you swallow, a series of muscle contractions called **peristalsis** (per ə stal´ sis) moves the food down this tube. The muscles just ahead of the food relax. Those just behind the food contract, squeezing the food down toward the stomach (fig. 16–3). If the food has been properly chewed and moistened, it moves nonstop to your stomach. Sometimes food becomes stuck in

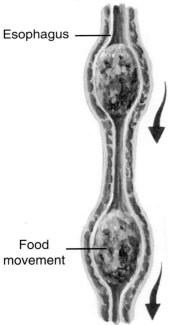

Esophagus

Food movement

Fig. 16–3 A series of muscle contractions moves food through the esophagus.

your throat when you swallow. If it does, you may need to drink some liquid or swallow again to move it all the way down to your stomach.

At the lower end of the esophagus is a muscular area that acts as a door to the stomach. When food arrives at this point, the door opens and food enters the stomach. Then the muscular area closes tightly to keep food from leaving the stomach and passing back into the esophagus.

TRY THIS 16–2A: How Sweet It Is

Materials:
  soda cracker

Procedure:
  1. Chew a soda cracker for two to three minutes without swallowing it.
     • How does the taste of the cracker change as you chew it?
     • Why does the cracker begin to have a sweet taste after it has been chewed for a long time?
     • Why is it important to chew your food well?

TRY THIS 16–2B: Sugar Cube

Materials:
  paper towels – 5   stopwatch
  plastic cups (clear) – 2   sugar cubes – 2
  plastic spoon   water

Procedure:
  1. Fill both cups about half full of water.
  2. Place one of the sugar cubes in one of the glasses of water. Use the stopwatch to time how long it takes the sugar cube to dissolve.
     • How long did it take the sugar cube to dissolve?
  3. Place the second sugar cube on the paper towel and use the spoon to crush it into small pieces.
  4. Place the crushed sugar cube into the other cup of water and time how long it takes for the crushed cube to dissolve.
     • How long did it take the sugar to dissolve?
     • How does this time compare to the time it took the other sugar cube to dissolve? Explain.
     • Why is it important to chew your food well?

REVIEW IT

  1. Where does digestion begin?
  2. Why is saliva important to the digestive process?
  3. What is peristalsis?

16–2 CLASS ACTIVITY: OK, Break It Up

Questions: Where does starch digestion begin?

Materials:

beaker (250 ml)	iodine solution
Benedict's solution	soda crackers – 2
graduated cylinder (10 ml)	test tubes – 3
hot plate	water

Procedure:
1. Label the three test tubes A, B, and C.
2. Crumble a soda cracker and put 1/4 of it in test tube A; add 3 ml of water.
3. Mix the cracker and water by rotating the test tube between the palms of your hands.
4. Add 3 or 4 drops of iodine solution to the test tube. Observe and record.
5. Place another 1/4 of the crumbled cracker in test tube B; add 5 ml of Benedict's solution.
6. Fill the beaker about half full of water and place test tube B in the beaker.
7. Chew a cracker for about one minute. Place the chewed cracker in test tube C. Add 5 ml of Benedict's solution.
8. Place test tube C in the beaker along with test tube B.
9. Heat the water in the beaker for about five to seven minutes. Observe and record.

Data:

TEST TUBE	OBSERVATIONS
A	
B	
C	

Questions:
1. What happened when the iodine solution was added to test tube A?
2. What was the difference between test tubes B and C after they had been heated?
3. What happened to the starch in the chewed cracker?
4. What is present in the mouth that begins to digest starches?
5. What is starch digested into?

Conclusion: Write 3–5 sentences about what you learned from this activity.

16–3 THE STOMACH

OBJECTIVE

- Describe the role of the stomach in digestion.

VOCABULARY
enzyme
gastric juice
stomach

The **stomach** is an organ made almost entirely of muscles. When empty, your stomach is about the size of your two fists. However, it can stretch large enough to hold almost any meal you eat.

The stomach begins to contract as food enters. The contractions squeeze and churn the food (fig. 16–4). At the same time, the food is mixed with the stomach's digestive juices.

Each day your stomach makes about 3 L (3 qts) of gastric juice. **Gastric juice** is a mixture of water, hydrochloric (hi drō klôr´ iK) acid, and **enzymes**—chemicals that help to break down molecules. It is produced by

The Stomach

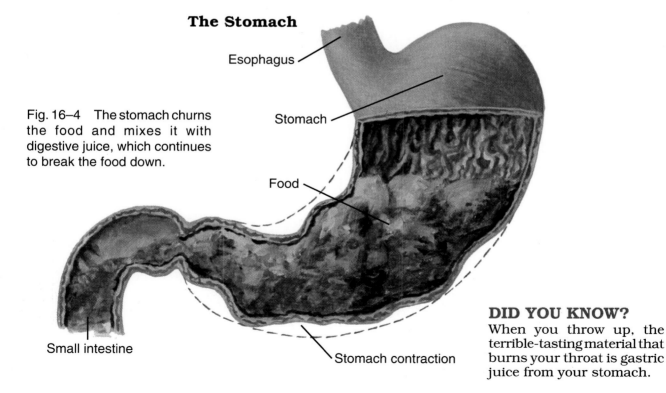

Fig. 16–4 The stomach churns the food and mixes it with digestive juice, which continues to break the food down.

Esophagus

Stomach

Food

Small intestine

Stomach contraction

DID YOU KNOW?

When you throw up, the terrible-tasting material that burns your throat is gastric juice from your stomach.

about 35 million glands that line the stomach. Gastric juice begins breaking down the large molecules of protein present in meat, milk, eggs, and legumes (leg´ yōōmz) into smaller molecules.

Food, water, acid, and enzymes make a thick, souplike mixture that leaves the stomach by passing through an opening into the small intestine. This opening is closed by a doughnut-shaped muscle (fig. 16–5).

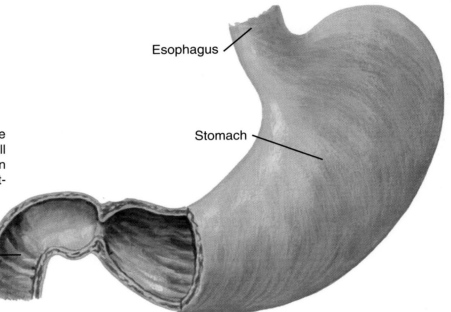

Esophagus

Stomach

Small intestine

Fig. 16–5   As food leaves the stomach on its way into the small intestine, it passes through an opening controlled by a doughnut-shaped muscle.

The stomach is a hard-working organ. Its job is made harder when you eat between meals or drink too much liquid at mealtime. Drinking too much liquid with your meal dilutes the digestive juices, and eating between meals causes the stomach to work overtime. You can make your stomach's job easier by chewing your food completely and eating only at mealtimes.

REVIEW IT

1. What is the function of the stomach?
2. What is the function of gastric juice?
3. What can you do to make your stomach's job easier?

16–4 THE SMALL INTESTINE

OBJECTIVES

- Explain the role of the small intestine in digestion.
- Compare and contrast intestinal juice, pancreatic juice, and bile.

VOCABULARY
bile
bile duct
intestinal juice
pancreas
pancreatic juice
small intestine
villi

The **small intestine** is about 3 m (10 ft) long and about 2 cm (.75 in) in diameter (fig. 16–6). Most food digestion takes place in this organ. Liquids in the small intestine break the partially digested food from the stomach into tiny molecules that can be absorbed. These liquids are intestinal juice, pancreatic (pan´ krē at ik) juice, and bile.

Small Intestine

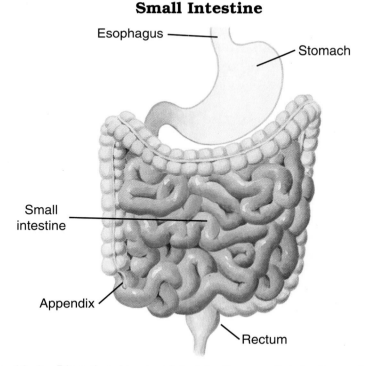

Esophagus

Stomach

Small intestine

Appendix

Rectum

Fig. 16–6 Digestion is completed in the small intestine, where the molecules are absorbed.

RESEARCH IT
What are gallstones, and how are they formed?

INTESTINAL JUICE is secreted by the wall of the small intestine. This liquid contains enzymes that help break down the molecules that were not broken down in the stomach.

PANCREATIC JUICE is similar to intestinal juice, but is stronger. It comes from the **pancreas**. Pancreatic juice contains three types of enzymes. One type of enzyme breaks starch into simple sugar. A second kind digests fats into fatty acids. A third type acts on proteins, breaking them into smaller units called amino acids.

BILE is produced by the liver and stored in the gallbladder. When bile is needed, it leaves the gallbladder through a small tube called the **bile duct**. In the intestine, bile breaks large drops of oil and fat into tiny droplets, much like dish detergent breaks up grease on dishes. These small drops are easily digested by the enzymes in the pancreatic juice.

The wall of the small intestine is lined with small fingerlike projections called **villi** (vil´ī) (fig. 16–7). One sq cm (.25 sq in) of small intestine contains about 8 000 villi. These villi greatly increase the surface area of the intestine and allow food to be absorbed more quickly.

The Villi of the Small Intestine

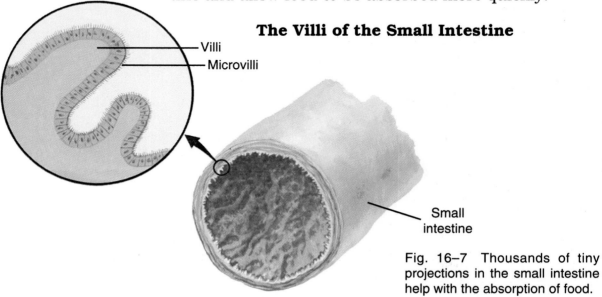

Villi

Microvilli

Small intestine

Fig. 16–7 Thousands of tiny projections in the small intestine help with the absorption of food.

Inside the villi are blood vessels and lymph vessels. Once amino acids and sugars are absorbed, they move into the blood vessels and start traveling to the cells. The fatty acids and some vitamins enter the lymph vessels, where lymph carries the fatty acids to the bloodstream.

TRY THIS 16–4: Food Mover

Materials:
    marble
    medicine dropper
    stopwatch
    tubing—40 cm (16 in) x 1 cm (0.5 in)
    vegetable oil 1 ml (1/4 tsp)
    water

Procedure:
1. Wet a piece of rubber tubing thoroughly.
2. Put a marble in one end of the tubing. Have your partner time how long it takes you to move the marble through the tube. Move the marble by squeezing the tubing just behind it, as shown.
    • How long did it take to move the marble through the tubing?
    • What caused the marble to move through the tubing?
3. Add 1 ml of oil to the inside of the tubing. Flatten the tubing to cover the entire inner surface with oil.
4. Repeat step 2.
    • How long did it take to move the marble through the tubing this time?
    • Through which tubing did the marble move faster? Why?
    • How does the model you have just made compare with what happens to food in the digestive tract?
    • In the digestive tract, what actually moves the food along?
    • What is produced in the digestive tract that acts like the oil?

REVIEW IT

1. What are the three liquids in the small intestine, and what does each do?
2. What structures actually absorb the digested food?

16–5 THE LARGE INTESTINE

VOCABULARY

anus
feces
fiber
large intestine
rectum

OBJECTIVES

- Identify the main function of the large intestine.
- Explain the importance of fiber.

The last part of the digestive tract is the **large intestine**. It is about 1.5 m (5 ft) long. It is called the large intestine because it is about 4 cm (1.5 in) in diameter. Fig. 16–8 compares the size of the large and small intestines.

Your body can't digest about one-tenth of the food you eat. About 300 ml (10 oz) of this undigested material, along with digestive juices, enters the large intestine every day. As the material moves past the villi of the large intestine, the villi absorb water and minerals, which are returned to the blood. If your intestines did not recapture this water, you would need to drink much more water every day.

Fiber, the part of food that cannot be digested, is important to the health of the large intestine. Fiber thickens the waste so that it can move more easily. Fiber also helps to absorb harmful chemicals present in the waste material. Some of these chemicals may

Large Intestine

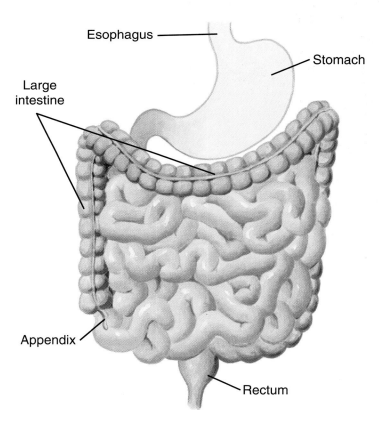

Esophagus

Stomach

Large intestine

Appendix

Rectum

Fig. 16–8   Water and minerals are absorbed in the large intestine.

cause cancer if they contact the lining of the intestine for a long time. Once the fiber absorbs these chemicals, they no longer touch the walls of the intestine.

The diet God provided for Adam and Eve at Creation provides all the fiber your body needs. Studies have shown that people who eat foods high in fiber have less intestinal cancer. Doctors recommend that you eat about 25–30 gm (1 oz) of fiber each day. A diet that includes plenty of natural foods will have enough fiber. Fiber-rich foods are pictured in fig. 16-9.

DID YOU KNOW?
Your appendix is located where the two intestines join. This organ helps the body fight infection. Appendicitis occurs when an infection causes the appendix to swell. This condition can be very painful and can cause death if not treated.

Fig. 16–9 Whole grains, nuts, fruits, and vegetables are excellent sources of fiber.

The undigested food remains in the large intestine for 8–10 hours. It becomes more solid as water is absorbed by the blood. The **feces**, or solid wastes, are now ready to leave the body. At the lower end of the large intestine is the **rectum**. During a bowel movement, the muscular rectum pushes the waste out of an opening called the **anus**, which is the end of the digestive tract.

DID YOU KNOW?
The length of time it takes for digestion to occur is 24 hours with fiber, 96 hours without.

REVIEW IT

1. What is absorbed in the large intestine?
2. What is the benefit of fiber?
3. About how long does undigested food remain in the large intestine?

16–6 THE LIVER AND PANCREAS

OBJECTIVES

- Describe the functions of the liver.
- Explain the role of the pancreas in digestion.
- Explain the importance of insulin.

The **liver** is your body's largest gland (fig. 16–10). This dark-red organ is located just above your stomach. When God designed you, He placed the liver behind the ribs for protection, because you cannot live without this organ.

The Liver

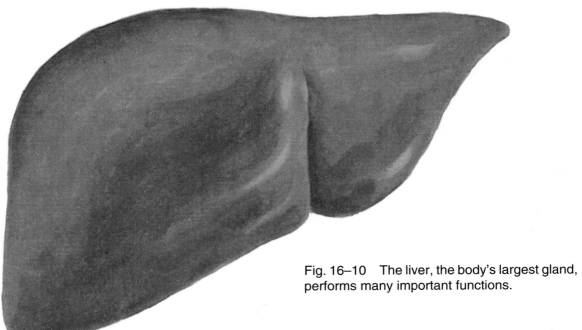

Fig. 16–10 The liver, the body's largest gland, performs many important functions.

The liver performs many vital functions. One of its most important functions is to produce bile. You read in section 16–4 that bile breaks down fats. The liver produces about 250 ml (8 oz) of this green liquid each day.

The liver also serves as a storehouse. Carbohydrates, fats, proteins, iron, and some vitamins are stored in the liver, then released into the blood as they are needed.

A third function of the liver is recycling broken and worn-out red blood cells. As the red blood cells are processed, the liver recycles their iron for use in new blood cells.

Filtering poisons out of the blood is perhaps the liver's most important job. Poisons entering the blood can come from food or water, or from drugs such as caffeine or alcohol. Alcohol can have a particularly damaging effect on the liver. Drinking excessive amounts of alcohol can lead to **cirrhosis** (sə rō′ sis), hardening of the liver, or liver cancer. The liver works hard to make the effect of alcohol and other harmful substances less poisonous and turn them into waste that can be removed from the body.

In severe cases of poisoning, though, the liver is the first organ to be damaged. People who die from poisoning usually suffer liver failure.

The pancreas is a feather-shaped gland that lies just below the stomach (fig. 16–11). Besides producing pancreatic juice,

The Pancreas

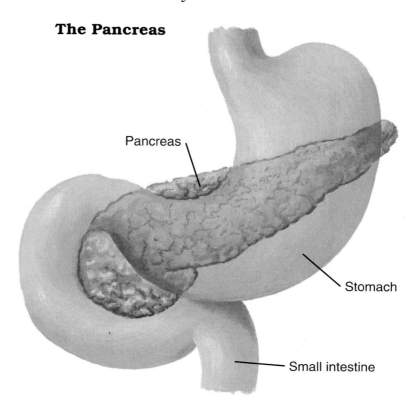

Pancreas

Stomach

Small intestine

Fig. 16–11 The pancreas, located below the stomach, helps with digestion and produces insulin.

which helps with digestion, the pancreas also produces **insulin**, a hormone that helps regulate the amount of sugar in the blood. Natural sugars are found in most of the foods you eat. Body cells need this sugar to produce energy. But it's dangerous for your blood to carry more sugar than the cells can use at any one time. If this happens, insulin turns the extra blood sugar into a substance that can be stored in the liver for later use.

Normally the amount of sugar in the blood is regulated correctly. However, when the pancreas does not make enough insulin, the body cannot handle blood sugar properly. This disease is called **diabetes** (dī ə bēt´ ēz), and people who suffer from it are called diabetics.

There are two kinds of diabetes: **insulin-dependent** and **non-insulin-dependent**. Diabetics who are insulin-dependent must take injections of insulin every day. Non-insulin-dependent diabetics don't need daily injections. Many are able to control their diabetes by regulating their diet and taking oral medication, if necessary.

Diabetes can lead to blindness, or even death, if it is not treated properly. Not too many years ago, most diabetics died of their disease. But much more is known about diabetes now, and most diabetics can get the help they need to live normal lives.

DID YOU KNOW?
Insulin was first isolated and prepared by a team of Canadian scientists at the University of Toronto. Insulin was first used in treating diabetic patients in 1922.

REVIEW IT

1. What are the four main functions of the liver?
2. Where is insulin produced, and what is its function?
3. How can diabetes be controlled?

FRONTIERS: The Blood Glucose Sensor

Nobody likes to get scratched or cut. The injury hurts, and it may bleed. People don't like to have a nurse give them a shot or have to have their fingers pricked to get a few drops of blood. But there are millions of people who must check a drop of their blood one, two, or even four times each day. These people have diabetes. Diabetes causes some people to have kidney and heart problems, others to become blind.

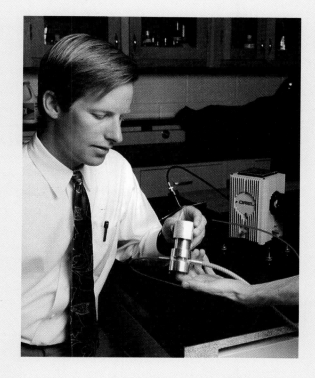

Diabetes is a disease that affects the pancreas. If the pancreas works properly, it makes the amount of insulin you need. Insulin controls the amount of glucose (sugar) in the blood. But the pancreas of a person with diabetes does not make enough insulin. This person must take insulin each day. Some diabetic people can swallow their insulin; others must give themselves shots. To know how much insulin they need, diabetics must know how much glucose there is in their blood.

In 1991 scientists at Sandia National Labs and the University of New Mexico School of Medicine, in Albuquerque, New Mexico, developed a device called a glucose sensor. It can measure the amount of glucose (sugar) in your blood without making you bleed.

To use this device, you place your finger into a tube-shaped monitor, as shown in the picture. The device shines a beam of invisible light through your finger. Some of the light, called near infrared light, is absorbed by the glucose in your blood. The light is changed when it is absorbed, and this allows the device to measure how much blood glucose you have.

Researchers hope to soon develop a home version of the glucose sensor that is inexpensive and easy to use. For the 2.5 million diabetic people in the United States and Canada, this would be mean no more finger pricks and no more pain. Because this test is painless, it can be done over and over if necessary.

Questions:
1. What causes diabetes?
2. Why must some diabetics check their blood?
3. How does the glucose sensor work?
4. What is the advantage of using a glucose sensor?

CHAPTER 16 WRAP-UP

SKILLS DEVELOPMENT

THINKING SKILLS: COMPARE AND CONTRAST

Most animals have a digestive system of some type. Look at the pictures below and examine the differences and similarities of the digestive systems represented; then answer the questions.

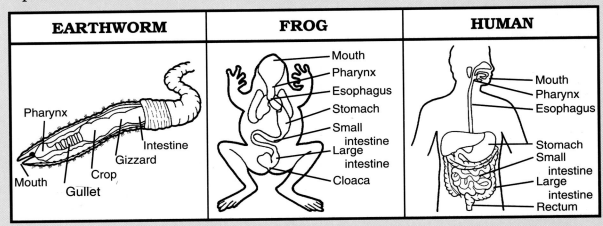

1. Which digestive tract is most similar to the human digestive tract? Explain your answer.

2. Which digestive tract is the most different from the human digestive tract? Explain your answer.

3. How are all of the digestive tracts similar?

4. Why do you think some animals have a more complex digestive tract than other animals?

5. Some animals, such as jellyfish and sea anemones, lack a digestive tract. How do you think these animals process their food?

QUESTIONS AND PROBLEMS

1. Trace the path of the food you eat through the five main parts of your digestive system.
2. How does saliva help with digestion?
3. Describe the composition and function of gastric juice.
4. What are the secretions of the small intestine, and what does each do?
5. Why is the wall of the small intestine covered by villi?
6. Why is fiber important to the health of the large intestine?
7. What are the four main functions of the liver?
8. What is insulin, what does it do, and where does it come from?
9. What causes diabetes?
10. Explain the difference between insulin-dependent and non-insulin-dependent diabetes.

RESEARCH

1. Discover the events that led to the development of the Kellogg Company and cold breakfast cereals. Learn what Kellogg's relationship was to the Seventh-day Adventist Church. Report your findings to the class.
2. Investigate over-the-counter products designed to relieve indigestion. Create a poster that compares 6–8 of these products as to their ingredients, recommended dosage, unit cost, and claims.
3. Interview an X-ray technologist or radiologist to discover how X-rays are taken of the digestive tract. Discover the type of tests used, what the patient is required to do, and what kind of information is learned. Give an oral report of your findings.
4. Find out what materials and programs are available in your community to help families with members who are insulin-dependent. Report your findings.
5. Write a creative story that compares your digestive system and the digestive processes of the body to something unrelated to the human body. Provide illustrations for your story.

REVIEW

HIGHLIGHTS

1. The purpose of the digestive system is to break down food so that it can be used by the body.
2. The parts of the digestive system include the mouth, esophagus, stomach, small intestine, and large intestine.
3. Digestion begins in the mouth as you chew your food and it is mixed with saliva.

4. Saliva keeps the mouth moist, lubricates the food to make it easier to swallow, and contains an enzyme that breaks down starch.
5. Peristalsis is a series of muscle contractions that moves food through the digestive system.
6. The contractions of the stomach mix the food with the digestive juices.
7. Most of digestion takes place in the small intestine.
8. In the small intestine, intestinal juice breaks down food arriving from the stomach. Pancreatic juice, secreted by the pancreas, helps digest carbohydrates, fats, and proteins. Bile, secreted by the liver, digests fat.
9. The large intestine absorbs water and many of the minerals resulting from digestion.
10. Fiber thickens the waste in the large intestine and absorbs harmful chemicals present in the waste.
11. The liver is the body's largest gland. It produces bile, stores nutrients needed by the body, recycles red blood cells, and filters the blood.
12. The pancreas is a feather-shaped gland. It produces pancreatic juice that aids digestion. The pancreas also produces insulin.
13. Insulin is a hormone that regulates the amount of sugar in the blood.

VOCABULARY LIST

anus
bile
bile duct
cirrhosis
diabetes
digestive system
enzyme
esophagus
feces

fiber
gastric juice
insulin
insulin-dependent
intestinal juice
large intestine
liver
molecule
mucus

non-insulin-dependent
pancreas
pancreatic juice
peristalsis
rectum
saliva
small intestine
stomach
villi

PRACTICE

Multiple Choice. Choose the best answer.
1. What important contribution did Dr. William Beaumont make to the understanding of the digestive system?
   a. how to chew food
   b. how the pancreas functions
   c. how the liver works
   d. how digestion takes place
2. Where does digestion begin?
   a. in the stomach
   b. in the esophagus
   c. in the small intestine
   d. in the mouth

3. When empty, how big is your stomach?
   a. the size of two fists
   b. the size of one fist
   c. the size of your head
   d. the size of your heart
4. Which of the following lists parts of the digestive system in the correct order?
   a. esophagus, stomach, large intestine, small intestine
   b. mouth, stomach, esophagus, small intestine
   c. stomach, small intestine, esophagus, large intestine
   d. esophagus, stomach, small intestine, large intestine
5. Which is not a part of gastric juice?
   a. enzymes
   b. hydrochloric acid
   c. saliva
   d. bile
6. Which is not a liquid in the small intestine?
   a. intestinal juice
   b. gastric juice
   c. pancreatic juice
   d. bile
7. What helps increase the surface area of the small intestine?
   a. the large intestine
   b. villi
   c. mucus
   d. water
8. What part of food cannot be digested?
   a. carbohydrates
   b. fiber
   c. feces
   d. fat
9. Which hormone helps to regulate the amount of sugar in the blood?
   a. bile
   b. adrenalin
   c. saliva
   d. insulin
10. Which can be used to control non-insulin-dependent diabetes?
   a. medication
   b. diet
   c. both a and b
   d. neither a nor b

Matching. Match each word with its definition or description.
1. a mixture of water, enzymes, and acid
2. tiny projections of the intestinal wall
3. solid waste from the body
4. an opening of the digestive tract
5. contractions that move food
6. an organ that filters poisons out of the blood
7. liquid stored in the gallbladder
8. a gland that produces insulin
9. a tube connecting the mouth and stomach
10. a disease created by insufficient insulin

   a. peristalsis
   b. esophagus
   c. gastric juice
   d. bile
   e. villi
   f. feces
   g. anus
   h. liver
   i. pancreas
   j. diabetes

CHAPTER 17

NUTRITION

INTRODUCTION

Do you ever dream of owning an expensive sports car? Or just the chance to drive one—taking a few friends along for a ride? If a wealthy relative decided to give you a sports car, how would you feel? Even though you had to wait a few years for a driver's license, you would probably keep the car shiny and in good repair. You would be careful whom you let drive it—or even touch it. You would read the owner's manual from cover to cover. Nothing but the best for your car!

Your body is a gift too. Not from a relative, but from the Creator. He has written the rules for its care in every cell and fiber. He expects you to learn everything you can about the way it is put together and how it works. For, unlike the sports car, you can't buy a new one when your body wears out. The best fuel for people, good nutrition, will help you get the most "trouble-free mileage."

SECTION TITLES

The Acura NSX, a luxury sports car.

17-1 NUTRIENTS

VOCABULARY
carbohydrate
fat
mineral
nutrient
protein
RDA
vitamin

OBJECTIVES

- Identify the basic nutrients.
- Describe the importance of each nutrient.
- Explain what is meant by RDA.

Do you like waffles? Would you want to eat them for every meal? Probably not. Eating the same food all the time would be boring. It would also be unhealthful. Eating a variety of foods is the best way to make sure you get all the nutrients you need. **Nutrients** are the chemicals in food that your body uses for energy, growth, and cell repair. There are six basic nutrients that your body cannot do without (fig. 17-1).

Fig. 17-1 The six basic nutrients include carbohydrates, fats, proteins, minerals, vitamins, and water.

NUTRIENTS THAT SUPPLY ENERGY

	NUTRIENT	IMPORTANCE	FOOD SOURCES
E **N** **E** **R** **G** **Y**	CARBOHYDRATES	Supply energy Digest easily	Bread, rice, potatoes, cereals, pasta, fruit, vegetables
	FATS	Supply energy Store vitamins	Dairy products, oils, meat, margarine, nuts, peanut butter, salad dressing
	PROTEINS	Supply energy Help with cell growth and repair	Dairy products, eggs, meat, fish, poultry, legumes, nuts, meat analogs (meat substitutes)

NUTRIENTS THAT DO NOT SUPPLY ENERGY

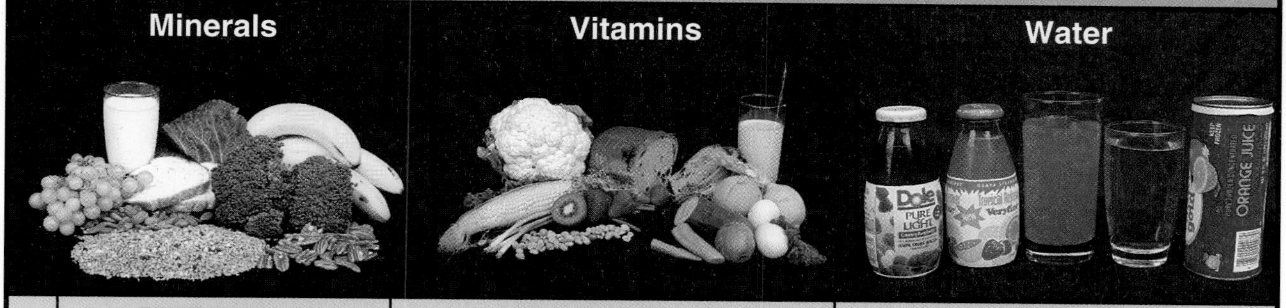

Minerals　　　　Vitamins　　　　Water

	NUTRIENT	IMPORTANCE	FOOD SOURCES
N O N E N E R G Y	**MINERALS**	Control body processes Help build new cells Carry oxygen in blood	Fruits, vegetables, dairy products, eggs, breads, cereals, meat
	VITAMINS	Control body processes Help build new cells Fight disease	Fruits, vegetables, dairy products, eggs, breads, cereals, meat
	WATER	Helps digestion Removes waste Main part of blood Controls temperature	Drinking water, milk, juice, soup, fruits, vegetables

Fig. 17–1 (cont.)

The United States and Canadian governments have recommended amounts of each nutrient that you need each day. These amounts are called the **RDA** (Recommended Dietary Allowance). Eating the RDA of each nutrient helps you stay healthy. Sometimes a doctor may suggest an amount different from the RDA if a person has a health problem. The list in fig. 17–2 gives the RDAs for 11- to 14-year-olds. Study this list. How well does your diet meet these standards?

DID YOU KNOW?

In each gram of carbohydrate and protein there are 4 calories of energy. In a gram of fat there are 9 calories.

Energy Intake		
	Age (years)	Average Energy Allowance Per Day
Males	11–14	2500
Females	11–14	2200

Recommended Dietary Allowances

	Age (Years)	Protein (g)	Fat-Soluble Vitamins			Water-Soluble Vitamins				
			Vita-min A (µg)	Vita-min D (µg)	Vita-min E (mg)	Vita-min C (mg)	Thia-min (mg)	Ribo-flavin (mg)	Niacin (mg)	Vita-min B (mg)
Males 11–14	11–14	45	1000	10	10	50	1.3	1.5	17	1.7
Females 11–14	11–14	45	800	10	50	50	1.1	1.3	15	1.4

	Minerals					
	Cal-cium (µg)	Phos-phorus (mg)	Mag-nesium (mg)	Iron (mg)	Zinc (mg)	Iodine (mg)
Males 11–14	1200	1200	270	12	15	150
Females 11–14	1200	1200	280	13	12	150

	Trace Elements				
	Copper (mg)	Man-ganese (mg)	Fluoride (mg)	Chromium (µg)	Molybdenum (µg)
Males and Females 11–14	1.5–2.5	2.0–3.0	1.5–2.5	50–200	75–250

Fig. 17–2   This chart lists the RDAs of several important nutrients for students your age.

REVIEW IT

1. What are the six basic nutrients needed by the body?
2. Which of the six nutrients supply energy? Which do not?
3. What is the RDA?

CLASS ACTIVITY 17–1: Vitamin C

Question: Which sample contains the most vitamin C?

Materials:

juice samples:	iodine solution
Hi-C fruit drink	medicine droppers – 2
orange juice	plastic cups (clear) – 7
pickle juice	starch solution
pineapple juice	test-tube rack
sauerkraut juice	test tubes – 6
tomato juice	

Procedure:

1. Label six of the plastic cups orange juice, pickle juice, sauerkraut juice, pineapple juice, tomato juice, and Hi-C fruit drink.
2. Label the test tubes A–F. Fill each 1/2 full of the starch solution.
3. Add four drops of iodine solution to each test tube.
4. Predict which of the samples you are testing contains the most vitamin C and which contains the least, ranking them from 1–6. Record your prediction in the Data section.
5. To test tube A use the medicine dropper to add orange juice drop by drop until the bluish color fades to white. Be sure to swirl the test tube after adding each drop. Record how many drops it takes to change the color of the starch solution.
6. Repeat step 5 with each test sample, using a clean test tube each time.
7. Again rank the samples from 1–6 with reference to the amount of vitamin C each contains and record in the Data section.

Data:

SAMPLE	PREDICTED RANKING	NUMBER OF DROPS	ACTUAL RANKING
Orange			
Pickle			
Sauerkraut			
Pineapple			
Tomato			
Hi-C			

Questions:

1. Which sample appears to be the best source of vitamin C? Which is the poorest?
2. How did the vitamin C content of Hi-C compare to the other juices?
3. Should vitamin C be the only nutrient considered when determining the nutritional value of various juice products? Explain.

Conclusion: Write 3–5 sentences about what you learned from this activity.

17–2 BALANCED DIET

VOCABULARY

balanced diet
combination food
food group
junk food

OBJECTIVES

- Identify the food groups necessary for a balanced diet.
- Identify sources for each food group.
- Explain how each food group benefits the body.

According to Genesis, Adam and Eve's first diet was fruits, grains, and nuts. Later, vegetables were added. After the Flood, God allowed people to eat meat. When people began to eat meat, their lives were shortened. The lesson is that the more closely you follow God's original diet, the healthier you will be. A healthful diet includes as many natural and unprocessed foods as possible.

A **food group** is made up of foods that contain the same kind of nutrients. A **balanced diet** is one that includes the right amount of foods from each group. There are four food groups that make up a healthful diet: fruits and vegetables, grains, milk foods, and protein foods (fig. 17–3).

Fig. 17–3   The four food groups include fruits and vegetables, grains, milk foods, and protein foods.

| Fruits and vegetables | Grains |

Fig. 17–3 (continued next page)

Milk foods	Protein foods

THE FOUR FOOD GROUPS		
FOOD GROUP	**IMPORTANCE**	**FOOD SOURCES**
FRUITS AND VEGETABLES	Supply: vitamin A, vitamin C; Help night vision; Fight disease; Provide fiber	Apples, grapes, plums, oranges, bananas, carrots, squash, peas, cabbage, broccoli, and others
GRAINS	Supply: carbohydrate, iron, niacin, thiamin; Provide energy	Breads, cereals, pasta, corn, rice
MILK FOODS	Supply: protein, calcium, riboflavin; Strengthen bones and teeth; Help vision; Ensure healthy skin	Milk, cheese, yogurt, ice cream, cottage cheese
PROTEIN FOODS	Supply: protein, niacin, iron; Build muscle, bone, and blood cells; Ensure healthy skin and nerves	Legumes, nuts, meat, fish, poultry, eggs, peanut butter, meat analogs

RESEARCH IT
Make a list of the most common excuses given by students your age for not eating breakfast. What are the most common excuses given by adults for skipping breakfast?

Many of the dishes a good cook prepares use foods from several groups. For example, a vegetarian roast may include cottage cheese, bread crumbs, eggs, and walnuts (fig. 17–4). When you eat the roast, you eat from several food groups at once. **Combination foods** like this supply a variety of nutrients and are an important part of a balanced diet.

Fig. 17–4 Macaroni and cheese, vegetarian loaf, pizza, and other combination foods supply a variety of nutrients.

Cake, cookies, candy, chips, and soft drinks provide quick energy but are low in vitamins, minerals, and fiber. That's why they are often called **junk foods** (fig. 17–5). These foods contain large amounts of fats, salt, and sugars. Eating too much junk food may cause malnutrition, bad teeth, and weight gain. Also, eating junk food may spoil your appetite for more nutritious food. It is better to eat only small amounts of junk foods.

Fig. 17–5   Junk foods provide quick energy but are low in nutrition.

REVIEW IT

1. What is a food group?
2. Which food group is made up of breads and cereals? Which is made up of legumes, nuts, and meat?
3. Which food group helps the body fight disease? Which helps strengthen bones and teeth?

CLASS ACTIVITY 17–2: Identifying Fat in Food

Question: Which sample contains the most fat?

Materials:
brown paper bag (small)
fatty food samples: banana, bread (wheat), cheese, chocolate, corn chips, mayonnaise, peanut butter, potato
scissors

Procedure:
1. Obtain a small sample of each item to be tested.
2. Use the scissors to cut open the paper bag so that it lies flat.
3. Predict which samples contain fat and which do not. Record your prediction in the Data section.
4. Place a small amount of each sample on the paper bag, labeling where each is placed.
5. Let the samples remain on the paper for about five minutes.
6. At the end of five minutes, remove the samples and examine the area of the paper beneath each sample. An oil spot on the paper indicates the presence of fat. Observe and record whether or not each sample contained fat.
7. Use your results to rank the samples from the one containing the most fat (1) to the sample containing the least fat (8). Record your ranking in the Data section.

Data:

	MAYO	PB	CHOC	BANANA	POTATO	CHIPS	BREAD	CHEESE
Prediction Fat/no fat								
Test Fat/no fat								
Ranking								

Questions:
1. Which foods contained fats? Which did not?
2. Which sample do you think contained the most fat? Why?
3. Which sample do you think contained the least fat? Why?
4. Which of these samples contained saturated fats?
5. Generally, what food group contains the least fat?
6. What problems can result from a diet high in fat?

Conclusion: Write 3–5 sentences about what you learned from this activity.

17–3 DIETARY GUIDELINES

OBJECTIVES

- Identify the seven dietary guidelines.
- Explain why following the dietary guidelines is important to your health.

VOCABULARY
saturated fat
unsaturated fat

A balanced diet includes a variety of foods from each food group. If you eat balanced meals, you will feel better and have more energy. The following guidelines will help you have a healthy diet.

Guideline 1. Eat a variety of foods.

Fifty different nutrients are needed for a healthful diet. It is important to eat a variety of foods from each food group each day (fig. 17–6). Don't limit your choices. God has created many delicious foods. The daily diet of someone your age should include these foods:

- four servings from the fruit and vegetable group
- four servings from the grain group
- four servings from the milk group
- two servings from the protein group

Fig. 17–6 It is important to eat a variety of foods from each food group.

DID YOU KNOW?
The dietary guidelines of the United States and Canada are very similar to the guidelines in *The Ministry of Healing*, a book written by Ellen White about 100 years ago.

Guideline 2. Be at your best weight.

Your best weight is the weight at which you look and feel the best. Carrying excess weight may cause health problems such as heart disease, high blood pressure, and diabetes. Exercise, a balanced diet, and eating more slowly will help you stay at your ideal weight.

Being underweight can be a sign of poor health. Underweight people may have less energy and may be more likely to have infections. Increasing exercise, eating more calories, and reducing stress may help people gain weight.

Guideline 3. Eat fewer fatty foods.

There are two kinds of fats (fig. 17–7). **Unsaturated** (un sach´ ə rāt id) **fats** come from vegetables, nuts and grains, and some fish and poultry. Vegetable oils used for cooking contain unsaturated fats. **Saturated fats** usually come from animal products such as dairy foods and most meat.

Too much fat in the diet contributes to increased weight and heart disease. A high-fat diet has also been linked to cancer. Limiting the amount of fat in your diet will promote good health.

Fig. 17–7   There are two kinds of fat in food: unsaturated fats (left) and saturated fats (right).

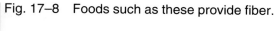
Fig. 17–8   Foods such as these provide fiber.

Guideline 4. Eat foods that contain fiber.

Fiber is the part of the food your body can't digest. It is present in fruit, grains, and vegetables (fig. 17–8). Fiber helps move waste through the intestine, thus reducing the risk of cancer.

Guideline 5. Eat less sugar.

Foods that are high in sugar are usually low in vitamins and minerals. These foods can cause weight gain and tooth decay. They may also contribute to heart disease. Plan your diet to include starches and limited amounts of sugar.

Guideline 6. Eat less salt.

Too much salt in the diet is related to high blood pressure and headaches. Less than one teaspoon of salt is needed each day (fig. 17–9). One serving of food often provides more than a day's requirement of salt.

Guideline 7. Do not drink alcohol.

Alcohol damages the liver and other body organs and increases the risk of stomach and liver cancer. Avoiding alcohol at any age promotes good health.

Fig. 17–9   Your body needs less than one teaspoon of salt each day.

REVIEW IT

1. What are the seven dietary guidelines?
2. Why is eating a variety of foods important?
3. Why is it important to eat fewer fatty foods?
4. How is too much sugar harmful to the body?

317

17–4 FOOD LABELS

VOCABULARY
additive
enriched food
fortified food
ingredient
preservative

NUTRITION INFORMATION PER PORTION	
PORTION SIZE	2 OZ. (ABOUT ½ CUP)
PORTIONS PER CONTAINER	30
CALORIES	240
PROTEIN, g	4
CARBOHYDRATE, g	37
FAT, g	8
POLYUNSATURATED, g	1
SATURATED, g	2
MONOUNSATURATED, g	5
CHOLESTEROL, mg	0
SODIUM, mg	700

PERCENTAGE OF U.S. RECOMMENDED DAILY ALLOWANCES (U.S. RDA)	
PROTEIN	6
VITAMIN A	*
VITAMIN C	*
THIAMIN	20
RIBOFLAVIN	15
NIACIN	10
CALCIUM	8
IRON	8

*CONTAINS LESS THAN 2 PERCENT OF THE U.S. RDA OF THESE NUTRIENTS.

INGREDIENTS: ENRICHED FLOUR BLEACHED (WHEAT FLOUR, NIACIN (a B VITAMIN), IRON, THIAMIN MONONITRATE (VITAMIN B₁) AND RIBOFLAVIN (VITAMIN B₂)), VEGETABLE SHORTENING (CONTAINS ONE OR BOTH OF THE FOLLOWING PARTIALLY HYDROGENATED OILS: SOYBEAN, COTTONSEED), LEAVENING (BAKING SODA, SODIUM ALUMINUM PHOSPHATE, MONOCALCIUM PHOSPHATE), WHEY, SALT, DRIED BUTTERMILK.

General Mills, Inc.
GENERAL OFFICES, MINNEAPOLIS, MN 55440
Made in U.S.A.
1.70 Kg

Fig. 17–10   Food labels provide important information to consumers.

Fig. 17–11   Enriched foods have nutrients added to them after processing.

OBJECTIVE

- Explain how food labels help you make good food choices.

Next time you go to the supermarket, take a look at some food labels. Labels are required on all packaged foods to let you know what you are buying. Each label must identify the name of the product, the name and address of the company, and the net quantity, which means the amount of food minus the container (fig. 17–10). Reading food labels will help you make smart choices.

The **ingredients** of a product must be listed. The first ingredient listed is the one present in the largest amount. The last ingredient listed is the one present in the smallest amount. Special foods such as low-calorie, reduced-calorie, low-salt, and low-sugar foods must meet certain requirements.

A label also lists additives used in the product. **Additives** are chemicals added to packaged foods to improve their taste and appearance. Certain additives, called **preservatives**, prevent food from spoiling. Some additives improve the nutritional value of foods. As food is

processed, some nutrients are lost or destroyed. These are sometimes replaced by adding similar nutrients to food after it has been processed. Such food is called **enriched food** (fig. 17–11). **Fortified foods** have extra vitamins and minerals added (fig. 17–12).

Fig. 17–12   Fortified foods have extra vitamins and minerals added to them during processing.

TRY THIS 17–4: Whazinit?

Materials:
cereal (single-serving box) – 3
Special Master R349

Procedure:
Carefully examine the labels on each box of cereal and complete the data table (Special Master).
- What is the main ingredient in each cereal?
- Which cereal do you think is the most nutritious? Why?
- Which cereal contains the most added sugar?
- Which cereal contains the most salt?
- What vitamins are provided by each cereal?
- Which cereal has added vitamins and minerals?
- Why do manufacturers add vitamins and minerals to packaged foods?
- Suppose someone is allergic to artificial coloring in food. Which of the three cereals should he or she avoid? Why?
- Suppose someone needed to avoid salt in his diet. Which of the three cereals would be safest to eat? Why?

REVIEW IT

1. In what part of a food label would you find the materials used to make the product?
2. List three reasons additives are added to food.
3. What are preservatives?

319

17–5 BODY COMPOSITION AND WEIGHT

VOCABULARY

body composition
desirable weight
fat tissue
lean tissue
pinch test
weight management

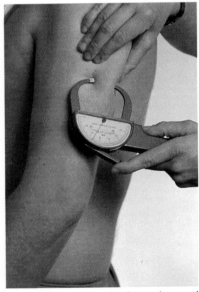

Fig. 17–13   The pinch test is used to determine the fat percentage of the body.

OBJECTIVES

- Compare and contrast fat and lean tissue.
- Define body composition.
- Explain what is meant by desirable weight.

Your body is made up of fat and lean tissue. **Fat tissue** lies beneath the skin and surrounds your muscles and internal organs. **Lean tissue** makes up your skeleton, muscles, skin, and internal organs. Your **body composition** is the ratio of fat to lean tissue in your body. A quick way of checking your fat percentage is the **pinch test** (fig. 17–13). Students age 10–13 should have about 10–15 percent fat tissue. The ratio increases with age. Men should have about 15 percent fat and women nearly 30 percent fat.

You need some fat tissue to help store vitamins and produce hormones. Fat also helps protect your internal organs and acts as insulation to keep you warm.

If you have too little fat, you may feel cold, and you may tire easily. On the other hand, having too much fat makes daily activities more difficult. It makes your heart work harder and may injure some joints.

You will be healthier if you are at your proper weight. Your **desirable weight** is determined by your age, sex, height, and body build (fig. 17–14).

Weight management is a plan that helps you maintain your ideal weight. The plan should include both regular exercise and a balanced diet.

REVIEW IT

1. What type of tissue makes up muscle and skin? What type surrounds internal organs?
2. What term is used to describe the ratio between fat and lean tissue?
3. What factors help determine your desirable weight?

Fig. 17–14   Your desirable weight is determined by your age, sex, height, and body build.

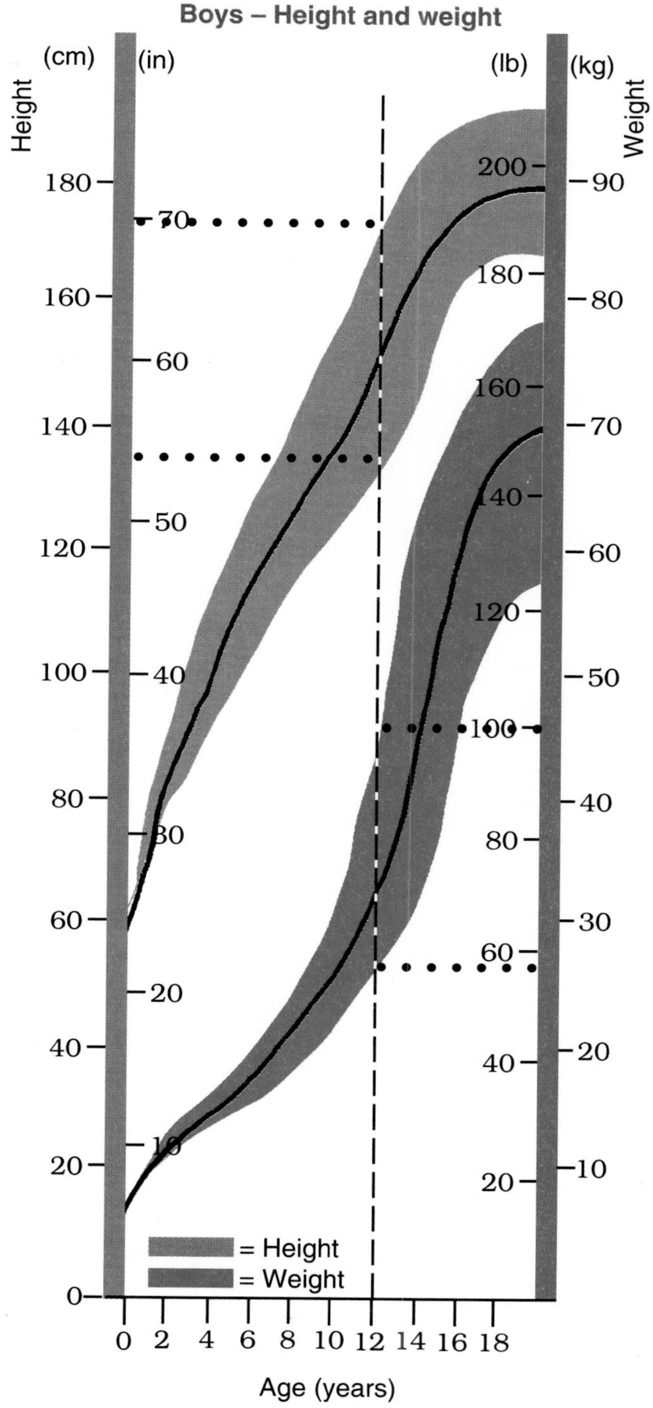

Boys – Height and weight

Girls – Height and weight

= Height
= Weight

Age (years)

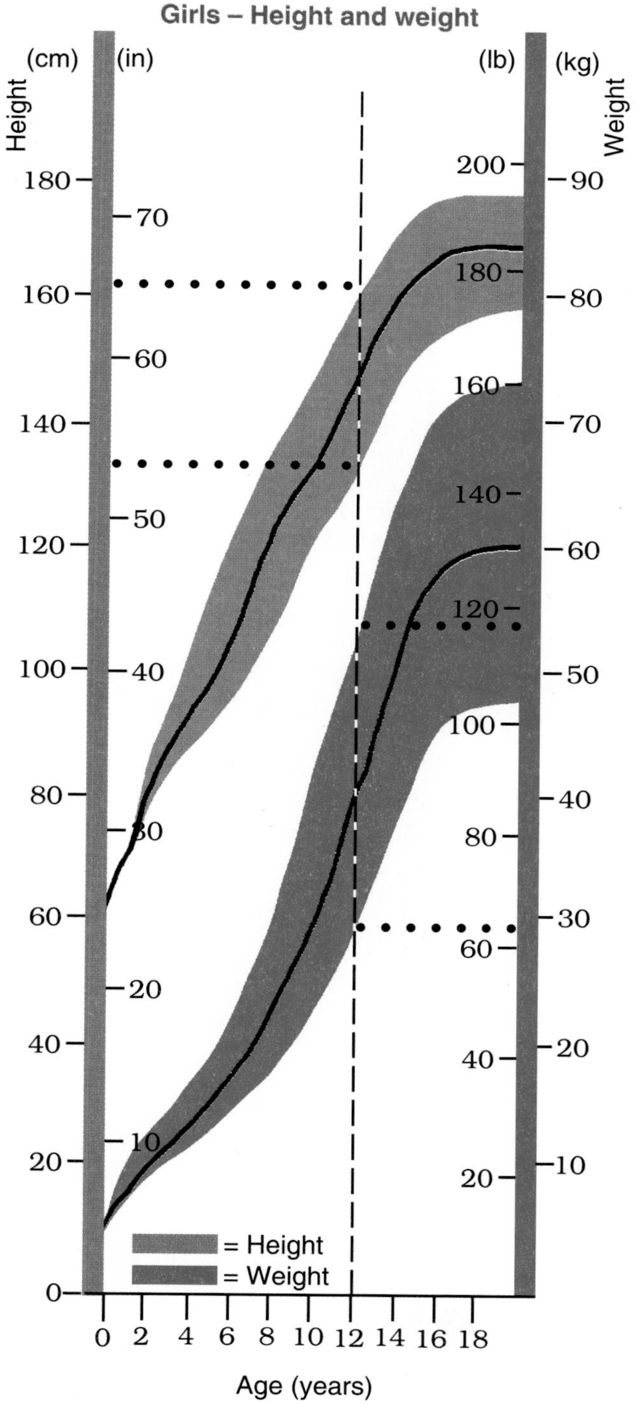

17–6 CALORIES AND METABOLISM

VOCABULARY
calorie
energy input
energy output
metabolic rate
metabolism

DID YOU KNOW?
An average boy's diet, 3000 calories, equals the energy contained in six pounds of TNT. A 300-calorie slice of pie has about the same energy as 50 gm of coal or 40 ml of gasoline.

OBJECTIVES

- Define calorie.
- Explain the relationship between calories and metabolic rate.
- Explain how weight can be managed.

Your food supplies energy as calories. A **calorie** is a unit of measure used to describe the amount of energy in food. Some foods contain more calories than others. For example, a gram of fat contains twice as many calories as a gram of carbohydrate or protein. Figure 17–15 shows the calorie content of common foods.

Good weight management relies on a knowledge of energy input and output. Your **energy input** is the number of calories you take in as food and drink. At your age you normally need between 2000 and 3000 calories every day. **Energy output** is the calories you burn as energy each day.

Breathing, digestion, and circulation go on whether you are awake or asleep. These processes are always using energy. The use of energy by your body is called **metabolism** (mə tab´ ə liz´m). The rate at which you use energy is your **metabolic rate**. When you are sleeping, your metabolic rate is low; when you exercise, your metabolic rate

Fig. 17–15   The calorie content of some common foods.

Food	Serving Size	Calories
Apple	3 inches	75
Avocado	1/2	190
Banana	1 large	170
Bread (wheat)	1 slice	60
Broccoli (cooked)	1 cup	40
Butter	1 tbsp	102
Cake (chocolate)	3 inches	350
Cheese (cheddar)	2 ounces	112
Cream cheese	2 tbsp	99
Cream of mushroom soup	7 ounces	149
Custard	1/2 cup	150
French fries	10	137
Ice cream sundae	regular	400
Lasagna	7 ounces	325
Lima beans	1/2 cup	127
Milk (whole)	1 cup	159
Orange	1 medium	70
Peanut butter	2 tbsp	172
Popcorn (plain)	1 cup	54
Spaghetti	1 cup	260
Walnut	8–15 (halves)	98

increases. The harder you exercise, the higher your metabolic rate. The higher your metabolic rate, the more calories you use. Figure 17–16 shows the number of calories used in common activities.

Weight management is based on balancing your energy input and output. To maintain your ideal weight, you must eat the same number of calories your body uses. You lose weight if you eat fewer calories than your body uses. It takes 3500 calories to make one pound of body fat. If you want to lose a pound, you must use 3500 calories more than you eat. Eating low or moderate amounts of fat and getting sufficient exercise will help prevent weight gain.

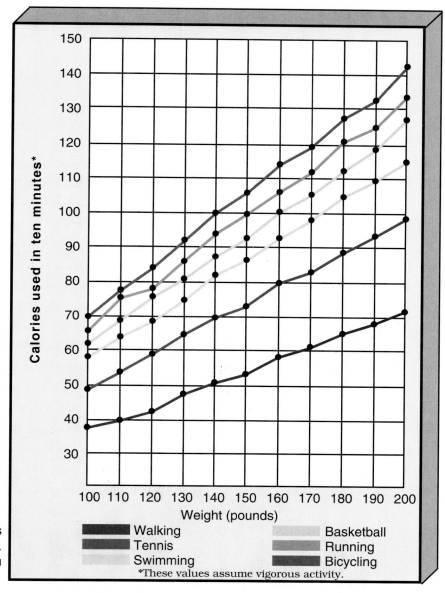

Fig. 17–16   The number of calories used in several common activities. The more you weigh, the more you use.

REVIEW IT

1. What is a calorie?
2. What happens to your calorie usage as your metabolic rate decreases?
3. What two things can you do to decrease your weight?

17-7 EATING DISORDERS

VOCABULARY
anorexia nervosa
bulimia

OBJECTIVES

- Identify common eating disorders.
- Explain the dangers of eating disorders.

Today's society is very concerned about weight. Commercials convey the message that "thin is beautiful." TV and magazine ads show slender women and men doing fun and exciting things. But many people can't live up to this standard. Are they less valuable because they don't have the beautiful bodies seen in the magazines and on television? Unfortunately, many young people are influenced by the messages of advertising. As a result, eating disorders in teenagers are on the rise. Look at figure 17-17. Which of these girls do you think has an eating disorder? You cannot always tell by looking at someone whether or not he or she has an eating disorder. Any one of these girls could have an eating disorder, but none of them does.

Fig. 17-17 It is difficult to determine if someone has an eating disorder by just looking at him or her.

Anorexia nervosa (an ə reks′ ē ə   nər vō′ sə) is a serious eating disorder that can result in starvation or death. It is caused by a poor self-concept and a fear of being overweight. Anorexia nervosa affects girls more than boys. It is estimated that 1 in 200 teenage girls is affected by anorexia. Those affected often diet and exercise excessively. Some even resort to using laxatives, diuretics (dī yo͞o ret′ iks), and forced vomiting. The resulting lack of nutrition causes serious physical problems, including erosion of tooth enamel, bone deterioration, and, in many cases, heart damage. Victims of anorexia nervosa also suffer emotional problems. They need medical attention and counseling to overcome this disorder.

Another eating disorder is **bulimia** (byo͞o lē′ mē ə). Like anorexia, it is caused by a poor or unrealistic self-image and a fear of being overweight. The main difference between anorexia and bulimia is that bulimia does not involve dieting or excessive exercise. A bulimic person consumes thousands of calories during periods of eating binges. This is often done in private. After eating, bulimics try to rid themselves of the food the same way anorexic people do, by vomiting or laxatives. Bulimics suffer physical and emotional problems similar to those suffered by victims of anorexia. Bulimics also require medical and psychological help to overcome their problem.

Being happy with yourself as a person will help you avoid the problems of eating disorders. To be happy with yourself, learn to recognize your strong and weak points. Know that you and others are valuable for yourselves, just the way you are.

REVIEW IT

1. What are the two most common eating disorders?
2. How do eating disorders endanger the body?

CHAPTER 17 WRAP-UP

SKILLS DEVELOPMENT

THINKING SKILLS: PREDICTING

Prediction is the process of estimating what you think will happen in a given situation. Although it is not exact, predicting is used frequently by scientists. Predicting helps scientists plan for events that have not yet occurred and to discover solutions to problems.

Below is a chart that is incomplete. You are to complete this chart by predicting how much the student will grow in the next few years. Study the numbers in each column to help you predict what numbers should go in the empty boxes. Be sure that you can offer reasonable support for your predictions.

AGE	HEIGHT	WEIGHT	SHOE SIZE	CALORIES PER DAY
8	4' 6"	75	4	2200
9	4' 8"	79	4.5	2300
10	4' 9"	84	4.5	2400
11	4' 11"	——	5.5	——
12	5' 3"	——	——	——
13	——	——	——	——
14	——	——	——	——
15	——	——	——	——

1. Does weight always increase with height? Explain.
2. How did the calories needed each day change as age increased? Why did this change occur?
3. On what did you base the weight prediction?
4. On what did you base the calorie prediction?
5. On what did you base the shoe size prediction?
6. Suppose you completed a similar chart of predictions for this person from age 20–30, what would be different about your predictions?

QUESTIONS AND PROBLEMS
1. Why is water important to the body?
2. Name a food that supplies all six nutrients.
3. Why are carbohydrates preferred by the body as a source of energy?
4. Make a list of the food you have eaten so far today. Identify the food group to which each item belongs.
5. Since your body needs salt, isn't it a good idea to add salt to the food you eat? Why?
6. What is the problem with junk food?
7. What is the advantage of preservatives being added to food? What is the disadvantage?
8. Which nutrient provides the most energy per gram?
9. What do you think is the best way to lose weight? Why?
10. How does TV and magazine advertising contribute to an increase in the occurrence of eating disorders?
11. How is anorexia nervosa different from bulimia?
12. Why are more girls affected by eating disorders than boys?
13. What would you do if you suspected that a friend might have an eating disorder?

RESEARCH
1. Investigate the different types of eating disorders and briefly describe each. Discover how many people are affected by each type of eating disorder. Make a poster that displays your findings.
2. Contact a hospital dietician and find out what his or her job is. Write a report on your findings.
3. Discover how scientists determine RDAs. Prepare an oral report and present it to the class.
4. Use pictures from newspapers and magazines to make a bulletin board that shows at least 20 examples of each food group.
5. Look through an *Index to the Writings of Ellen G. White* and find references that correspond to the seven dietary guidelines. Present your findings to the class.

REVIEW
HIGHLIGHTS
1. The main nutrients needed by the body are carbohydrates, fats, proteins, vitamins, minerals, and water.
2. The importance of each nutrient is identified on pages 306 and 307.
3. RDA stands for the Recommended Dietary Allowance and represents the amount of each nutrient needed each day by the body in order to maintain health.
4. There are four main food groups: fruits and vegetables, grains, milk foods, and protein foods.

5. The sources and benefits of each food group are found in the chart on page 311.
6. The seven dietary guidelines are identified on pages 315–317.
7. Following the dietary guidelines will help you feel better, have more energy, and reduce the risk of certain diseases, such as heart disease and cancer.
8. Reading food packaging labels will help you make smart food choices.
9. Fat tissue lies just beneath the skin and surrounds the muscles and internal organs. Lean tissue makes up the skeleton, muscles, and organs.
10. Body composition describes the ratio of fat tissue to lean tissue.
11. Your desirable weight is the weight at which your body functions best. It is determined by your age, sex, height, and body build.
12. A calorie is the unit of measure used to describe the amount of energy in food.
13. The greater your metabolic rate, the more calories (energy) you need. The lower your metabolic rate, the fewer calories (energy) you need.
14. Weight can be managed by taking in the same number of calories (energy) as your body uses. If weight gain is desired, increase the calories eaten and decrease exercise. If weight loss is desired, decrease the calories (energy) eaten and increase exercise.
15. Two common eating disorders are anorexia nervosa and bulimia. Both of these disorders are related to poor self-image and require medical attention and counseling.
16. Eating disorders lead to many health-related problems, including damage to the bones and teeth, problems relating to the digestive and nervous systems, and damage to the heart.

VOCABULARY LIST

additive
anorexia nervosa
balanced diet
body composition
bulimia
calorie
carbohydrate
combination food
desirable weight
energy input
energy output

enriched food
fat
fat tissue
food group
fortified food
ingredient
junk food
lean tissue
metabolic rate
metabolism
mineral

nutrient
pinch test
preservative
protein
RDA
saturated fat
unsaturated fat
vitamin
weight management

PRACTICE

Multiple Choice. Choose the best answer.
1. Carbohydrates are important because they:
   a. supply energy
   b. fight disease
   c. repair cells
   d. remove waste

2. Eating the RDA for each nutrient allows you to:
   a. eat more
   b. stay healthy
   c. both a and b
   d. neither a nor b
3. A food source for the grain food group is:
   a. milk
   b. fruit
   c. legumes
   d. bread
4. The milk foods group supplies:
   a. protein
   b. riboflavin
   c. calcium
   d. all of these
5. A food that supplies a variety of nutrients is known as a
   a. multiple food
   b. mixture food
   c. combination food
   d. none of these
6. There are ___ dietary guidelines.
   a. four
   b. seven
   c. eight
   d. five
7. Indicate the one that is not a dietary guideline.
   a. eat less salt
   b. eat fewer fatty foods
   c. eat more sugar
   d. eat a variety of foods
8. The information on the label of a food container must contain:
   a. the size of the can
   b. the name of the product
   c. the color of the contents
   d. the weight of the can
9. A plan that helps you maintain your ideal weight is known as:
   a. weight management
   b. body management
   c. mass management
   d. exercise management
10. A serious eating disorder that often results in starvation or death is:
   a. bulimia
   b. metabolism
   c. anorexia nervosa
   d. diabetes

Matching. Match each word with its definition or description.
1. nutrient that helps carry oxygen in the blood
2. nutrient that helps the body fight disease
3. the use of energy by the body
4. the materials used in food products
5. fats that come from nuts and grains
6. unit used to measure the energy in food
7. amount of nutrient needed each day
8. foods with added nutrients
9. fats present in animal products
10. nutrient that supplies materials for growth and repair

a. ingredients
b. calorie
c. enriched foods
d. metabolism
e. minerals
f. proteins
g. vitamins
h. saturated fats
i. RDA
j. unsaturated fats

CHAPTER 18

DRUGS

INTRODUCTION

Imagine sitting around a campfire and enjoying its warmth. The fire is inviting. It warms your hands. You may roast corn or marshmallows in it. Now think of a forest fire or house fire. These fires are dangerous, destructive, and can be deadly.

Drugs are much like fire. Though some drugs can help you, others are harmful and can destroy your mind and body. What are drugs? How do drugs affect your body? Why do some people misuse drugs? This chapter will help you understand drugs and how to avoid their dangers.

SECTION TITLES

Fire can be beneficial or harmful, depending on its use.

18–1 DRUGS AND THE BODY

VOCABULARY
drug
immunization

OBJECTIVES

- Define a drug.
- Distinguish between drugs that are medicine and those that are not.

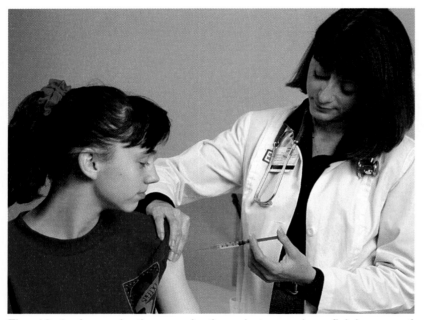

Fig. 18–1   Immunizations and other shots are beneficial ways of using drugs.

When you get a cold, the coughing, sneezing, and sniffling can make you feel miserable. You may take medicine to help you feel better. Most students have had injections to prevent measles, mumps, and other diseases. Such injections contain **drugs**, chemicals that change the way the body works. Some drugs, called **immunizations** (im´ myo͞o nīz ā shənz), help to prevent diseases, as did your shots for measles (fig. 18–1). Other drugs, such as cold medicines or antibiotics, are used to treat diseases. Both kinds of drugs are medicines and can be very helpful.

When you are sick, you may use over-the-counter (OTC) medicines (fig. 18–2). If so, you should follow the directions on the label carefully. If you go to a doctor and he or she prescribes a medicine for you, use it exactly as directed (fig. 18–3).

Other kinds of drugs, the kind you have heard about the most, are not medicines. Drugs such as cocaine,

DID YOU KNOW?
The most prescribed drug in the world is Zantac, a drug used to treat ulcers.

marijuana, and alcohol are harmful and illegal. They are not used to treat disease or to prevent illness. Instead, they are used for the effect they produce.

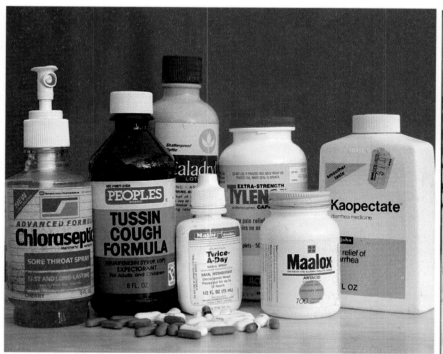

Fig. 18–2   These medications are examples of OTCs (over-the-counter) drugs.

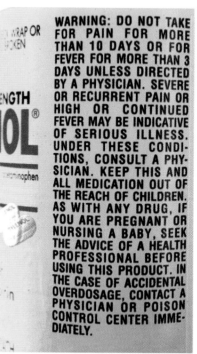

WARNING: DO NOT TAKE FOR PAIN FOR MORE THAN 10 DAYS OR FOR FEVER FOR MORE THAN 3 DAYS UNLESS DIRECTED BY A PHYSICIAN. SEVERE OR RECURRENT PAIN OR HIGH OR CONTINUED FEVER MAY BE INDICATIVE OF SERIOUS ILLNESS. UNDER THESE CONDITIONS, CONSULT A PHYSICIAN. KEEP THIS AND ALL MEDICATION OUT OF THE REACH OF CHILDREN. AS WITH ANY DRUG, IF YOU ARE PREGNANT OR NURSING A BABY, SEEK THE ADVICE OF A HEALTH PROFESSIONAL BEFORE USING THIS PRODUCT. IN THE CASE OF ACCIDENTAL OVERDOSAGE, CONTACT A PHYSICIAN OR POISON CONTROL CENTER IMMEDIATELY.

Fig. 18–3   Legal drugs come with directions on how to use them properly.

You will have to make choices about the kinds of drugs you will use. Choosing to use drugs that are not medicines can cause a lot of trouble. Those who use cocaine often commit crimes in order to support their drug habit. People who drink alcohol and drive may kill themselves or others in accidents. They may hurt family members or friends. When Solomon wrote in Proverbs 20 that "wine is a mocker, strong drink is raging," he was telling about the dangerous effects of the drug alcohol.

RESEARCH IT

Find out which vaccine or vaccines were discovered by each scientist: Jenner, Koch, Salk, Pasteur.

REVIEW IT

1. What is a drug?
2. How are medicines different from other drugs, such as cocaine?

CLASS ACTIVITY 18–1: Aspirin

Question: Which aspirin brand is the better buy?

Materials:
    aspirin samples:
        Anacin
        Bayer aspirin
        Bufferin
        children's aspirin
        generic aspirin
    balance

Procedure:
1. Calculate the cost of each tablet. Divide the price of the container by the number of tablets contained. Record the cost/tablet.
2. Divide the price of each tablet by the number of grains in each tablet. Record the cost/grain.
3. Weigh 10 tablets of each brand. Divide the mass by 10 to get the average mass per tablet (round to the nearest gram). Record the mass/tablet.
4. Divide the number of grains in each tablet by 15. Record this as the amount of aspirin/tablet.
5. To find out what percentage of a tablet is really aspirin, divide the number in the fourth column (aspirin/tablet) by the third column (mass/tablet) and multiply by 100. Record the percent aspirin/tablet.

Data:

BRAND	COST/ TABLET	COST/ GRAIN	MASS/ TABLET	ASPIRIN/ TABLET	% ASPIRIN/ TABLET
Store brand					
Bayer					
Bufferin					
Anacin					
Children's					

Questions:
1. Which aspirin brand had the most aspirin per tablet? Which had the least?
2. Which aspirin brand cost the most per tablet? Which cost the least?
3. Which aspirin brand is the best buy? Which is the worst?
4. Do you think it is better to buy name brand medicines or store brand medicines? Why?

Conclusion: Write 3–5 sentences about what you learned from this activity.

18–2 WHY PEOPLE ABUSE DRUGS

OBJECTIVE

• Explain why people abuse drugs.

Drug abuse in America is a national problem. Many people believe it is the most serious problem affecting society. Knowing why people abuse drugs can help you avoid abusing them yourself. The most common reasons people abuse drugs are peer pressure, curiosity, low self-image, and rebellion.

PEER PRESSURE. Taking a drug just because someone else does it is foolish. But this is the most common reason why teenagers begin to abuse drugs. The invitation to "try it just once" sounds harmless, until you find yourself doing things you really don't want to do. Peer pressure can push you into habits you know aren't good for you (fig. 18–4).

CURIOSITY. Curiosity and risk taking are often reasons why some teenagers use drugs. While these are normal urges, experimenting with drugs is never safe.

LOW SELF-IMAGE. Some young people start using drugs to overcome a poor self-image. They feel lonely and depressed. They use drugs to make themselves feel better. But when the effects of the drugs wear off, the lonely, depressed feelings return.

Fig. 18–4 Peer pressure is the most common reason young people begin to abuse drugs.

RESEARCH IT
What methods are used to help people give up smoking? Which method is most successful?

Fig. 18–5 Some teenagers abuse drugs because they are rebelling against parents or others in authority.

REBELLION. Many teenagers who are unhappy or rebellious use drugs as a means of "getting even" with parents or others in authority (fig. 18–5). Rebellion that involves drug abuse is dangerous and does not solve problems.

Usually, more than one reason is involved when someone chooses to use drugs. If you know someone who is having trouble with drugs, encourage that person to talk with a parent, teacher, or other trusted adult (fig. 18–6).

Fig. 18–6 If someone is having trouble with drugs, encourage him or her to talk to a trusted adult.

TRY THIS 18–2: Why Smoke?

Materials:
none needed

Procedure:
1. Conduct a survey of five adult smokers. Ask why they started smoking and why they continue to smoke. Record the responses in a notebook.
2. Conduct a survey of five adult nonsmokers. Ask why they do not smoke. Record responses in a notebook.
3. Compile a class list of reasons why people begin to smoke, why they continue to smoke, and why some people don't smoke.
   • According to your class list, what is the most common reason people begin to smoke?
   • According to your class list, what is the most common reason people continue to smoke?
   • According to your class list, what is the most common reason people do not smoke?
   • What evidence did you gather that suggests that smoking is an addiction?
   • Why has smoking been banned in many public places?

REVIEW IT

1. What is the most common reason teenagers try drugs?

CLASS ACTIVITY 18–2: Magazine Advertising

Question: What information is given in OTC drug advertising?

Materials:
magazines

Procedure:
1. Find seven advertisements for over-the-counter medicines. Complete the chart for each advertisement. Use the number codes provided when filling out the chart for Intended Purpose and Intended User.

Intended Purpose

1. allergies	5. first-aid cream	9. pain relief
2. colds	6. headache relief	10. personal hygiene
3. coughs	7. fever reducer	11. sleep
4. eye/ear drops	8. laxative	12. stomach problems

Intended User

1. young children	3. men	5. adults (men/women)
2. older children	4. women	6. senior citizens

Data:

PRODUCT	PURPOSE	INTENDED USER	INSTRUCTIONS GIVEN		WARNING GIVEN	
			YES	NO	YES	NO

Questions:
1. Which purpose was the most common? Which was the least?
2. Did most advertisements indicate who the medicine was intended for?
3. What type of instructions were included in the advertisements?
4. What warnings were given?

Conclusion: Write 3–5 sentences about what you learned from this activity.

18–3 EFFECTS OF DRUGS ON THE BODY

depressant
gateway drug
hallucinogen
stimulant

DID YOU KNOW?

Wounded soldiers of the Civil War were given morphine to relieve their pain. However, many of these soldiers became addicted to morphine. Heroin was developed to help them overcome their morphine addiction. Unfortunately, heroin proved to be even more addictive than morphine.

OBJECTIVES

- Identify factors that determine the effect of a drug on the body.
- Describe the way in which drugs affect the body's nervous system.
- Classify drugs according to their effects on the body.
- Describe the mind-altering effects of some drugs.

Four factors determine the effect of a drug on the body.

1. **AMOUNT.** Usually, the larger the dose, the greater the effect.
2. **WEIGHT.** The greater a person's weight, the larger the dose needed for the desired effect.
3. **PHYSICAL HEALTH.** Drugs more easily affect people who are in poor health than those in good health.
4. **EXPECTATION.** If people expect an effect, they may feel an effect even when they have taken no drug at all.

Once drugs enter the bloodstream, they affect the brain almost immediately. As a result, drugs that are injected into a vein act quickest of all. Drugs that are swallowed, inhaled, or held under the tongue act more slowly because it takes longer for them to get into the bloodstream (fig. 18–7).

Fig. 18–7 Drugs enter the body by injecting (left), inhaling (center), or swallowing (right).

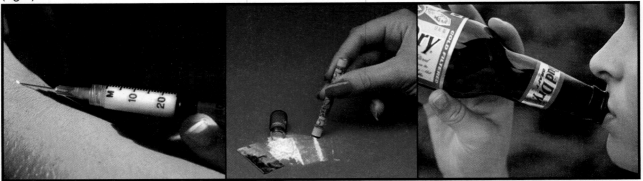

Drugs act on the nerves that transmit signals to the brain and on the brain itself. Often drugs act on the part of the nervous system that automatically controls the heart and breathing rate. Some drugs speed up these processes; others slow them down. An overdose of a drug can dangerously affect the heart and breathing and can cause death. This is often called "OD ing."

Drugs are classified according to the ways in which they affect the body and the chemicals they contain. Study fig. 18–8 to learn the effects of specific drugs.

Fig. 18–8 Most drugs are classed as either depressants, stimulants, or hallucinogens.

DRUGS AND THEIR EFFECTS			
	DRUG GROUP	KINDS OF DRUGS	EFFECTS OF DRUGS
	Depressants—drugs that slow down body processes.	• drugs made from opium: morphine, codeine, heroin, cough syrups • barbiturates • tranquilizers • alcohol	• Alter the perception of pain. Cause sleep and drowsiness. • Used as sedatives or anesthetics. Produce physical and mental dependence.
	Stimulants—drugs that speed up body pro-cesses.	• amphetamines • cocaine, crack • caffeine • nicotine	• Increase perception, nervousness, and blood pressure. Dull the appetite. • Used to reduce fatigue and depression. • Produce physical and mental dependence.
	Hallucinogens—drugs that change how the brain works.	• marijuana • LSD • PCP	• Alter the thinking and interpreting processes of the brain. Interfere with judgment and cause the user to perform strange and some-times violent acts. • Produce mental dependence.

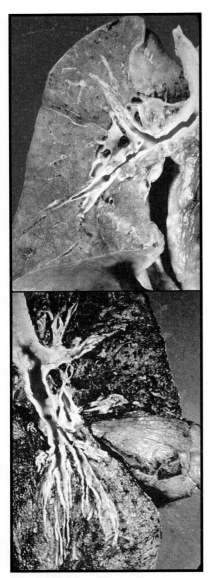

People continue to take drugs for the effect they get. However, for every effect of a drug, there is usually an equal and opposite later reaction to the drug (fig. 18–9). For example, people take caffeine because it is a stimulant. At first, caffeine does stimulate the brain. But after that effect wears off, there is a depressing effect on the brain. When people feel this reaction, they want more caffeine to "pep them up" again. Such reactions cause people to continue using drugs.

Some drugs are dangerous because they alter the way people act. When people use alcohol, cocaine, or LSD, they may injure themselves or others. Other drugs, such as tobacco, cause the greatest damage to the user (fig. 18–10). Still other drugs are called **gateway drugs** because they make it easier for people to use stronger and more harmful drugs. Marijuana is a gateway drug.

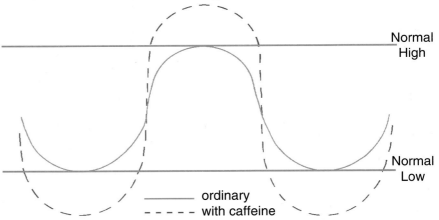

Fig. 18–9   For every effect a drug produces, there is an opposite effect that occurs once the drug wears off.

Fig. 18–10 Cigarettes cause emphysema. A healthy lung (top) can become diseased by smoking (bottom).

REVIEW IT

1. What four factors help to determine the effect of a drug?
2. How do drugs affect the body's nervous system?
3. What class of drugs speeds up the body's processes?
4. What do marijuana and LSD have in common?

18-4 DECISIONS ABOUT DRUGS

OBJECTIVES

- Explain where your values come from.
- Identify the steps in decision making.
- Identify personal and community resources that help people who abuse drugs.

When you see a TV or billboard ad for alcohol or tobacco, what message do you get (fig. 18-11)? What message do you think the advertiser wants you to get? Advertising costs enormous amounts of money, but companies are willing to pay for it because they know that advertising sells more of their products. You must know what things are most important to you to be able to resist some advertising.

Your values, or ideas of what are most important in life, come from your home, your church, your friends, and your school (fig. 18-12). When you need to make decisions about things in your life, you should think about the following questions:

Fig. 18-11 Advertisements influence many young people to drink alcoholic beverages.

Fig. 18-12 Your friends have a great impact on the values you accept.

DID YOU KNOW?
Nicotine is used as an ingredient in some insecticides.

1. Is this what I choose to do? Or is someone choosing for me?
2. What is my goal in making this choice? Have I thought of other ways to reach my goal?
3. What are the facts?
4. Have I thought about the consequences?
5. How important is what I have chosen?
6. Am I willing to share my decision with people who are important to me?
7. What does God say to me about such a decision?

If you practice these steps in making small decisions, you will be more likely to use them in important decisions. What you decide about drug use will affect the rest of your life. Since many drugs affect your brain and the way you think, they can also affect your relationship to God. God speaks to you through your brain. If your brain is affected by drugs, you will have a very difficult time thinking about God or hearing what He says to you.

Your decision about drug use needs to be made before you have the chance to use them. Practice ahead of time what you will say or do. Just as practice in sports helps you pitch a better ball or balance on a bar, so practice in refusing to abuse any drugs will help you stick to your decision (fig. 18–13).There are many people who can help

Fig. 18–13   Practicing helps you become a better gymnast. Practicing how to refuse drugs will help you stay drug free.

you if you are tempted to use drugs. Here are some suggestions:

- Find and make friends with people who do not use drugs.
- Talk with a family member, church youth leader, or teacher who cares about you.
- Ask for information about community groups, such as Alateen or Al-Anon.
- Go to community organizations such as the YWCA or YMCA.
- Talk to a doctor, nurse, pharmacist, or other health professional.

Although you may feel that no one will understand your problems, don't give up until you find someone who will help you (fig. 18–14). God has promised never to leave you alone; He often sends just the person you need to talk to. You are very important to Him. He wants to help you make right decisions.

Fig. 18–14 Talking to a friend can often help you with your problems.

REVIEW IT

1. What are the sources of a person's values?
2. What are the steps of decision making?
3. Who can help you make good choices concerning drugs?
4. What community resources are available to help teens who have difficulty with drugs?

CHAPTER 18 WRAP-UP

SKILLS DEVELOPMENT

THINKING SKILLS: MAKING A TABLE (This activity requires R381 and R383)

A table is used to place a lot of information in a relatively small space and make it easier to understand. The materials below provide information concerning types of drugs, examples, immediate and long-term effects, and whether the drugs cause physical or mental dependence. Your task is to organize the information into the table provided. The first one has been done as an example for you. When putting information into table form, avoid using sentences or long phrases.

Scientists identify several types of drugs. Drugs can be grouped as either beneficial drugs, such as medicines, or drugs of abuse. Drugs of abuse include cannabis, depressants, narcotics, stimulants, hallucinogens, and inhalants.

The cannabis group includes marijuana and hashish. The immediate effects of these drugs include increased heart rate and confusion. The long-term effects include lung disease and possible brain damage. These drugs cause mental dependence.

The depressant group includes alcohol, barbiturates, and tranquilizers. The immediate effects of these drugs include drowsiness, dizziness, and loss of coordination. The long-term effects include decreased blood pressure, diseases of the liver, stomach, heart, and brain, possible death. These drugs cause both mental and physical dependence.

The narcotic group includes heroin, morphine, and codeine. The immediate effects of these drugs include drowsiness, blurred vision, nausea. The long-term effects include infection from unsterile needles, painful withdrawal, infections of the heart and lungs. These drugs cause both mental and physical dependence.

The stimulant group includes cocaine, amphetamines, nicotine, and caffeine. The immediate effects of these drugs include increased heart rate and blood pressure, sleeplessness, loss of appetite. The long-term effects include nervousness, mental disorders, and diseases of the heart and lungs. These drugs cause both mental and physical dependence.

The hallucinogen group includes LSD and PCP. The immediate effects of these drugs include loss of control over thoughts, hallucinations, loss of memory. The long-term effects include mental illness. These drugs do not cause physical dependence but may cause mental dependence.

The inhalant group includes various glues, solvents, and sprays present in household products. The immediate effects of these drugs include dizziness, loss of memory, lack of coordination, nausea, and possible death. The long-term effects include damage to kidneys, liver, lungs, and brain. It is unknown whether these drugs cause physical or mental dependence.

QUESTIONS AND PROBLEMS

1. Which of the drugs of abuse is as old as Earth's history?
2. Why are some drugs of abuse (such as alcohol) legal while others (such as heroin) are illegal?
3. Why is drug abuse such a worldwide problem?
4. Why do people choose to abuse drugs even though they know the harmful effects of the drugs?
5. Why are gateway drugs so dangerous?
6. In what ways could your church help young people avoid drug abuse? What could your community do?
7. What problems can occur from taking over-the-counter drugs?
8. What counsel does the Bible give concerning the use of alcohol?
9. What additional danger is present in "street drugs"?
10. What effect does the regular use of caffeinated beverages have on the body? What happens to users when these beverages are not available?
11. How would you reply to individuals who want to legalize marijuana? List the reasons for your opinion.

RESEARCH

1. Contact local law-enforcement agencies and determine the costs of drug abuse in your community. Prepare a chart or graph to present your findings.
2. Draw a diagram of the body showing the areas affected by various drugs such as caffeine, alcohol, heroin, marijuana, and cocaine.
3. Write a report on the relation of AIDS to intravenous drug abuse.
4. Interview several cigarette smokers and find out how much they smoke each day, how much they spend for a pack of cigarettes, and how they feel about continuing to smoke. Prepare a chart of your findings and present an oral report.
5. Find out what medicines come from plants and how the medicines are made. Make a poster of your findings.

REVIEW

HIGHLIGHTS

1. A drug is any chemical that changes the way the body works.
2. Drugs that are medicines are designed to treat or prevent illness. Drugs that are not medicines are used simply for the effect they give.
3. People abuse drugs for many reasons. Four of the most common are peer pressure, curiosity, low self-image, and rebellion.

4. The effect a drug has on the body is determined by the dosage, body weight, physical health, and expectations.
5. Drugs either slow down the nervous system (depressants), speed up the nervous system (stimulants), or alter the way the brain works (hallucinogens).
6. Drugs are classified according to the way they affect the body. The chart on page 339 provides a summary of drugs and their classification.
7. Drugs such as marijuana and LSD alter the thinking and interpreting processes of the brain and interfere with judgment.
8. Your values are influenced by your parents, church, friends, and school.
9. In making decisions, it is best to think through what you will do before a situation happens. Asking yourself the questions listed on page 342 will help you make final decisions you will be happy with.
10. Several resources are available to help people who experiment with or abuse drugs, including family members, church youth leaders, teachers, Alateen, YMCA or YWCA, doctors, nurses, pharmacists, or other health professionals.

VOCABULARY LIST

depressant	gateway drug	immunization
drug	hallucinogen	stimulant

PRACTICE
Multiple Choice. Choose the best answer.
1. Which is not a medicine?
   a. immunization
   b. marijuana
   c. antibiotic
   d. aspirin
2. Solomon warned against which drug?
   a. LSD
   b. tobacco
   c. alcohol
   d. caffeine
3. Which of the following is important when taking medicines?
   a. read the label
   b. follow the directions
   c. both a and b
   d. neither a nor b
4. Which of the following reasons for abusing drugs is the most common reason teens try drugs?
   a. risk-taking
   b. self-image
   c. rebellion
   d. peer pressure
5. Drugs injected directly into the bloodstream cause the quickest reaction because they reach which organ first?
   a. heart
   b. lungs
   c. liver
   d. brain

6. Which is used to classify drugs?
   a. their effect on the body
   b. their relative cost
   c. their legal status
   d. their source
7. Some drugs, such as cocaine and amphetamines, can cause death by dangerously damaging which organ?
   a. stomach
   b. heart
   c. brain
   d. liver
8. Beer is classed as what type of drug?
   a. depressant
   b. hallucinogen
   c. stimulant
   d. barbiturate
9. Which helps form one's values?
   a. school
   b. church
   c. parents
   d. all of these
10. Which is considered a gateway drug?
    a. cocaine
    b. LSD
    c. heroin
    d. marijuana

Matching. Match each word with its definition or description.
1. LSD
2. morphine
3. cigarettes
4. cola drinks
5. wine
6. sleeping pills
7. marijuana
8. cocaine
9. cough syrup
10. diet pills

a. stimulant
b. depressant
c. hallucinogen

CHAPTER 19

SAFETY

INTRODUCTION

Mountain climbing is a challenge, even to experienced climbers. Scaling a sheer cliff can be scary. What if your foot slips? What if the rope breaks? What if you fall? Most mountain climbers do not take chances. They plan very carefully. Each piece of equipment, each piton, each rope is tested. The route is mapped out to the last detail. The climber's life and those of her or his climbing companions depend on careful preparation. With preparation, accidents are less likely to happen.

You may not climb mountains every week, but your need for accident prevention is just as real. Falling off a bicycle or getting hit by a car can smash you up as quickly as if you fell off a mountain. Take a clue from mountain climbers and learn about safety.

SECTION TITLES

Being careful protects this girl from injury as she climbs in Yosemite National Park.

19-1 ACCIDENTS AND FALLS

OBJECTIVES

- Identify the major causes of accidental death.
- Describe ways of preventing falls.

DID YOU KNOW?
Ninety percent of all accidents happen because of something someone did or did not do. Very few accidents occur because of equipment that does not work properly or breaks or because of natural disasters.

RESEARCH IT
What is the most common cause of accidental death of children under 10 years of age?

In recent years, the number of home and school accidents has gone up. The good news is that fewer people died from those accidents because of better trained and better organized emergency medical systems. In many areas, calling 9-1-1 is all that's needed to quickly send emergency rescue workers to the scene of an accident. Sometimes, trained personnel can give you lifesaving directions over the phone.

Still, about 100,000 people die from accidents in Canada and the United States each year. Accidents are the main cause of death in young people. For young people your age, most fatal accidents happen at home or when they ride on bicycles or in cars. At home, most accidents are caused by falls, fire, suffocation (including choking), poisoning, and guns. Most of these deaths can be prevented.

Falls can occur anywhere in your house. Most of them can be avoided by following a few precautions (fig. 19-1).

TRY THIS 19-1: Paper Accidents

Materials:
   local newspapers

Procedure:
1. Find five newspaper articles that describe accidents.
2. For each accident supply the following analysis:
   a. Describe how the accident occurred.
   b. Describe the types of injuries that resulted.
   c. Explain how you think each accident could have been prevented.

WAYS TO AVOID FALLS

1. Use a sturdy ladder. Don't climb on chairs or tables.

2. Use nonskid strips or mats in tubs and showers to prevent slipping.

3. At school, walk when in the buildings and on the sidewalks. Save your running for the playground.

4. Use caution and follow directions when playing sports or on the playground.

Fig. 19–1

REVIEW IT

1. For people your age, what is the most common type of accidents away from home?
2. What can you do at school to prevent accidents?

CLASS ACTIVITY 19–1: Mapping Accidents

Question: Where do most accidents occur at school?

Materials:
    graph paper

Procedure:
1. Draw a detailed map of your school on the graph paper. Label all rooms and areas of the school.
2. With your partner, make a list of all the accidents and injuries that have happened at school. Briefly describe each accident, the date of the accident, and where the accident occurred. Record your list in your notebook. Your teacher, school secretary, or principal may be able to help you.
3. Mark on your map where each accident occurred.
4. Complete the Data table.

Data:

DESCRIPTION	DATE	LOCATION	SERIOUSNESS	
			MINOR	SERIOUS

Questions:
1. What was the most common type of accident?
2. Which of the accidents was the most serious?
3. Where did most of the accidents occur?
4. Which accident would have been the easiest to prevent? Explain.
5. Does your school have any rules designed to reduce the chances of accidents happening at school? List some of these rules.
6. If you were asked to make your school safer, what would you do?

Conclusion: Write 3–5 sentences about what you learned from this activity.

19–2 FIRES AND SUFFOCATION

OBJECTIVES

- Describe how to prevent injuries caused by fire.
- Identify ways of preventing suffocation.

VOCABULARY
suffocate

Fires cause many home accidents. People are burned by grease, hot liquids, gasoline, paint thinner, and fireworks. Most people, however, are injured when houses burn. Most deaths from house fires are caused by smoke inhalation. But knowing a few simple precautions can help you survive a house fire. Since smoke tends to rise, breathe the air near the floor. Keep your head near the floor if you are in a burning building. If you can't get out, stay near a window and call for help. If your clothes catch on fire, **STOP, DROP, AND ROLL** (fig. 19–2). If you see someone else whose clothes are on fire, cover him or her quickly with a jacket, blanket, or towel and roll him or her on the ground. You can help reduce injuries caused by fire by following these safety practices (fig. 19–3).

Fig. 19–2 If your clothes catch on fire, STOP, DROP, and ROLL to put the flames out.

Fig. 19–3

FIRE SAFETY
1. Do not play with matches.
2. Do not use flammable liquids indoors.
3. Do not overload electrical outlets or cords.
4. Be careful around heaters, stoves, and campfires.
5. Turn handles of pans toward the center of the stove.
6. Use potholders when removing hot pans from stoves, ovens, and microwaves.
7. Have working smoke detectors on each floor of your home.
8. Know the fire-escape plan for your home and school. Take practice drills seriously.

RESEARCH IT
Find out from the local recreation department what the requirements are to become a lifeguard at a public pool.

DID YOU KNOW?
In 1736 Benjamin Franklin founded the first fire department in the U.S. in Philadelphia.

Many accidents that happen at home are a result of suffocation. When victims cannot breathe oxygen into their lungs, they **suffocate**. Choking is a common cause of suffocation. Small children may choke on small objects inhaled through the mouth into their air passages. In older children and adults, choking is usually caused by food stuck in the air passage.

People have suffocated by inhaling smoke from fires and from being trapped under a heavy object. Small children have suffocated by putting plastic bags over their heads or by being trapped inside freezers, refrigerators, or clothes dryers.

You can help reduce accidents caused by suffocation by observing a few safety measures (fig. 19–4).

Fig. 19–4

PREVENTING SUFFOCATION

1. Keep plastic bags away from small children.

2. Keep small objects away from small children.

3. Chew your food well before swallowing.

4. Avoid laughing while eating.

5. To keep children out of a broken refrigerator, dispose of it or remove the door.

6. Do not get under any heavy object unless it is well supported.

REVIEW IT

1. How does **STOP, DROP, AND ROLL** help reduce injury?
2. What is suffocation?

19–3 POISONING AND GUNS

OBJECTIVES

- Identify household poisons.
- Describe ways of preventing poisoning.
- Describe gun safety.

If someone were to ask you where you keep the poisons in your home, how would you answer? You would probably say that you don't have poisons in your home. While you may not think you have poisonous substances at home, many household products are poisonous. Cleaning liquids, gasoline, paints, paint thinners, weed killers, ant and roach sprays, and snail bait are all common poisons found in kitchens, bathrooms, basements, and garages. Even many medicines are poisonous if taken improperly. Poisonous substances may also be used in a science class at school.

Every year thousands of people are accidentally poisoned by these substances. Figure 19–5 shows a few safety precautions you can take to help prevent accidental poisoning.

Fig. 19–5

PREVENTING POISONING

1. Keep poisonous materials locked safely away.
2. Dispose of unused or outdated poisons properly.
3. Never store poisons in unmarked containers or containers that once held food or drink.
4. Teach small children never to eat or drink something without checking with an adult.
5. Do not taste unknown substances.
6. Avoid breathing toxic fumes.
7. Avoid poisonous plants and animals.
8. Know where to find the phone number of the nearest poison control center.

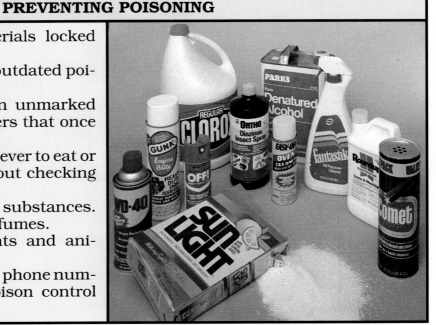

Misusing guns is another cause of accidents. People are often careless with guns. If they think a gun is not loaded, they may point it at someone for fun. When they pull the trigger, someone may get hurt or killed. When guns are not in use, they should be unloaded and stored in a locked case. GUNS ARE NOT TOYS. Never play with them under any circumstances. Figure 19–6 describes safety precautions relating to guns. Of course, the best way to avoid problems with guns is to not have any.

GUN SAFETY

1. When not in use, keep guns unloaded and locked up.

2. When carrying a gun, keep it pointed toward the ground.

3. Keep the safety on and your finger off the trigger until you are ready to shoot.

Fig. 19–6

REVIEW IT

1. Where can you find the telephone number of the nearest poison control center? What is that number?
2. What are three ways of preventing accidental poisoning at home?
3. What is the safe way to handle a loaded gun?

CLASS ACTIVITY 19–3: DANGER! POISON!

Question: What kind of poisons are kept in your home?

Materials:
   none needed

Procedure:
1. Survey your home and list all of the products that contain poisons.
2. Next to each product, list the specific poisonous ingredients.
3. For each poisonous ingredient you listed, list the antidote, if given.
4. Record whether or not each product you listed has been stored properly.
5. Complete the Data table.

Data:

PRODUCT	POISONOUS INGREDIENT	ANTIDOTE	SAFELY STORED

Questions:
1. How many poisonous products did you find? Was this more or less than you expected?
2. What types of warnings were provided on the labels of the products you listed?
3. Did any products not list antidotes for the poisons contained? Which ones?
4. Did you find any hazardous products that you didn't know existed?
5. Were poisonous products safely stored?
6. If someone were poisoned at your home, what would be the best thing for you to do?

Conclusion: Write 3–5 sentences about what you learned from this activity.

19–4 OUTDOOR SAFETY

OBJECTIVE

- Explain how to be safe when walking, bicycling, riding in motor vehicles, swimming, playing sports, or camping.

Fig. 19–7 Accidents occur when people are careless.

Each year more than ten million young people are injured as a result of accidents that happen during recreation (fig. 19–7). When you begin to play a board game, you read the rules. The rules make the game more enjoyable. In the same way, following safety rules makes many recreational activities more enjoyable. Obeying the rules reduces the risks of getting hurt. Most safety rules involve common sense and are simple to remember. The following is a list of rules for pedestrian, bicycling, motor vehicle, water, sports, and outdoor safety (fig. 19–8).

Fig. 19–8

SAFETY RULES

PEDESTRIAN SAFETY More than 6500 pedestrians are killed in the United States each year.	1. Use sidewalks and paths when possible. 2. Walk or run in the opposite direction of traffic. 3. Obey traffic signs. Cross streets only at crosswalks. 4. Wear bright or reflective clothing. 5. Avoid narrow or winding roads. 6. Anticipate what the drivers of motor vehicles may do.

Fig. 19–8 cont.

SAFETY RULES

BICYCLE SAFETY Many people are seriously injured in bicycle accidents.	1. Wear a safety helmet when riding a bicycle. 2. Make sure any bike you ride works properly and is adjusted to suit you. 3. Do not ride double. 4. Ride with the flow of traffic. Use bike lanes when available. 5. Obey traffic signs. Use hand signals when making a turn. 6. Wear bright or reflective clothing. 7. Avoid narrow and winding roads. 8. Yield the right-of-way to pedestrians.
MOTOR-VEHICLE SAFETY Wearing seat belts can prevent most serious injuries in automobile accidents.	1. **ALWAYS** wear a seat belt. 2. Keep body parts inside a moving vehicle. 3. Do not distract the driver or interfere with his or her view. 4. Lock doors when small children are passengers.

Fig. 19—8 cont.

SAFETY RULES

WATER SAFETY Drowning is the second leading cause of death in young people.	1. **LEARN TO SWIM** or wear a life jacket when near water. 2. Wear life jackets when boating. 3. Swim only in supervised areas. 4. Know the depth of water before jumping or diving. 5. Don't dive in shallow areas, near rocks or logs, or where you can't see the bottom. 6. Always leave the water during a thunderstorm. 7. Never swim alone.
SPORTS SAFETY Following rules and wearing the right equipment can reduce the number of sports injuries.	1. Wear the proper equipment. 2. Know and obey the rules of the game. 3. Exercise caution when playing. 4. Obey the instructions of coaches and teachers.

Fig. 19–8 cont.

SAFETY RULES

OUTDOOR SAFETY	
Many trips that start out fun end sadly because someone was a victim of an accident.	1. **NEVER PARTICIPATE IN OUTDOOR ACTIVITIES ALONE.** 2. Use maps and compasses when hiking, backpacking, or cross-country skiing. 3. Wear proper shoes and clothing. 4. Take along first-aid supplies, matches, and a flashlight. 5. Build campfires only in designated areas and keep them small. 6. Be sure campfires are completely out (cold to the touch) before leaving. 7. When skiing, stay on marked trails and runs.

REVIEW IT

1. What single safety practice can prevent most injuries due to auto accidents?
2. What single safety practice can prevent most drowning accidents?
3. Compare your position in traffic when you are walking to when you are riding a bicycle.

19–5 NATURAL DISASTERS

VOCABULARY
flash flood
natural disaster

OBJECTIVES

- Identify the most common natural disasters.
- Analyze appropriate safety procedures in dealing with disasters.
- Identify organizations involved in disaster relief.
- Analyze reasons for SDA involvement in disaster relief.

Natural disasters are destructive events caused by weather and movements of Earth (fig. 19–9). Satan's influence has destroyed God's perfect Earth. Disorder and chaos are common. If it were not for God's protection, many more natural disasters would occur.

You have seen the terrible results of natural disasters on TV or in newspapers. Usually you hear of disasters that happen somewhere else. But if a disaster occurred where you live, you should know ahead of time what to do.

Fig. 19–9 Flooding (left), earthquakes (top right), tornadoes (bottom right), and other natural disasters cause widespread damage.

Find out what disasters are most likely to occur where you live. Stock your home with necessary supplies (fig. 19–10). Learn about first aid. And find out about government and private organizations that can provide help.

RESEARCH IT
Which natural disasters are given the names of people? Make a chart listing the names selected for this year's storms.

Fig. 19–10 How might these items help you in a natural disaster?

No part of the world is safe from disasters. Drought and famine occur in many parts of the world. Volcanoes, earthquakes, avalanches, and forest fires create havoc where they occur. Below is a discussion of several common disasters that occur in North America. By knowing what to do, you can help your family and neighbors survive should one of these disasters strike where you live.

TRY THIS 19–5: Where Do They Occur?

Materials:
   Special Master R397

Procedure:
1. Use your library resources to determine in which states and provinces tornadoes, hurricanes, and earthquakes are common.
2. On Sheet A mark the types of natural disasters common to each state or province. Mark a "T" for the areas where tornadoes are common, a "H" where hurricanes are common, and an "E" where earthquakes are common.
   • Are any states completely safe from natural disaster? Explain.
   • Which state do you think is the safest to live in? Why?
   • Which state do you think is the most dangerous to live in? Why?
   • What natural disasters are common to the area in which you live?

EARTHQUAKES are hard to predict and difficult to plan for because they happen suddenly. The best protection for those living in earthquake areas is to plan buildings and highways to withstand earthquake shocks and to know what to do during and following an earthquake. To protect yourself from injury in an earthquake, follow the safety procedures in fig. 19–11.

Fig. 19–11

EARTHQUAKES
1. If you are outside, stay in the open.
2. If you are inside, stand in a doorway or get under a table, desk, or bed.
3. Stay away from windows, bookshelves, or anything heavy that could fall.
4. Stay inside until the shaking stops.
5. When the shaking stops, leave the building. Watch for downed wires and debris that could fall.
6. After an earthquake, **DO NOT USE ELEVATORS**.
7. Once outside, get away from the building.
8. If you are home, turn off the gas and electricity.
9. DO NOT reenter a building until it is safe to do so.

HURRICANES AND FLOODS can usually be predicted (except for flash floods). Preparing for these disasters is easier than preparing for earthquakes or tornadoes, for which there is little or no warning.

Following the safety measures in fig. 19–12 can protect your family from many injuries associated with hurricanes and floods.

Fig. 19–12

HURRICANES AND FLOODS
1. Listen to a TV or radio for information about the path of a hurricane.
2. Bring small objects such as tools, garbage cans, and bicycles indoors.
3. Protect windows by boarding them up.
4. Turn off the gas and electricity.
5. Move valuables to high ground if possible.
6. Stay inside if possible, but be ready to leave the area if advised to.
7. Avoid crossing streams more than knee deep. Don't drive on flooded roads.
8. Drink only bottled water.

TORNADOES regularly hit certain areas of Earth. The areas most often struck by tornadoes in the United States are shown in fig. 19–13. Weather observers watch tornadoes carefully. They can never tell where or when a tornado might touch down, but they can

DID YOU KNOW?
Over 700 tornadoes hit the United States each year. The worst tornado to hit the U.S. occurred in 1925 and lasted more than three hours. Nearly 700 people died as a result of this tornado. In 1981 a tornado lifted a baby in his stroller 50 feet into the air and set the stroller and the baby down 300 feet away. The baby slept through the entire ordeal.

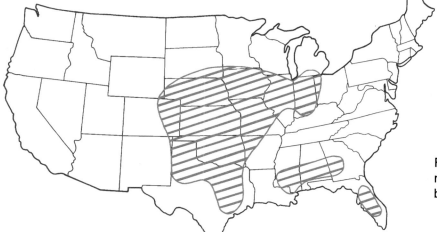

Fig. 19–13 The red shaded areas mark the regions most often struck by tornadoes.

Fig. 19–14 Tornadoes often cause massive damage.

warn people where tornadoes may form. Tornadoes are very powerful storms that affect only the area they touch. They can overturn cars, demolish houses, uproot trees, and make fences disappear (fig. 19–14). People have been killed by flying debris during a tornado. To protect yourself from injury during a tornado, obey the safety rules in fig. 19–15.

Fig. 19–15

TORNADOES
1. Go indoors and open windows.
2. Take cover in a sheltered area. Basements, storm cellars, or under staircases are usually safest.
3. Stay away from windows.
4. If you are in a car, **GET OUT** and lie face down in a low area.
5. If you must stay outside, lie face down in a low area.

SNOWSTORMS or blizzards can isolate your family. You may become stranded. If the snow is heavy, stay home and do not travel by car. There are several steps your family can take that will help you survive a severe snowstorm (fig. 19–16).

Fig. 19–16

SNOWSTORMS
1. Have an emergency supply of food.
2. Stay indoors.
3. Have a radio, flashlight, extra clothing, and blankets.
4. Have a wood, oil, or kerosene heater available.
5. If you live in an area where snowstorms occur, keep chains, a shovel, blankets, and a flashlight in your car.
6. Don't travel by car. If stranded in a car, stay inside with the engine turned off and wait for help.

THUNDERSTORMS are common in most areas of North America. Though thunderstorms are not feared as much as hurricanes or tornadoes, they kill more people each year. Most of the deaths due to thunderstorms occur when people are struck by lightning or falling objects blown by the storm's strong winds. You can protect yourself from injury during a thunderstorm by following the precautions listed in fig. 19–17.

Fig. 19–17

THUNDERSTORMS
1. If there is lightning, go indoors or get into an automobile.
2. If you must stay outside, **DON'T** stand near a tree or other solitary object. Lie face down in a low area.
3. If outdoors, **DON'T** touch metal objects during a thunderstorm.
4. **DO NOT** touch electrical wires that have fallen.

In a disaster, government leaders ask public and private organizations to help. Public agencies include local health departments and law enforcement officers, state or provincial police, and in some cases the military. Private organizations that offer aid during disasters include the Red Cross, local hospitals, and church groups.

Seventh-day Adventists have gained a reputation for helping in disasters because they plan ahead. Warehouses are filled with food and clothing ready to be shipped when needed. In some areas, vans carrying medical supplies, food, blankets, and clothing are ready to drive to disaster areas (fig. 19–18). Many Seventh-day Adventist volunteers help after disasters. Perhaps you have helped or know someone who has.

Seventh-day Adventists offer this aid to relieve suffering. Jesus taught us to help those in need. Helping others is the Golden Rule in action. You may have a Community Services Center where you live. If you do, learn what it does. Ask what you can do to help.

Fig. 19–18   Many federal, state, and community organizations provide aid to victims of natural disasters.

REVIEW IT

1. What two natural disasters pose the greatest danger in your community?
2. Which natural disasters can be most easily predicted?
3. If you are outside and can't get to a house or car, how can you protect yourself during a thunderstorm?

CHAPTER 19 WRAP-UP

SKILLS DEVELOPMENT

THINKING SKILLS: READING A DIAGRAM

Many accidents occur every day because the basic rules of safety are not followed. In this chapter you have learned many of these safety rules. Hidden in the diagram below are nine safety rules that are NOT being followed. Find the nine and explain what the students should be doing.

QUESTIONS AND PROBLEMS

1. Why do fewer people die from accidents today than in the past?
2. Describe the most serious accident you have had this year. What safety precautions could have helped to prevent it?
3. Describe, in order, the rescue procedures for someone whose clothes are on fire.
4. What danger is caused by freezers, refrigerators, and dryers?
5. What are several ways of protecting young children from accidental poisoning?
6. Explain the rule "Never go alone" and how it helps provide outdoor safety.
7. Which of the natural disasters is least likely to affect you? Why?
8. If a natural disaster struck your community, what resources are available to help the victims?
9. What could be done in your home to make it safe from accidental poisoning?
10. Why is it necessary for even good swimmers to wear life jackets when boating in rough or cold water?

RESEARCH

1. Collect information regarding accidents involving school-age children. Design a "Safety Newspaper" in which to report each accident. Include picture suggestions of how the injuries could have been prevented.
2. Discover which natural disasters are signs of Jesus' second coming. Prepare a worship talk to present your findings.
3. Investigate the history of the Red Cross and write a report.
4. Prepare a full-page newspaper advertisement for smoke detectors. Explain how they work, where to install them, their price range, and their importance in fire safety. Include pictures.
5. Make a diagram showing the fire-escape routes for your school. Include the position for each class outside the buildings. Color code escape routes and label all structures.

REVIEW

HIGHLIGHTS

1. Most accidental deaths of young people occur at home or when they are riding in motor vehicles.
2. Falls can be prevented by thinking ahead and by following the safety precautions identified on page 351.
3. Injuries caused by fire can be reduced by following the safety guidelines listed on page 353.

DGC—24

4. Following the safety suggestions listed on page 354 can help to prevent suffocation.
5. Many household products are poisonous. They should be used with caution and stored properly. Household poisons include cleaning liquids, gasoline, paints and thinners, weedkillers, and pesticides such as insect sprays and snail bait.
6. Accidental poisonings can be reduced if you follow the guidelines listed on page 355.
7. Gun safety includes keeping guns unloaded and locked up when not in use, keeping the gun holstered or pointed at the ground when you are walking, keeping the safety on and your finger off the trigger until you are ready to shoot.
8. Accidents that occur when walking, bicycling, riding in motor vehicles, swimming, playing sports, or camping can be reduced by following the safety guidelines listed in the charts on pages 358–361.
9. The most common natural disasters are earthquakes, hurricanes and floods, tornadoes, and snowstorms.
10. Safety procedures relating to each natural disaster are identified on pages 364–366.
11. Organizations involved in disaster relief include local health, fire and police departments, state or provincial police, military, Red Cross, local hospitals and churches.
12. The Seventh-day Adventist Church is involved in disaster relief to relieve suffering and to put the Golden Rule into action.

VOCABULARY LIST

flash flood	natural disaster	suffocate

PRACTICE

Multiple Choice. Choose the best answer.
1. What is the safest thing to do following an earthquake?
   a. turn off the lights   c. get under a table
   b. turn off the gas   d. leave the building
2. Which is the correct place to ride a bicycle along a road?
   a. with traffic
   b. against traffic
3. Which natural disaster occurs with little or no warning?
   a. earthquakes   c. blizzards
   b. hurricanes   d. flash floods

4. Which private organizations provide aid during a disaster?
   a. state police
   c. the military
   b. public health departments
   d. churches
5. Which are causes of home accidents?
   a. choking and suffocation
   c. falls and fires
   b. poisoning and guns
   d. all of these
6. When does suffocation occur?
   a. when food blocks the airway
   b. when exhaling too quickly
   c. when inhaling too quickly
   d. when breathing freezing air
7. In North America, which natural disaster kills the most people?
   a. tornadoes
   c. thunderstorms
   b. hurricanes
   d. earthquakes
8. What is the best way to get emergency help?
   a. dial 9–1–1
   c. call a neighbor
   b. call the police
   d. call a doctor
9. Which storm requires seeking shelter in a basement?
   a. thunderstorm
   c. tornado
   b. hurricane
   d. all of these
10. When you are riding a bicycle, to whom must you give the right of way?
    a. the biker
    c. the car
    b. the pedestrian
    d. another biker

Matching. Match the related phrases or ideas.
1. ride with traffic flow
2. point toward ground
3. wear correct equipment
4. take someone along
5. install smoke detectors
6. wear seat belts
7. dispose of properly
8. use mats in showers
9. learn to swim
10. face traffic

a. motor-vehicle safety
b. water safety
c. poison safety
d. home safety
e. sports safety
f. pedestrian safety
g. gun safety
h. bicycle safety
i. fire safety
j. outdoor safety

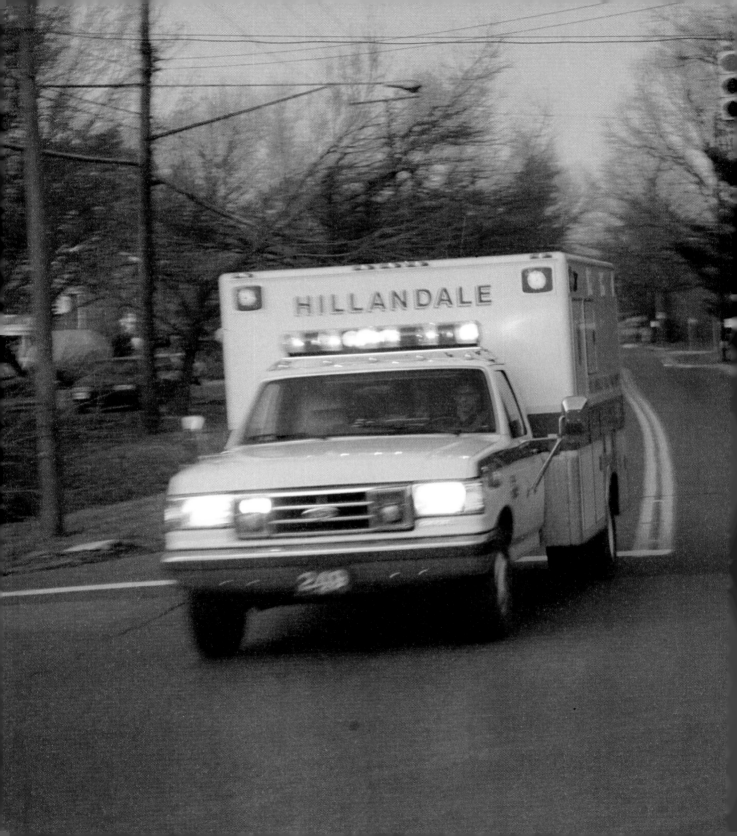

CHAPTER 20

FIRST AID

INTRODUCTION

Red light flashing, siren screaming, an emergency vehicle darts past your car. The traffic is thick, but you'd like to follow it. You know those paramedics are on their way to an accident. Just once, you would like to see what they do.

Paramedics are in the exciting business of saving lives. But someday, you, too, may be called on to save a life. Do you know how to help a person who is choking or who has stopped breathing? Can you help a small child who has swallowed poison? It may be up to you before the paramedics arrive.

SECTION TITLES

Paramedics and other emergency medical personnel save many lives.

20–1 WHAT IS FIRST AID?

VOCABULARY

artificial respiration
CPR
first aid

OBJECTIVES

- Define first aid.
- Explain why some emergency procedures should not be attempted without training.
- Identify ways of responding to medical emergencies.

Have you ever cut yourself or sprained your ankle? If you have, you or someone else probably washed the wound, applied medicine, and covered the injury with a bandage (fig. 20–1). This immediate treatment is called **first aid**. With some injuries, such as minor cuts and scrapes, the first aid you give is sufficient. Other problems, such as stopped breathing or heart attack, are more serious and require additional treatment.

Many situations, such as drowning, electric shock, or heart attack, cause a person to stop breathing. If breathing has stopped, **artificial respiration** can be used to get breathing started again. One type of artificial respiration is done mouth-to-mouth (fig. 20–2). Often, artificial respiration is used as part of cardiopulmonary resuscitation (kär dē ō pool´ mə ner ē) **(CPR)** to restore the heartbeat of

RESEARCH IT

Contact the Red Cross to find out the requirements to become certified in First Aid. Include how many hours must be spent in training.

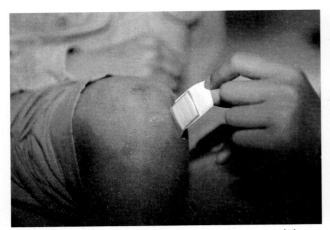

Fig. 20–1   First aid can be as simple as applying a bandage.

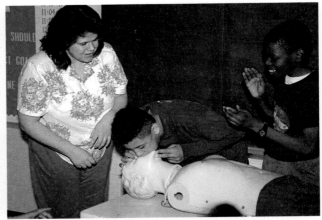

Fig. 20–2   Artificial respiration can save lives.

someone whose heart has stopped. You should not use CPR unless you have been trained because you may cause further injury to the victim by using improper procedures (fig. 20–3).

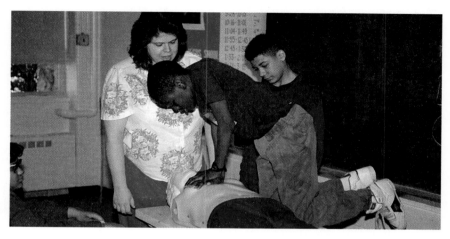

Fig. 20–3   Only people who have completed a CPR class should administer CPR.

You may know some first aid already. It is good to know what to do, or what not to do, to help an injured person. What you learn about first aid is good only if you remember and practice it. When you are older, take a class in first aid, taught by your local chapter of the Red Cross or your city recreation department (fig. 20–4). The Heart Association and local fire departments teach classes in CPR. If you learn first aid or CPR, you may be able to save a life one day. You might even save your own life.

DID YOU KNOW?
The most commonly injured part of the body is the hand. Accidents involving the hand usually result from not paying attention. The most common hand injury is getting a finger crushed in a car door.

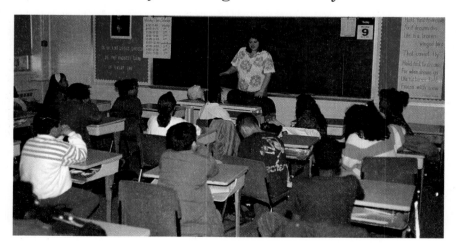

Fig. 20–4   The American Red Cross and many local agencies offer classes in first aid and CPR.

At your age, you may not know what to do in all emergencies. But there are five things you can always do, no matter what the emergency is:

1. **Stay calm.**
2. **Do not move the victim.**
3. **Try to make the victim comfortable.**
4. **Call 9–1–1 for medical help** (fig. 20–5).
5. **Encourage the victim to stay calm.**

Fig. 20–5 Dialing 9-1-1 connects you with people who can help in an emergency.

A person who knows first aid will look for several major problems. An injured person may have a broken neck or back and should not be moved. If breathing has stopped, it must be restarted. Heavy bleeding must be stopped immediately. When a person swallows poison, something must be taken to dilute the poison or to counteract it. Once these major problems have been taken care of, there is time to look for less serious injuries such as broken bones or cuts. Injured persons should be covered to keep them warm and comfortable and to prevent shock. Then call for help. If other people are present, ask them to call for help immediately.

REVIEW IT

1. What is first aid?
2. Why shouldn't you treat serious injuries or administer CPR unless you have been trained?
3. What should you do in response to any emergency?

CLASS ACTIVITY 20–1: WHATCHUGOT?

Question: What first-aid materials do you have at home?

Materials:
none needed

Procedure:
1. Make a list of all the medicines in your home that could be used in administering first aid.
2. For each item you list, briefly explain how it could be used and whether it would be used for minor or serious injuries.
3. Complete the Data table.

Data:

ITEM	DESCRIPTION OF USE	TYPE OF INJURY	
		MINOR	SERIOUS

Questions:
1. Which of the items did you not know you had at home?
2. Which items would you use for minor cuts and scrapes?
3. Which items would you use if there were serious bleeding?
4. Which items would you use if someone broke his or her wrist?
5. Which of the items do you think is the most important to have?
6. Does everyone in your family know where the first-aid supplies are kept?
7. What first-aid supplies should your family get that it doesn't currently have?

Conclusion: Write 3–5 sentences about what you learned from this activity.

20-2 GENERAL FIRST-AID PROCEDURES

VOCABULARY

direct pressure
Heimlich maneuver
poison control center
shock

OBJECTIVES

- Explain why some injuries should be treated before others.
- Describe first-aid procedures for blocked air passage, bleeding, poisoning, and shock.
- Describe the Heimlich maneuver.

Imagine that you are the first to arrive at the scene of a serious accident. What is the first thing you should do? The most important thing you should do is to determine who needs to be helped first. While many injuries are severe, the most serious are bleeding, blocked airway, shock, and poisoning. A person who has suffered any one of these four problems may die if first aid is not given immediately. This section will help you know what to do and what to avoid in each of these situations.

Fig. 20–6

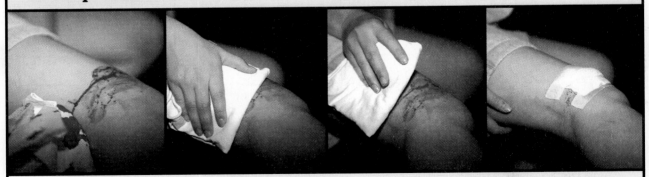

BLEEDING

A person can bleed to death in a few minutes. Serious bleeding is stopped with **direct pressure**.

1. Place a clean cloth or other piece of fabric on the wound and PRESS FIRMLY.
2. When you think the bleeding is stopped, slowly lift your hand. If bleeding starts, press on the wound again.
3. When bleeding stops, cover the wound with a clean cloth.
4. Call for help.

Fig. 20–7

BLOCKED AIR PASSAGE

Brain damage can start just two or three minutes after a person stops breathing. The **Heimlich** (hīm´ lik) **maneuver** (steps 3–8) can be used to help choking victims.

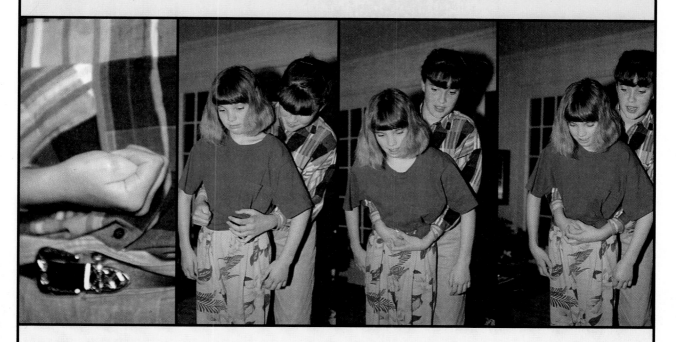

PROCEDURE:

1. Hit the person with a flat hand between the shoulder blades. A small child should be hit more softly than an adult.
2. If this does not work, use the Heimlich maneuver as described in steps 3–8.
3. Stand behind the choking victim.
4. Make a fist with one hand and wrap your other hand over your fist. Place both your hands against the person's abdomen. Make sure your thumb is touching the victim just above the navel (belly button) and below the ribs.
5. Quickly press your fist up and into the victim's abdomen. This should dislodge whatever is blocking the air passage.
6. If the person is too big, lay him down face up. Place your hands on his abdomen and quickly push up and in.
7. For babies, press the abdomen with your fingers, since too much pressure can injure the baby.
8. Repeat the process if the victim is still choking.

Fig. 20-9

SHOCK

Shock is the shutting down of the body, and it can cause death. Any person who is injured should be treated for shock.

1. Lay the person on his back.
2. Raise his legs slightly. **DON'T DO THIS IF YOU SUSPECT THERE IS NECK OR BACK INJURY**.
3. Keep the victim warm and call for help.

TRY THIS 20-2: Shock: What Do You Do?

Materials:
blanket
pillow

Procedure:
1. Imagine your partner has been in an accident. Demonstrate how you would properly treat him or her for shock.
   - Why is it important to keep a shock victim warm?
   - Should someone who is injured in an accident always be treated for shock? Explain.
   - What are the symptoms of shock?
   - Why is shock considered so serious?

Fig. 20–9

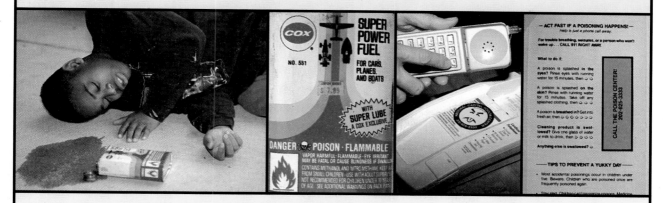

POISONING

Children are the most common victims of poisoning. If you suspect poisoning, call the **POISON CONTROL CENTER** telephone number listed in your phone book.

1. Identify the poison that has been swallowed.
2. **CALL THE POISON CONTROL CENTER** (the telephone number should be listed in your phone book). Otherwise, call **9–1–1**.
3. Follow the directions given by the emergency personnel.
4. If you are unable to get help quickly, do the following:
   a. If the person is awake, give the antidote listed on the container. If you don't know what the victim swallowed or what antidote to use, give the victim milk or water.
   b. Make the person vomit; give him warm salty water or stick your finger in his throat. (**CAUTION: NEVER MAKE THE VICTIM VOMIT HARSH CHEMICALS SUCH AS GASOLINE OR DRAIN CLEANER.**)
   c. After the person has vomited, lay him on his side or stomach so that vomited material stays out of the lungs.
   d. Get the person to a doctor.

REVIEW IT

1. Why should blocked airway and severe bleeding be treated first?
2. What do you do first for poisoning?
3. What do you do first for bleeding?

20–3 OTHER EMERGENCIES

VOCABULARY

concussion
fainting
fracture
seizure

OBJECTIVE

- Describe first-aid treatment for burns, fractures, concussion, fainting, insect bites and stings, snake-bite, seizures, and eye injury.

Blocked air passage, bleeding, poisoning, and shock are life-threatening emergencies that require immediate first aid. However, other emergencies can become serious and life threatening if first aid is not provided. These emergencies include burns, fractures, concussions (kən kush´ nz), fainting, insect bites and stings, snake-bites, seizures, and eye injuries. The pictures and procedures that follow explain what to do in these emergencies.

Fig. 20–10

BURNS

BURNS. Burns occur when the skin comes in contact with fire, hot objects, strong chemicals, or too much sunlight.

1. Keep the burn cool.
2. If the burn is small, run cool water over it. Apply a cold, wet cloth to a burn if it is large. (Use smooth cloth like a sheet. **DO NOT** use a towel or flannel cloth.)
3. If there are blisters or charred skin, cover the area with a wet cloth, and do not disturb it.
4. Call for help.

Fig. 20–11

FRACTURES, CONCUSSION, FAINTING

FRACTURES. Most bone **fractures** cannot be easily seen. But they can be identified by pain, swelling, and discoloration.

1. Keep the victim still. Motion causes pain.
2. Use a splint to hold the injury still. (Any stiff material can work.)
3. Tie the splint above and below the suspected fracture.
4. Place ice on the fracture to reduce swelling.
5. Call for help.

CONCUSSION. A **concussion** usually occurs because of a fall or a blow to the head. Concussions often cause unconsciousness. If severe, they may cause death.

1. If the person is not breathing, start artificial respiration.
2. Treat the person for shock.
3. Call for help.
4. Check the victim every 15 minutes for alertness.
5. Once the victim is stable, let him sleep, but check him every two hours for alertness.

FAINTING. Fainting occurs when there is a temporary loss of blood to the brain.

1. If a person feels faint, have him sit with his head between his knees.
2. If a person faints, elevate the legs about 6–12 inches.
3. When the person becomes alert, keep him comfortable.
4. Call for help.

Fig. 20–12

SEIZURES, EYE INJURY, INSECT BITES AND STINGS

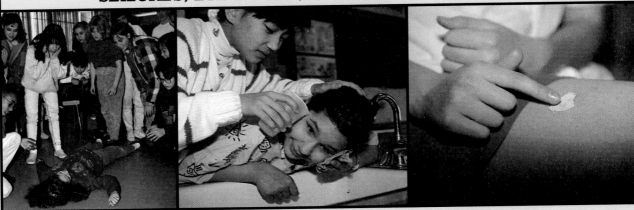

SEIZURES. Seizures occur when a person loses muscle control. Most seizures are not serious and last less than a minute.

1. Make sure the person is lying on the floor or ground.
2. Let the person move, but keep objects away from him.
3. After the seizure, turn the person on his side. This will keep the throat open should the person vomit.
4. Keep the person comfortable.

EYE INJURY. Eye injuries not treated properly may cause partial or complete blindness.

1. Rinse the eye with water, or use the corner of a clean cloth to lift an item out of the eye.
2. If a liquid splashes into the eye and stings, immediately rinse the eye with water for 10–20 minutes.
3. If the injury is severe, cover both eyes with a loose-fitting patch.
4. Any eye injury should be examined by a doctor.

INSECT BITES AND STINGS. Most insect bites and stings are not serious. Some people, however, are allergic to insects and may have a dangerous reaction.

1. Wash the area and remove the stinger if present.
2. Apply medication if available. If there is no medicine, run cold water over the affected area.
3. If the victim has an allergic reaction, get medical help.

Fig. 20–13

SNAKEBITE

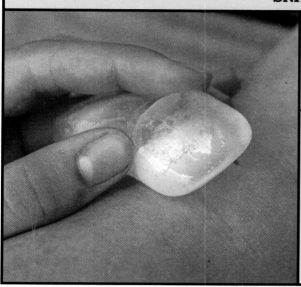

SNAKEBITE. In North America, more people die from insect bites than from snakebites.

1. Nonpoisonous snakebites should be washed and bandaged.
2. Victims of poisonous snakebites must be kept calm.
3. Keep the bitten area below the level of the heart.
4. Apply ice or cold water to the injury.
5. Get the victim to a doctor.

TRY THIS 20–3: Wrap It Up

Materials:
    cloth strips (6 cm x 60 cm) – 5
    newspapers – 2

Procedure:
1. Imagine your partner has just broken his lower right leg. Demonstrate what first aid you should administer.
    • What is the purpose of a splint?
    • What danger could result if the splint is secured too tightly? If it is not secured tightly enough?
    • What other material is available at school that could be used to splint a fracture?
    • What other material is available at home that could be used to splint a fracture?
    • Is the fracture the only condition that should be treated? Explain.

REVIEW IT

1. What can cause burns?
2. What is the most important first aid for a broken bone?
3. What injury can be caused by a blow to the head?
4. What is the most important action when someone has a seizure?
5. What should be done for eye injuries?

RESEARCH IT
List the four North American animals that are most responsible for poisonous bites.

20–4 FIRST AID FOR HEAT AND COLD

VOCABULARY

frostbite
heat exhaustion
heatstroke
hypothermia

DID YOU KNOW?

Because most ultraviolet rays pass through the clouds, you can get a serious sunburn on a cloudy day.

OBJECTIVE

- Describe first-aid procedures for the effects of extreme temperature.

Have you ever been playing outside on a hot summer day and felt yourself become nauseated (nô´ shē āt id)? If this has happened to you, it could have been a warning sign of heat exhaustion. Heat exhaustion and heatstroke are two emergencies that may develop if people get too hot. Hypothermia and frostbite are two emergencies that can occur if people get too cold. Look at the pictures below and read the first-aid procedures to discover how to help someone suffering from one of these problems.

Fig. 20–14

SUNBURN

SUNBURN. Each year many people spend too much time out in the sunshine and get sunburn. Besides being painful, sunburn can lead to skin cancer.

1. Cool the area with a wet cloth.
2. Use a first-aid cream or spray designed to relieve the pain of sunburn.
3. If blisters form, a doctor should examine the sunburn.

Fig. 20–15

HEATSTROKE AND HEAT EXHAUSTION, HYPOTHERMIA, FROSTBITE

HEATSTROKE AND HEAT EXHAUSTION. Heatstroke causes the body to lose its ability to cool itself. **Heat exhaustion** causes the victim to feel faint and nauseated.

1. Move the victim to a cool area.
2. Lay the person down and raise his or her legs and head.
3. Remove extra clothing.
4. Rinse the person with cool water.
5. Get medical help.

HYPOTHERMIA. Hypothermia occurs when the body gets too cold and cannot maintain normal body temperature. Death may result if hypothermia is not treated.

1. Do not put the person in a hot shower or bath.
2. Replace wet clothes with dry ones or blankets.
3. Give the person warm, not hot, liquids to drink.
4. If you can't go indoors, put the victim in a sleeping bag or wrap him in a blanket or coat.

FROSTBITE. Frostbite occurs when areas of skin freeze.

1. Get the victim out of the cold.
2. Gently warm the affected area. **CAUTION:** Do not massage the injured area or use hot water to warm the area.
3. Get medical help.

REVIEW IT

1. How is heatstroke different from heat exhaustion?
2. What is the most important action when treating a victim of hypothermia?
3. What is frostbite?

CHAPTER 20 WRAP-UP
SKILLS DEVELOPMENT

THINKING SKILLS – SEQUENCING

It is important to properly sequence the steps in lifesaving techniques. If one step happens to be left out or placed in the wrong sequence, it could result in a more serious injury or even death. The following are first-aid procedures, but the sequencing of the steps is not correct. Number each set of steps in the proper order.

1. Blocked Air Passage

    ____ Quickly press your fist up and into the victim's abdomen.

    ____ Stand behind the choking victim.

    ____ Make a fist with one hand.

    ____ Hit the person with a flat hand between the shoulders.

    ____ Wrap your other hand over the fist.

2. Fractures

    ____ Place ice on the fracture to reduce swelling.

    ____ Tie the splint above and below the suspected fracture.

    ____ Keep the victim still.

    ____ Use a splint to hold the injury still.

3. Concussion

    ____ Check the victim every 15 minutes for alertness.

    ____ If breathing has stopped, begin artificial respiration.

    ____ When stable, let the victim sleep, but check every two hours.

    ____ Treat the person for shock.

    ____ Call for help.

4. Seizures

    ____ Keep the person comfortable.

    ____ After the seizure, turn the person on his side.

    ____ Let the person move, but keep objects away from him.

    ____ Make sure the person is lying on the floor or ground.

QUESTIONS AND PROBLEMS
1. What kind of work do emergency paramedics do?
2. Is first aid the only treatment necessary for injuries? Explain.
3. What organizations offer classes in first aid?
4. If an accident victim has several injuries, what should you do?
5. How does the Heimlich maneuver differ for adults and small children? Why?
6. What long-range danger is associated with sunburn and tanning?
7. Why shouldn't towels or flannel fabric be used to cover a burn?
8. Why should a concussion victim be checked every two hours while sleeping?
9. Explain why more people in North America die from beestings than snake-bites.
10. Why shouldn't hot water be used to treat frostbite?

RESEARCH
1. Construct a poster or bulletin-board display on any one of the following injuries: burns, fractures, or insect bites. Discuss the types of each specific injury and the appropriate treatment. Include pictures.
2. Identify several common household poisons. Discuss several ways of preventing poisoning with these chemicals and discuss first-aid treatment. Present an oral report that includes visual aids.
3. Report on community organizations that offer first-aid training. List when, where, and how long the classes are, and the fees charged.
4. Make a collection of newspaper and magazine articles concerning individuals who performed necessary first aid on accident victims. Present your findings.
5. Visit a local ambulance company. Interview a paramedic and find out the information below:
   a. The training required to become a paramedic.
   b. The most common types of medical emergencies he or she responds to.
   c. The rewards of being a paramedic.

REVIEW

HIGHLIGHTS
1. First aid is the immediate treatment given to an injured person.
2. Some emergency procedures, such as artificial respiration and CPR, require special training to prevent additional injury to the victim as a result of first-aid treatment.
3. In any medical emergency, you can help by doing the following: stay calm, do not move the victim, make the victim comfortable, call 9–1–1, and encourage the victim to stay calm.

4. Blocked airway, bleeding, poisoning, and shock are all conditions that may result in death if first-aid treatment is not given immediately. For this reason, these conditions should always be treated first.
5. First-aid procedures for bleeding, blocked airway, shock, and poisoning are identified on pages 378–381.
6. The Heimlich maneuver can be used to help people who are choking. This procedure is described on page 379.
7. First-aid treatment of burns, fractures, concussions, fainting, insect bites and stings, snakebites, seizures, and eye injuries are identified on pages 382–385.
8. First-aid procedures for the effects of extreme temperature are listed on page 386, 387.

VOCABULARY LIST

artificial respiration	first aid	Heimlich maneuver
concussion	fracture	hypothermia
CPR	frostbite	poison control center
direct pressure	heat exhaustion	seizure
fainting	heatstroke	shock

PRACTICE

Multiple Choice. Choose the best answer.

1. What is the main business of a paramedic?
   a. making medicine
   b. running pharmacies
   c. saving lives
   d. running hospitals
2. Which is not an example of first aid?
   a. taking an X-ray
   b. bandaging an injury
   c. washing a wound
   d. applying medicine
3. Which procedure should be used on someone who is not breathing?
   a. apply direct pressure
   b. artificial respiration
   c. keep him warm and comfortable
   d. apply a splint
4. Which is most important to do for any injury victim?
   a. raise the victim's legs
   b. keep the victim calm
   c. move the victim to a safe place
   d. give the victim food to eat
5. What is the first thing that should be done at a serious accident?
   a. send for help
   b. call 9–1–1
   c. move the victim
   d. determine the type of injuries
6. How quickly can brain damage occur after someone has stopped breathing?
   a. 2–3 minutes
   b. 20–30 minutes
   c. 10–15 seconds
   d. 2–3 hours

7. What type of people are helped by the Heimlich maneuver?
   a. AIDS patients
   b. burn victims
   c. choking victims
   d. heatstroke victims
8. Which procedure should be performed first for a victim of serious bleeding?
   a. CPR
   b. apply direct pressure
   c. apply a tourniquet
   d. clean the wound
9. In case of accidental poisoning, what should be done first?
   a. give the antidote
   b. call the police
   c. call a doctor
   d. call the poison control center
10. Which is not usually true of fractures?
   a. they can be easily seen
   b. they often swell
   c. they are painful
   d. they often have discoloration

Matching. Match each word with its definition or description.
1. makes the body unable to cool itself
2. caused by too little blood to the brain
3. used to help choking victims
4. occurs when the body gets too cold
5. causes the body systems to shut down
6. can lead to skin cancer
7. may be caused by a blow to the head
8. immediate treatment of injuries
9. provides first-aid classes to the public
10. causes nausea and fainting

a. fainting
b. concussion
c. shock
d. Heimlich maneuver
e. first aid
f. Red Cross
g. hypothermia
h. sunburn
i. heatstroke
j. heat exhaustion

CAREERS

Dietitian

Description of Work
Dietitians help individuals and families choose foods that benefit health. They also supervise the preparation and service of food to groups, develop special diets, participate in research, and supervise the nutritional aspects of health care.

Personal Qualifications
Dietitians must be tactful and analytical. They must also have good health and good organizational skills and be able to supervise people.

Requirements
High-school diploma plus four years of college.

Career Information
The American Dietetic Assn.
216 W. Jackson Blvd.
Chicago, IL 60606–6995

Registered Record Administrator (RRA)

Description of Work
Registered Record Administrators manage medical information systems. They develop and maintain manual and computerized record-keeping systems. RRAs develop department policies and budgets, and evaluate employee performance.

Personal Qualifications
RRAs must be honest, sensitive to others, and good communicators and motivators. They must be able to plan, organize, and use good judgment.

Requirements
A high-school diploma plus four years of college.

Career Information
American Medical Record Assn.
875 N. Michigan Ave.
Chicago, IL 60611

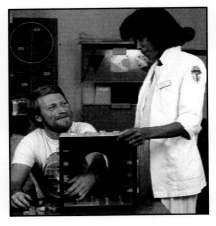

Occupational Therapist

Description of Work
Occupational therapists help people whose lives have been disrupted by injury, illness, or other problems. Through the use of various activities, they help patients become self-reliant and enjoy a balanced lifestyle.

Personal Qualifications
Occupational therapists must have a knowledge of science and how people behave. They need to be good problem solvers, tactful, resourceful, and have a desire to help others.

Requirements
A high-school diploma plus four years of college.

Career Information
American Occupational Therapy Assn.
P.O. Box 1725
Rockville, MD 20800–4375

Safety Engineer

Description of Work
Safety engineers study materials, standards, processes, and laws on health and safety. They inspect to see that buildings are constructed and equipped safely. Safety engineers work to protect workers and conduct classes in safety and first aid. They also study accidents to learn their cause and how to keep them from recurring.

Personal Qualifications
Safety engineers must be able to apply engineering principles. They need to be organized and able to communicate well.

Requirements
A high-school diploma and a college degree or completion of an approved program in occupational and industrial safety.

Career Information
American Society of Safety Engineers
1800 E. Oakton St.
Des Plaines, IL 60018

Emergency Medical Technician (EMT)

Description of Work
EMTs are often the first to treat people in medical emergencies. They must determine the patient's illness or injury and decide on what first aid to give. At the hospital the EMT reports to the hospital emergency staff.

Personal Qualifications
EMTs must have good health, eyesight, and coordination. They must be able to lift at least 100 lbs. EMTs must use good judgment, have leadership ability, and have a pleasant personality.

Requirements
A high-school diploma and the completion of an approved program in emergency medical care.

Career Information
National Assn. of Emergency Medical Technicians
9140 Ward Parkway
Kansas City, MO 64114

Pharmacist

Description of Work
Pharmacists advise people on the selection and use of medicines. They dispense medicines prescribed by doctors. Pharmacists must understand drugs and their effects. In small pharmacies, pharmacists often buy and sell items other than drugs and oversee the operation of the pharmacy.

Personal Qualifications
Pharmacists must be intelligent, accurate, and aware of details. They must also be able to communicate well and be well organized.

Requirements
A high-school diploma and a college degree or training to qualify for a state license.

Career Information
American Assn. of Colleges of Pharmacy
1426 Prince St.
Alexandria, VA 22314

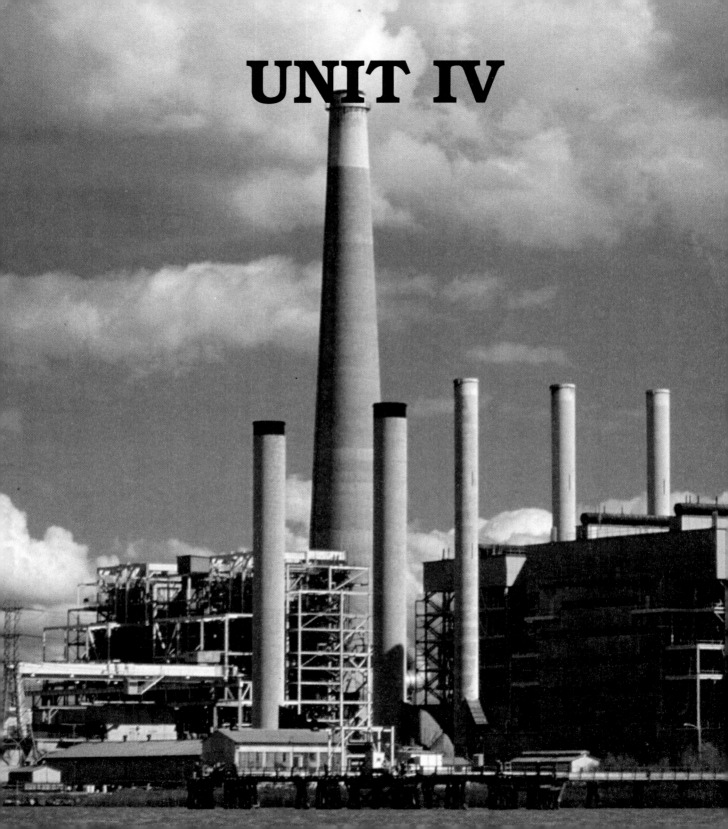

UNIT IV

ELECTRICITY AND MAGNETISM

INTRODUCTION

Take a look around your home and see how many things are plugged into electrical outlets. Most of the appliances we rely on to help with everyday tasks require electrical power. A power plant, such as the one in the picture, supplies all the electrical power needed to light up our homes and run our household appliances.

We need different kinds of power to function as human beings. God is the power supply for all our spiritual needs. Second Timothy 1:7 says, "God hath not given us the spirit of fear; but of power." Just as we can turn on the power from the power plant and light up our homes, we can turn on the power of God to light up our lives. When we need strength and wisdom, we should remember that God's power is available to us. As Paul says in Philippians 4:13, "I can do all things through Christ which strengtheneth me." Let's turn on the Power!

CHAPTER TITLES

Large electrical generating plants such as this produce the electricity we depend on.

CHAPTER 21

EXPLORING ELECTRICITY

INTRODUCTION

When we think of electricity, we usually think of current electricity, the kind that has to do with wires and plugs, light bulbs and power plants, circuits and batteries. But there is another kind of electricity that does not depend on any of these things. It makes your hair stand up, your clothes cling, and gives you a shock when you touch something on a dry, windy day. It also causes lightning. It's called static electricity.

In this chapter we will explore both types of electricity.

SECTION TITLES

Van de Graaff generators, like this one at the Ontario Science Center, Ontario, Canada, produce static electricity.

21-1 STATIC ELECTRICITY

VOCABULARY

electron
electroscope
lightning
neutron
proton
static charge
static discharge

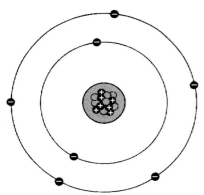

Fig. 21-1 Atoms are made up of a nucleus containing protons and neutrons and of electrons that whirl around the nucleus.

OBJECTIVES

- Identify the cause of the electrical force.
- Describe ways static charge is produced.
- Explain how an electroscope measures static electricity.
- Describe the interaction of charged objects.

Before we can understand static electricity, we must first understand something about atoms. An atom is made up of three kinds of tiny particles called protons, electrons, and neutrons (fig. 21–1). Protons and electrons each have one unit of charge. The charge on these little particles is similar to the charge on a flashlight battery, only much weaker (fig. 21–2). The **proton** has a positive charge (+), and the **electron** has a negative charge (–). The **neutron** is neutral and has no charge.

The charges of the protons and electrons that make up an atom can be likened to the opposing players in a soccer game (fig. 21–3). When you play soccer, both teams need the same number of players. For every player on Team A there is a player on Team B. Each player tries to cancel the effort of the other team's players. If a team member is missing, the other team has an advantage.

Fig. 21-2 A battery has both a positive and a negative charge.

Fig. 21-3 The charged particles in an atom cancel each other out, just as players on one team cancel out the effort of the players on the other team.

Just as opposing players in a soccer game try to cancel out each other's plays, protons and electrons cancel out each other's charge when there are the same number of protons and electrons.

Protons and neutrons are tightly packed together in the center, or nucleus, of the atom. Electrons whirl around the nucleus as shown in fig. 21–1. When an atom has the same number of electrons whirling around its nucleus as it has protons in its nucleus, the atom is neutral. The positive charges of the atom's protons cancel the negative charges of the electrons.

Electrons sometimes move from one atom to another, creating an electrical force. When an atom picks up an extra electron, that atom becomes negatively charged because it has one more electron than it has protons (fig. 21–4). The atom that lost the electron becomes positively charged because it has one more proton than it has electrons. Therefore, as electrons move from one atom to another, both atoms become electrically charged.

DID YOU KNOW?
On a dry, windy day, you can produce a static discharge of about three or four thousand volts by scuffing across a carpet or by pulling off a sweater over your head.

Fig. 21–4 Atoms become electrically charged when they gain or lose electrons.

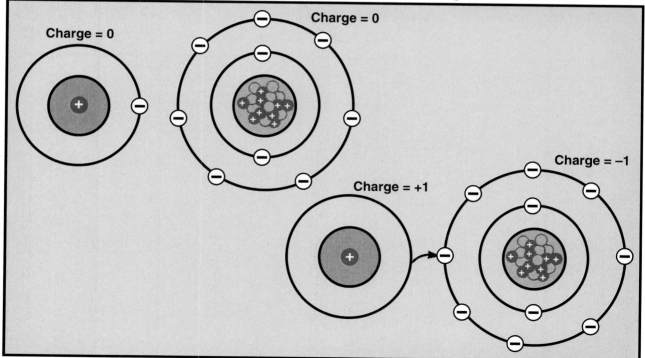

The same thing can happen to you when you walk across a carpet on a cold day. You become charged because electrons move from the atoms of the carpet to you. The extra electrons give you a **static charge**. When you touch someone who has no charge, the extra electrons jump from you to them (fig. 21–5). This sudden flow of electrons causes a shock called a **static discharge**. After the discharge, you become neutral again. The greater the static charge, the stronger the discharge or shock.

In fig. 21–6, the cloud has more electrons than the ground and is statically charged. When the difference is large enough, an electrical discharge occurs between the cloud and ground, causing **lightning**. Lightning may also occur between two differently charged clouds.

An object with a positive charge and an object with a negative charge attract each other. Sometimes when you comb your hair, electrons move from your hair to the comb. The comb then has a negative charge, and your hair has a positive charge. The negative comb and the positive hair attract each other. This causes the hair to stand out toward the comb.

Fig. 21–5 On a dry, windy day you can create an electric discharge (a shock) by touching something or someone else.

Fig. 21–6 When the difference between the electrical charge in a cloud and the charge in the ground becomes great enough, lightning occurs.

DID YOU KNOW?
A lightning bolt lasts less than 1/10,000th of a second. In this short time, a bolt may produce 15 million volts of electricity and may heat up to 28,000° C (50,000° F).

Positive and negative attraction can also be seen when clothes are dried in a dryer. Some clothes become positively charged, while others become negatively charged. This is why clothes from a dryer often stick together (fig. 21–7).

A statically charged object also attracts an uncharged object. For example, rubbing a balloon on a sweater creates a static charge in the balloon and the sweater. When the negatively charged balloon is placed near an uncharged wall, the balloon sticks to the wall. When the balloon loses its charge, it falls from the wall.

These examples demonstrate that unlike charges attract. The following example shows that like charges repel (fig. 21–8).

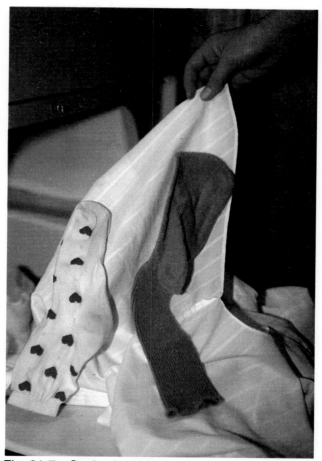

Fig. 21-7 Static electricity is what causes clothes to "stick" together when they are taken out of a clothes dryer.

STATIC CHARGES	
Like Charges	Repel
Opposite Charges	Attract
Charged Objects	Attract neutral objects

Fig. 21–8

RESEARCH IT
Report on Benjamin Franklin's contribution to the knowledge of static electricity.

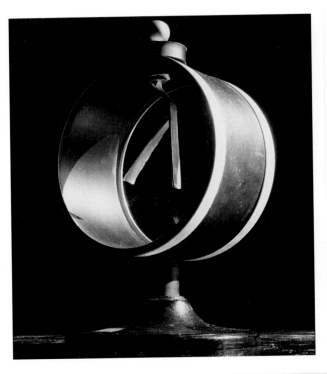

Scientists use an **electroscope** to detect static charges (fig. 21–9). When no charge is present, the two strips of metal hang parallel. But when a charged object touches the ball on top of the electroscope, both strips get the same charge, and the strips spread apart. This happens because objects with the same charge repel.

The picture on page 396 shows a girl with her hair standing straight out. How is her hair like the metal strips in an electroscope?

Fig. 21–9   The metal strips of an electroscope detect static electricity.

TRY THIS 21–1: Salt and Pepper

Materials:
- bond paper
- pepper
- salt

test materials: comb, eraser, pencil, plastic bag, plastic cup, plastic pen, toothpick, water.

Procedure:
1. Mix the salt and pepper together on a sheet of paper.
2. Try to separate the salt and pepper using the test materials listed above.
   - What method did you use to separate the salt and pepper?
   - Why?

REVIEW IT

1. What is an electron?
2. What happens when electrons move from one atom to another?
3. What does an electroscope do?
4. What happens when a positively charged object comes close to a negatively charged object?

21-2 CURRENT ELECTRICITY

OBJECTIVES

- Describe electric current.
- Distinguish between alternating and direct current.

VOCABULARY
alternating current
current
direct current

When you turn on the light switch in your home, moving electrons create the electricity, to light the bulb (fig. 21-10). Unlike a discharge of static electricity, which moves in bursts, these electrons move in a constant stream. The constant flow of electrons is called **current**. When the light switch is on, the light stays on because a current keeps flowing through the light. When you turn off the swiitch, the light goes off because the connection is broken, and the electrical current is stopped.

Fig. 21–10 Turning on a light switch allows electricity to flow to a light bulb and produce light.

Electric current can be direct or alternating (fig. 21–11). Current from batteries is **direct current** (DC) and flows in only one direction from the battery through the wires. **Alternating current** (AC) occurs when the electrons move first in one direction, then stop and go the other direction. The current changes direction so quickly that you do not notice it.

The electricity in your home is alternating current. Power plants generate AC current because it can be sent over power lines more easily. It flows each way 60 times per second in the lines that run from the power plant to your home. If it did not change directions so quickly, your lights would flicker or flash.

DID YOU KNOW?

AC current changes directions 120 times per second, too fast to be seen.

Fig. 21–11   Direct current (A) moves in only one direction. Alternating current (B) moves back and forth.

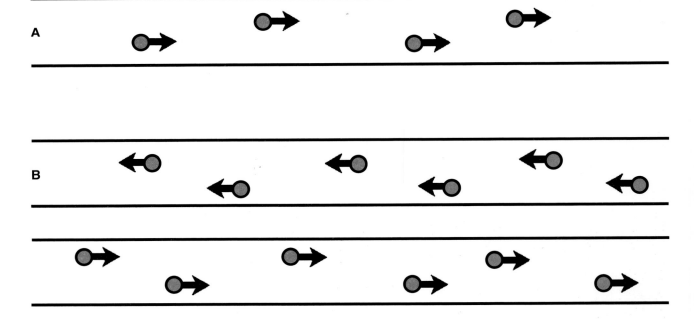

REVIEW IT

1. Why does an electric light go off when the switch is turned off?
2. How is alternating current different from direct current?

21–3 CONDUCTORS AND INSULATORS

OBJECTIVES

- Distinguish between insulators and conductors.
- Explain the effect of resistance on current.

VOCABULARY
conductor
insulator
ohm
resistance

Electrons, which make up electric current, flow easily through metals. A substance through which electrons flow easily is called a **conductor**. Silver and gold are two of the best conductors, but are too expensive to use for ordinary electrical wire. The wire in most homes is copper because it costs less and works well.

Although conductors let electrons move through them, they also resist the flow of electrons. This **resistance** is measured in units called **ohms** (ōmz). Good conductors, such as gold or copper, have little resistance. Iron has more resistance than gold or copper and is not as good a conductor.

Resistance to the flow of electrons creates heat. In some cases this heat is useful. Special wires are used to produce heat for electric heaters, stoves, and toasters (fig. 21–12). Light bulbs have very thin wires that create so much resistance that light is produced.

DID YOU KNOW?
Plastic can be made to conduct electricity.

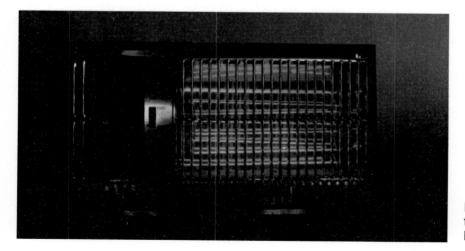

Fig. 21–12   A wire's resistance to the flow of electricity creates heat.

TRY THIS 21–3: Insulators/Conductors

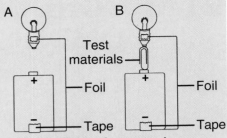

Materials:
>   aluminum foil
>   D-cell
>   flashlight bulb
>   transparent tape

test materials: foil, glass, paper, paper clip, penny, rubber band, styrofoam.

Procedure:
1. Using tape, connect a piece of aluminum foil to the D-cell and bulb as shown in A.
2. Touch the base of the bulb to the positive (+) end of the D-cell.
   - What happens?
   - Why?
3. Place the test materials between the bulb and the D-cell (as shown in B) to discover which are insulators and which are conductors. Make a table that displays your results.

Fig. 21–13 The heat created by overloading extension cords or wall sockets can cause fires.

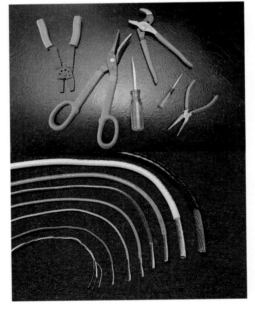

Fig. 21–14 Insulation on tools and electrical wires prevents electric shock.

Resistance can also be dangerous. Extension cords, when improperly used, may become so hot that they start a fire (fig. 21–13).

Some materials, called **insulators**, do not let electrons flow through them. Rubber, ceramic, glass, and plastic are good insulators. Electrical wire and many tools are insulated with one of these materials to protect people from electrical shock (fig. 21–14).

REVIEW IT

1. Why is electrical wiring wrapped in plastic?
2. Why do some wires get warm when electricity moves through them?

21–4 VOLTAGE AND AMPERAGE

OBJECTIVE

- Distinguish between voltage and amperage.

An electric current flows through a wire the way water flows through a pipe (fig. 21–15). Water must be pushed through a pipe, usually by a pump. In a similar way, electrons must be pushed along a wire to make an electric current. The pressure, or push, on electrons may come from a battery or from a generator. The strength of the push is called **voltage** and is measured in units called **volts**. The voltage of an electric current tells how much pressure is pushing the current along the wire. The greater the voltage, the greater the push on the electrons.

Fig. 21–15 The movement of water through a pipe demonstrates how electricity moves through wire.

407

Another measure of electricity is amperage. **Amperage** measures how many electrons per second are moving through a wire. Amperage is affected by two factors, voltage and the size of the wire (fig. 21–16). When the voltage is greater, the amperage is usually greater. The size of wire is the second factor that affects amperage. Just as more water can move through a large pipe, so more electric current can flow through a large wire than through a small wire because a smaller wire has a greater resistance to the flow of electricity.

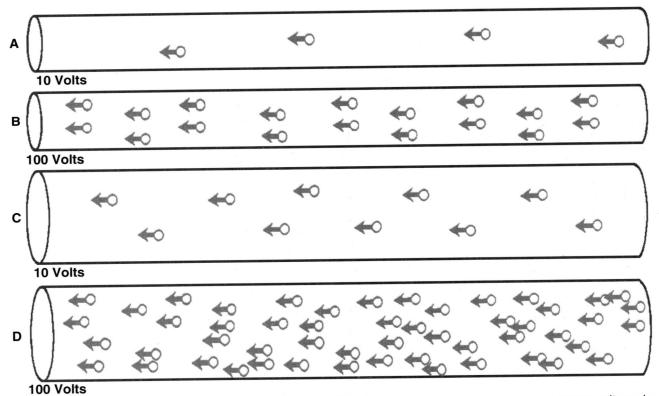

Fig. 21–16 Wire size and voltage affect amperage. Wire B has more amperage because more voltage is passing through wire B than wire A. Wire C has more amperage than wire A because it is larger. Wire D has the most amperage because it is the largest wire and has the highest voltage.

RESEARCH IT

Write a biographical report on one of these people: Oersted, Ampère, Faraday, Tesla, Edison, Volta.

REVIEW IT

1. What is voltage?
2. What factors affect amperage?

21–5 CELLS AND BATTERIES

OBJECTIVES

- Distinguish between electrical cells and batteries.
- Distinguish between dry and wet electrical cells.
- Compare and contrast rechargeable and non-rechargeable dry cells.

VOCABULARY
battery
dry cell
electrical cell
rechargeable cell
wet cell

The items in fig. 21–17 produce electricity and are called **electrical cells**. When several of these cells are connected, they make a **battery**, such as the 9-volt battery used in radios and toys (fig. 21–18).

RESEARCH IT
Research the use of solar cells in homes, industry, space.

Fig. 21–17   Electrical cells come in many sizes.

Fig. 21–18   A battery, such as this 9-volt battery, is made up of several electrical cells.

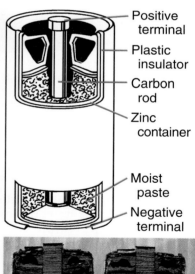

Positive terminal

Plastic insulator

Carbon rod

Zinc container

Moist paste

Negative terminal

A zinc case with a pencil-sized carbon rod in the center (fig. 21–19) is a **dry cell**. Dry cells really aren't dry but contain a moist chemical paste that surrounds the rod. The paste makes electrons move from the carbon rod to the zinc case. When a dry cell is connected to a circuit, the electrons flow out of the dry cell in a steady current.

Fig. 21–19   The inside of a dry cell.

409

DID YOU KNOW?
Some of the early automobiles were electric powered and ran by using batteries.

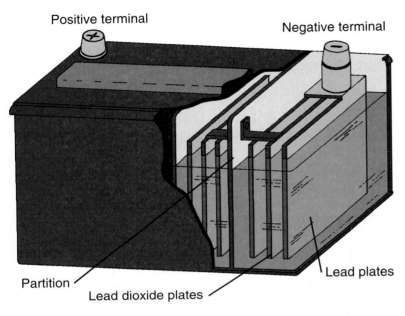

Positive terminal

Negative terminal

Partition

Lead dioxide plates

Lead plates

Fig. 21–20   In a car battery and other wet cells, metal plates are surrounded by an acid.

Most dry cells have the same voltage (1.5 volts) regardless of their size. Larger dry cells work longer than smaller dry cells but do not have a greater voltage. When the chemical paste stops reacting, the electrons quit moving, and the dry cell has no voltage.

A cell containing liquid acid is a **wet cell**. A 12-volt car battery is made of six 2-volt wet cells. This type of battery has metal plates hanging in sulfuric acid (fig. 21–20). As the plates react chemically with the acid, electrons move out of the battery in a constant current of electricity. Eventually, wet cells quit working because the chemicals are exhausted and stop reacting. When this happens, the battery needs to be recharged or replaced.

MINIBIOGRAPHYMINIBIOGRAPHYMINIBIOGRAPHYMINIBIOGRAPHYMINIBIOGRAPHY

ALESSANDRO VOLTA

My name is Alessandro. My friend Luigi was dissecting a frog. He found that he could cause the muscles in a frog's leg to twitch when his steel scalpel simultaneously touched a muscle in the leg and a brass hook holding the frog.

At first I did not believe what was happening. But by experimenting I learned that zinc and silver produced the greatest movement in the frog. Another time I touched two metal strips to my tongue, expecting my tongue to move. It didn't, but I tasted a very sour taste. I decided that moisture on my tongue helped with this electric current.

Next, I soaked some cardboard in brine and placed it between the two different kinds of metal strips. It produced electricity! Then I found that I could produce even more electricity with a stack of metal pieces with the cardboard in between. This has come to be called the Voltaic pile (the world's first battery).

MINIBIOGRAPHYMINIBIOGRAPHYMINIBIOGRAPHYMINIBIOGRAPHYMINIBIOGRAPHY

Most wet and dry cells can be recharged by running electric current through them. Car batteries are recharged by connecting them to an automotive battery charger (fig. 21–21).

You may have recharged dry cells with a household battery charger (fig. 21–22). This type of battery charger works only with rechargeable dry cells. **Rechargeable cells** are usually made from nickel and cadmium instead of zinc and can be recharged 500 or more times. **DO NOT** recharge dry cells unless they are labeled rechargeable. They may explode.

Fig. 21–21   Car batteries are designed to be recharged.

Fig. 21–22   Some dry cells are designed to be "rechargeable."

REVIEW IT

1. What is the relationship between an electrical cell and a battery?
2. What are the differences between dry and wet cells?

21–6 CIRCUITS

circuit
circuit breaker
fuse
parallel circuit
series circuit

OBJECTIVES

- Define a circuit.
- Distinguish between series and parallel circuits.
- Explain the purpose of fuses and circuit breakers.

Figure 21–23 shows a water fountain. The water sprays out of the fountain, into the pool, and through the pump, ready to be sprayed again. Just as the water in the fountain flows through a certain pathway, electricity must flow through a pathway called a **circuit**. A circuit must have three parts: a source that pushes the electrons, a device for the electrons to flow through, and a conductor that carries the electrons from the source to the device.

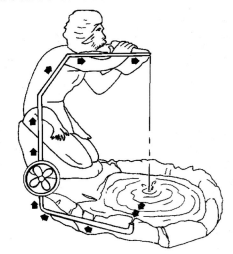

Fig. 21–23 The movement of water through a fountain demonstrates how electricity moves through an electrical circuit.

The dry cell (fig. 21–24) is the source of the push, and the light bulb is the device. The wire acts as the conductor to carry the current. Notice that a circuit makes a complete path. The electricity must be able to move through the entire circuit and back to the dry cell. If the path is broken, the electrons cannot flow through the circuit.

Fig. 21–24 Every circuit must have a source (the battery), a conductor (the wire), and a device (the light bulb).

There are two kinds of circuits: series circuits and parallel circuits. A **series circuit** has only one path for the current to flow through (fig. 21–25). If there is a break in a series circuit, the current stops. A flashlight is a good example of a series circuit. If the light bulb burns out or the dry cell quits, the flashlight stops working because the circuit is not complete.

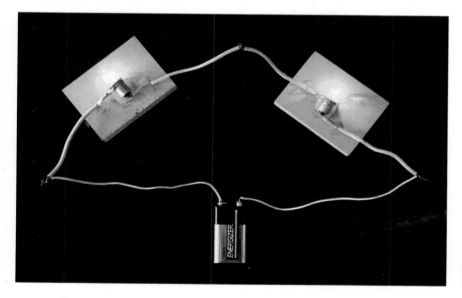

Fig. 21–25 In a series circuit, electricity has only one path to follow.

The second type of circuit, a **parallel circuit**, has more than one path that the current can follow. Look at Fig. 21–26. What will happen if you remove one of the bulbs?

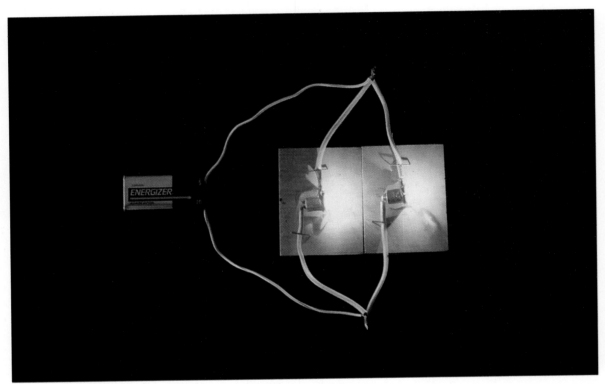

Fig. 21–26 In a parallel circuit, electricity has more than one path to follow.

A series circuit permits you to control several lights or appliances with one switch. Both a bathroom light and fan can be turned on with one switch if they are connected by a series circuit. A series circuit may also be used to turn on several outside lights at the same time.

However, if all the appliances in your house were on a series circuit, one switch would control everything. If you turned on the TV, you would also turn on the microwave, electric range, radio, and all the lights. When you turned off the TV, everything else would go off, including your refrigerator. A parallel circuit allows you to turn one item at a time on or off. What type of circuit is most common in your house? Can you find examples of both types of circuits?

TRY THIS 21–6: Making Circuits

Materials:
>   aluminum foil
>   bell wire (30 cm) – 2
>   D-cell
>   flashlight bulbs – 2

Procedure:
1. Set up the apparatus as shown in A.
2. Touch the wire from bulb 1 to the top of the D-cell. Touch the wire from bulb 2 to the base of bulb 1. Now touch the base of bulb 2 to the foil as shown in B.
   • What happens?
3. Remove the wire from the base of bulb 1.
   • What happens?
4. Reconnect bulb 1 and lift bulb 2 from the foil.
   • What happens?
   • Is this a series or parallel circuit? Why?
5. Set up apparatus as shown in C.
   • What happens?
6. Disconnect bulb 1.
   • What happens?
7. Reconnect bulb 1 and lift bulb 2 from the foil.
   • What happens?
   • Is this a series or parallel circuit? Why?
   • What are some differences between the series and parallel circuits?

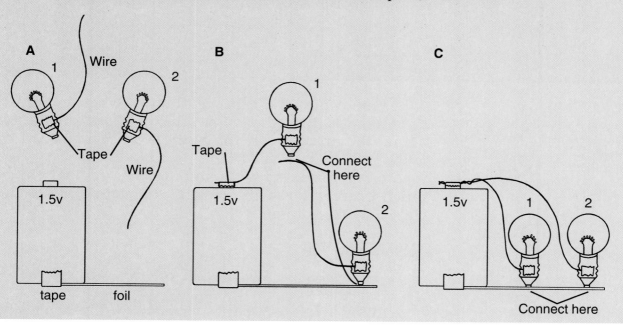

Each circuit can handle only a certain amount of current. If too many appliances are connected to one circuit, the wire will become hot and may cause a fire. Fuses and circuit breakers are safety devices that keep wires from overheating (fig. 21-27).

Fig. 21-27 Circuit breakers (left) and fuses (right) protect against electrical fires created by over-heated electrical wires.

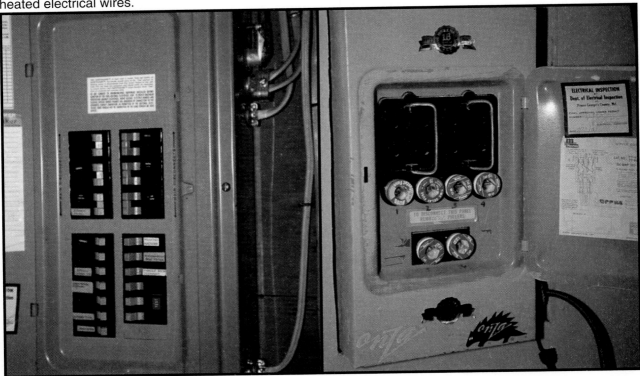

RESEARCH IT

Research the use of circuit breakers and fuses in homes, cars, and electrical appliances. Collect the devices and report to the class.

A **fuse** contains a thin metal strip. When too much current flows through the fuse, the metal strip melts and breaks the circuit before the wiring overheats and causes a fire.

A **circuit breaker** is an automatic switch. When too much current flows through it, the switch shuts the electricity off automatically.

REVIEW IT

1. How is a parallel circuit different from a series circuit?
2. Why aren't only series circuits used in houses?

CLASS ACTIVITY 21–6: WILITLITE

Question: Can you make a complete electrical circuit?

Materials:

aluminum foil
bell wire (30 cm) – 2
construction paper
D-cell

flashlight bulb
hole punch
transparent tape

Procedure:

1. Cut the sheet of construction paper in half (fig. A).
2. On one piece of the paper, punch six holes (fig. B).
3. Place the punched paper on top of the unpunched paper and mark the holes on the unpunched paper as shown in fig. C. Label one set of holes A and the other set B.
4. Cut the aluminum foil into 1 cm (0.5 in) wide strips.
5. On the unpunched paper, tape a foil strip between one of the marks on the left side and a mark on the right side as shown in fig. D.
6. Repeat step 5 until all marks in set A have been matched with marks in set B. Be sure to insulate with tape whenever foil strips cross. Make note of which marks are connected.
7. Tape the punched sheet over the foiled sheet (fig. E).
8. Set up apparatus as shown in fig. F using the D-cell and wire.
9. By touching wire 1 to the hole on side A and wire 2 with the correct hole on side B, the bulb will light up.

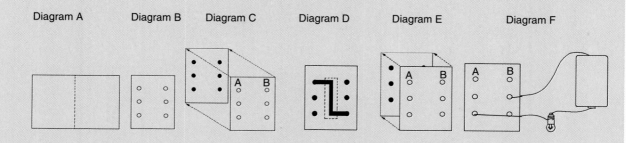

Diagram A   Diagram B   Diagram C   Diagram D   Diagram E   Diagram F

Questions:

1. How do you know whether a circuit is formed when connecting a hole from side A with a hole from side B?
2. Why is insulation necessary between foil strips that cross?
3. Why didn't the bulb light each time two holes were connected?

Conclusion: Write 3–5 sentences about what you learned from this activity.

CHAPTER 21 WRAP-UP

SKILLS DEVELOPMENT

THINKING SKILLS: DESIGNING AN EXPERIMENT

Using two brands of flashlight dry cells, determine which dry cell lasts longer. Use the scientific method for constructing your experiment.

1. State the problem.
2. Gather information.
3. Form a hypothesis.
4. Experiment to test the hypothesis.
5. Record the data.
6. Analyze the data.
7. Make a conclusion.

QUESTIONS AND PROBLEMS

1. Which type of lightning occurs more often: cloud-to-cloud or cloud-to-ground?
2. What makes clothes cling together in a clothes dryer?
3. What do AC and DC mean?
4. A 100 ft roll of copper wire weighs 3 lbs and costs $10. How much would an identical roll of gold wire cost? (Clue: check troy ounces)
5. Does increased voltage mean increased amperage? Why?
6. How many dry cells are in a 9-volt battery?
7. What is the advantage of rechargeable dry cells, when they cost so much more than regular dry cells?
8. What type of electrical current is used in automobiles?
9. What is "parallel" about parallel circuits?
10. What is the advantage of fuses and circuit breakers?

RESEARCH

1. Find out why static electricity increases on cold, dry days. Write a report on your findings.
2. Find out how fabric softeners reduce static cling. Survey a local supermarket to discover the cost of fabric softener products. Make an oral report on your findings. Include visual aids.
3. Find out how many different types of circuits there are. Draw a diagram of each and explain their differences.
4. Find out what Benjamin Franklin did with electricity after his famous kite experiment. Construct a series of posters that tells the story.
5. Find out how to make wet cells using fruits and vegetables. Conduct a demonstration that shows how these cells work.

REVIEW

HIGHLIGHTS

1. The movement of electrons creates an electrical charge.
2. Static charge is produced by a buildup of electrons. Rubbing your feet on a carpet and brushing your hair are two ways to produce static charge.
3. Electroscopes are used to show the presence of static electricity.
4. Opposite charges attract, and like charges repel.
5. Electric current is the flow of electrons.
6. Direct current flows in only one direction. Alternating current flows back and forth in both directions.
7. Conductors, such as copper and gold, allow electricity to pass through them. Insulators, such as glass and rubber, resist electric current.

8. Resistance makes it harder for current to flow.
9. Voltage is the strength of the push on electrons. Amperage is the number of electrons moving in a current.
10. An electrical cell is a single unit that produces electricity. A battery is two or more cells working together.
11. Most dry cells use a moist paste surrounding a rod to produce electricity. A wet cell uses liquid acid that reacts with metal plates to produce electricity.
12. Nonrechargeable dry cells cannot be recharged. Rechargeable dry cells can be recharged many times.
13. A circuit is a pathway through which electricity can flow.
14. A series circuit has only one path through which the current can flow and allows one switch to control several devices. A parallel circuit has two or more paths through which the current can flow and allows one device to be turned off or on while not affecting other devices in the circuit.
15. Fuses and circuit breakers are devices designed to keep electrical wires from overheating and starting fires.

VOCABULARY LIST

alternating current	electrical cell	proton
amperage	electron	rechargeable cell
battery	electroscope	resistance
circuit	fuse	series circuit
circuit breaker	insulator	static charge
conductor	lightning	static discharge
current	neutron	volt
direct current	ohm	voltage
dry cell	parallel circuit	wet cell

PRACTICE
Multiple Choice. Choose the best answer.
1. Which has the least resistance?
   a. a copper wire
   b. a gold wire
   c. a steel wire
   d. an aluminum wire
2. What kind of electrical circuit is mostly used in homes?
   a. a series circuit
   b. a parallel circuit
   c. a simple circuit
   d. a copper circuit
3. Voltage is similar to
   a. water pressure
   b. lightning
   c. amperage
   d. alternating current

4. Balloons can be made to stick to a wall because of
   a. magnetism
   b. suction
   c. gravity
   d. static charge
5. Which is used in making a dry cell?
   a. iron
   b. silver
   c. aluminum
   d. carbon
6. What causes a static charge?
   a. a neutron is added to the nucleus of an atom
   b. a proton moves from one atom to another
   c. an electron moves to another atom
   d. the nucleus of the atom falls apart
7. Which unit is used to measure resistance?
   a. ohms
   b. watts
   c. volts
   d. kilograms
8. For circuits to work, they must
   a. be made with wire
   b. form a complete path
   c. be insulated
   d. have switches
9. How does alternating current differ from direct current?
   a. it changes direction
   b. it is stronger
   c. it makes a brighter light
   d. it needs a larger wire
10. In which of the following is a series circuit used?
   a. a flashlight
   b. a light bulb
   c. a battery
   d. all of these

Matching. Match each word with its definition or description.
1. causes electrical wiring to become hot
2. produces 1.5 volts of electricity
3. several electrical cells joined together
4. a measure of the push of the electrons
5. the positive particle of an atom
6. the negative particle of an atom
7. a pathway for the flow of electrons
8. a shock caused by the flow of electrons
9. the number of electrons that flow through a wire
10. allows electricity to move through it

a. amperage
b. battery
c. circuit
d. conductor
e. dry cell
f. electron
g. proton
h. resistance
i. static discharge
j. voltage

CHAPTER 22

MAKING AND USING ELECTRICITY

INTRODUCTION

The cockpit of a 747 jumbo jet has a dazzling array of dials and gauges. Pilots use these instruments to determine altitude, fuel levels, and other essential information. Pilots also use this equipment to communicate with other planes and control towers.

The airplane makes and uses its own supply of electricity to keep all this equipment working. Without such a supply of energy, the plane could not fly.

The cockpit of a Boeing 747.

22-1 MAKING ELECTRICITY

generator
transformer

OBJECTIVES

- Explain how a generator produces electricity.
- Identify sources of energy used to power generators.
- Explain the purpose of transformers.

Fig. 22-1 The electricity that lights the headlight of this bicycle is produced by a simple generator (bottom).

The headlight on the boy's bike has no batteries (fig. 22-1). Mounted on the bicycle is an electric generator that touches the wheel. As the wheel turns, the **generator** spins and makes electricity for the headlight. When the bicycle stops moving, the generator no longer spins, and the headlight goes out.

Electricity is usually made at power plants by large generators. Fig. 22-2 shows a diagram of a bicycle generator. Although the power-plant generator is much larger, both generators have similar parts. The bicycle generator is made of a wire coil that rotates between a set of magnets. When the wire coil turns past the magnets, electrons begin to flow in the wire to the headlight. The large generator also has a wire coil and magnets. The electricity it makes moves out over wires to homes and factories.

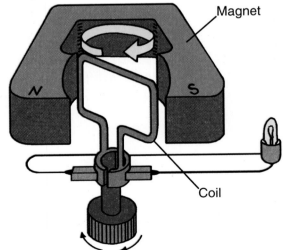

Fig. 22-2 The generator on a bicycle generates electricity in the same way the generator of a large power plant does.

In the United States and Canada, most power plants burn coal or oil to turn water into steam. The steam then turns large turbines attached to generators (fig. 22–3).

Steam can also be produced in other ways (fig. 22–4). In nuclear power plants, uranium creates heat that turns water into steam. Steam also can be made with energy from sunlight. In some places, natural steam from geysers runs generators.

RESEARCH IT

Research the electrical backup systems hospitals have in case there is a power failure.

Fig. 22–3 Water provides the power to push the blades of this turbine, which turns the generator.

Fig. 22–4 Steam to power electrical generators can be produced by nuclear power (left), solar power (center), or harnessing the steam from geysers (right).

Wind Water

DID YOU KNOW?

Solar cells are used to power pocket calculators, security lights, and lights used in advertising. They are even used to power experimental cars.

Some power plants generate electricity without steam. Most of these use the force of moving water from lakes and reservoirs to turn the generators. The water moves down long pipes, or penstocks, until it becomes a strong jet of water. As the water hits the blades of the turbine, it spins the generator rapidly (fig. 22–5).

Fig. 22–5   The energy produced by the force of water flowing downhill can turn the turbines of a generator to produce electricity.

Fig. 22–6   Wind causes the blades of these windmills to turn, producing electricity.

Windmills can also produce electricity (fig. 22–6). As wind turns the windmill blades, the generator turns. This method is being used more each year.

Both water power and wind power are relatively clean ways of producing electricity. They do not pollute the air as do coal- and oil-burning power plants. But while dams and windmills are desirable sources of electricity, they cannot be used everywhere. Dams are expensive and cannot be built on all rivers. And in many areas the wind doesn't blow hard enough to turn windmills.

CLASS ACTIVITY 22–1: Lemon Power

Question: How can a lemon be used to produce electricity?

Materials:

bell wire (30 cm)	lemon
dimes – 2	paper clip
directional compass	sandpaper (fine)

Procedure:
1. Roll the lemon on a desk, pressing on it, so that it becomes soft and juicy.
2. Clean the coins with fine sandpaper.
3. Use a pair of scissors to make two slits in the lemon 1 cm apart as shown.
4. Wrap the wire 10 times around the compass in a N–S direction.
5. Insert the paper clip in one slot of the lemon and one of the dimes into the other slot.
6. Touch one end of the wire to the paper clip. Watch the compass as you touch the other end of the wire to the dime. Record data.
7. Reverse the ends of the wire on the paper clip and dime. Record data.
8. Replace the paper clip with the second dime. Touch the dimes with the ends of the wire. Record data.

Data:

HOOKUP	RESULTS
clip/dime (step 6)	
dime/clip (step 7)	
dime/dime (step 8)	

Questions:
1. Is current produced when a paper clip and dime are used?
2. Is current produced when two dimes are used?
3. Why is there a difference?

Conclusion: Write 3–5 sentences about what you learned from this activity.

Solar

Fig. 22–7 When sunlight hits these solar panels, electricity is produced.

Solar cells are also used to produce electricity (fig. 22–7). These devices are put together in panels. Sunlight hits the panels, causing electrons to flow out of them. Hundreds of panels can supply a good deal of power. But though solar panels cause no pollution, they are expensive to purchase and install.

Fig. 22–8 Power lines such as these carry high-voltage electricity.

Fig. 22–9 Transformers lower the voltage of electricity so it can be used in our homes.

DID YOU KNOW?
Nikola Tesla, an American scientist, invented the AC transformer. Today transformers can be seen on power poles throughout North America.

All of these sources of power generate high-voltage electricity, which is carried over high-voltage power lines (fig. 22-8). High-voltage power lines sometimes carry more than 500,000 volts. Before the electricity is used in your home, its voltage is lowered by a **transformer** such as you see on power poles (fig. 22-9). The transformer changes the electricity to 120 volts before it enters your house. Almost all electrical devices in your house run on 120 volts. Those that run on less than 120 volts, such as televisions, radios, stereos, and computers, all have built-in low voltage transformers.

REVIEW IT

1. How do generators make electricity?
2. What sources of power are used to turn generators?
3. What do transformers do?

22-2 MEASURING ELECTRICITY

OBJECTIVES

- Explain how electrical use is measured.
- Define watt, watt-hour, and kilowatt-hour.
- Identify ways of conserving electricity.

VOCABULARY
electric power
kilowatt-hour
watt
watt-hour

An electric company employee reads the meter on the outside of your house to see how much electricity your family uses each month (fig. 22–10). As power enters your house, the meter turns. In the first picture, the meter reads 4139. The next day the meter reads 4228. This means 89 units of power were used from one day to the next (fig. 22–11).

Fig. 22-10 Electricity meters measure how much electricity is used.

The rate at which electric energy is used is called **electric power**. Electric power is measured in units called **watts**. Some equipment is marked with the amount of power it uses (fig. 22–12). For instance, a light bulb that uses 100 watts per hour is marked "100 watts." A bulb that uses only 60 watts per hour is marked "60 watts." A typical hair dryer uses 1500 watts of energy per hour.

A **watt-hour** is the measure of the rate at which power is used. If a 100-watt light bulb is operated for one hour, it will use 100 watt-hours of energy. If you forget to turn it off for one day, it will use 2400 watt-hours of energy. A toaster uses energy at the rate of 1500 watts per hour, but it only takes a few minutes to make toast. So making toast would take only 25–50 watt-hours of electricity. Large amounts of electrical power are measured in kilowatt-hours (kwhr). One kilowatt-hour is 1000 watt-hours.

Fig. 22–11 The amount of electricity usage is measured as the difference between the reading on an electric meter on one day and the reading on the meter another day.

Fig. 22–12 Many manufacturers include the power rating of appliances on the product label.

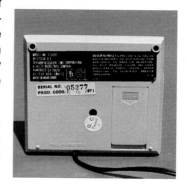

TRY THIS 22-2: Meter Reading

Materials:
   electric meter (home)

Procedure:
1. Locate your electric meter at home.
2. Record the reading.
3. Return at the same time the next day and record the reading again.
4. Determine the number of kwhrs by subtracting the smaller number from the larger.
   • If electricity costs $0.10/kwhr, what is the cost of the electricity used?
   • How does $0.10 compare to the actual rate you are charged?

Typical Energy Useage by Some Home Appliances			
Hair dryer, blower	1000	Television	200
Microwave oven	1450	Electric toothbrush	7
Radio/tape player	100	100 watt light bulb	100
Range/oven	2600	40 watt fluorescent light bulb	40
Refrigerator/freezer	600		

Fig. 22-13 The amount of electricity used by common household appliances.

The average American family uses more than 30,000 watt-hours (30 kwhr) of electricity each day. For instance, a boy might use 375 watt-hours to dry his hair. His sister might use 500 watt-hours to dry her hair. To boil a small pot of water on an electric stove might take 125 watt-hours. To make two pieces of toast requires about 25 watt-hours of energy. All of these activities add up to 1025 watt-hours.

You can help your family save money by conserving energy. It is helpful to know which electrical devices use the most power (fig. 22-13). Whenever you leave a room for even a minute or two, turn off the light. Turn heaters down, and always remember to close refrigerator doors.

DID YOU KNOW?

Thomas Edison developed the first company that supplied electrical power. He generated alternating current.

REVIEW IT

1. In what units does the utility company measure the electricity used in your home?
2. What units are used to measure electric power?
3. How can you help conserve electricity in your home?

22–3 ELECTRONICS

OBJECTIVES

- Define electronics.
- Identify the historical development of electronics.
- Analyze the impact of electronics.

VOCABULARY
electronics
integrated circuit
microchip
transistor
vacuum tube

Electronics is the study of electrons and how they move. Electronic devices control moving electrons to create pictures on TV screens, produce sounds on stereo equipment, and calculate the answers to math problems (fig. 22–14). These devices work because of the electrons that move inside them.

Fig. 22–14   Electronic devices include TVs, stereos, and computers.

The first important electronic invention was the **vacuum** (vac´ yōō əm) **tube** (fig. 22–15). The vacuum tube worked as a valve to control the flow of electrons. It could "open and close" to let different amounts of electrons flow through. Vacuum tubes were used from the 1920s to the 1950s in radios and early television sets to create sounds and pictures. They were large, expensive, became hot, and wore out quickly. So scientists worked to invent smaller and more-reliable devices.

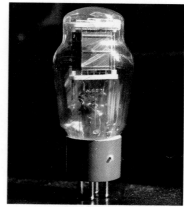

Fig. 22–15   Vacuum tubes, the first electronic invention, are used in picture tubes of TVs and in microwave ovens.

Fig. 22–16 Transistors did the same job as vacuum tubes but were much smaller.

In 1947 the **transistor** was invented (fig. 22–16). It was small and did the same job as a vacuum tube. The transistor lasted longer and gave off little heat. Transistors were used in everything from radios to toys. Because transistors were small, electronic devices could be made smaller (fig. 22–17).

In 1959 scientists developed the **integrated circuit**. The thousands of transistors that make up an integrated circuit are made and connected at one time (fig. 22-18). These circuits are always made on a piece of silicon, which is the main element in sand. Integrated circuits use little power and produce little heat.

Fig. 22–17 The use of transistors in electronics allowed radios and other equipment to be made smaller.

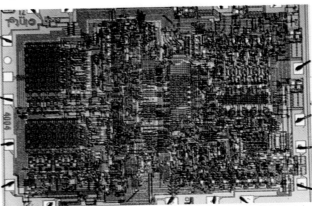

Fig. 22–18 The integrated circuit uses little power and produces little heat.

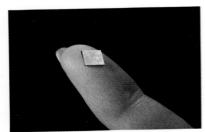

Fig. 22–19 Microchips are tiny integrated circuits.

These circuits were made smaller and smaller until they became microscopic and were called **microchips**, or "chips" for short (fig. 22–19). Microchips are used in toys, watches, calculators, computers, cameras, VCRs, and microwaves.

New advances are being made in electronics every day. Devices impossible or too expensive to make today may be available in just a few years.

REVIEW IT

1. In what way are transistors better than vacuum tubes?
2. What is a microchip?

432

22–4 COMPUTERS

OBJECTIVES

- Describe how computers have benefited society.
- Explain the advantage the human mind has over the computer.

VOCABULARY
microprocessor
program

Microchips, transistors, and integrated circuits are components used to make small computers. Early computers were huge and couldn't do any more than a good pocket calculator can do today. ENIAC (ē´ nē ak), a computer made in 1947, took up the space of an average house, weighed 30 tons, and included more than 18,000 vacuum tubes (fig. 22–20). It broke down often because one or more of its vacuum tubes would overheat and stop working.

DID YOU KNOW?
One of the earliest computers was the abacus used by the ancient Chinese and Greeks.

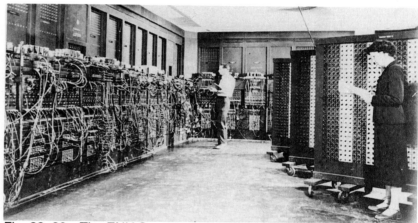

Fig. 22–20 The ENIAC computer was large and awkward to operate.

In 1971 the microprocessor was invented (fig. 22–21). A **microprocessor** is a large chip that is the "brain" of a computer. A set of commands, called a **program**, tells the microprocessor what to do (fig. 22–22). The microprocessor controls the computer by handling the mathematical computations. As microprocessors became better, computers could work faster.

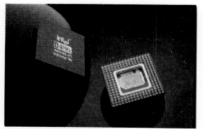

Fig. 22–21 Microprocessors similar to this one serve as the "brains" of computers.

```
1    REM  *********************************************
2    REM  * THIS PROGRAM TESTS YOU ON STATE CAPITALS *
3    REM  *********************************************
4    REM
10   READ I$
20   PRINT I$
30   PRINT
40   READ N
50   LET S = 0
60   LET L$(0) = "TRY AGAIN"
70   LET L$(1) = "THE CORRECT ANSWER"
75   LET L$(2) = L$(1)
80   REM
100  FOR I = 1 TO N
110       READ Q$, A$
120       LET T = 0
130       PRINT Q$;
140       INPUT B$
150       IF A$ = B$ THEN 200
160       PRINT L$(T);
170       LET T = T + 1
180       IF T = 1 THEN 140
190       PRINT A$
192       LET T = 2
194       GOTO 130
200       LET S = S + 2-T
210       PRINT
220  NEXT I
230  REM
300  LET S1 = S/(2*N)
310  PRINT "YOUR SCORE IS "; INT(S1*100+0.5); "%"
320  REM
900  DATA NAME THE CAPITAL OF THE FOLLOWING STATES
901  DATA 15
902  DATA NEW YORK, ALBANY, NORTH DAKOTA, BISMARCK
903  DATA OHIO, COLUMBUS, NEVADA, CARSON CITY
904  DATA NEW HAMPSHIRE, CONCORD, MAINE, AUGUSTA
905  DATA MARYLAND, ANNAPOLIS, MICHIGAN, LANSING
906  DATA HAWAII, HONOLULU, ARIZONA, PHOENIX
907  DATA COLORADO, DENVER, MONTANA, HELENA
908  DATA NEW MEXICO, SANTA FE, OREGON, SALEM
909  DATA VERMONT, MONTPELIER
999  END
```

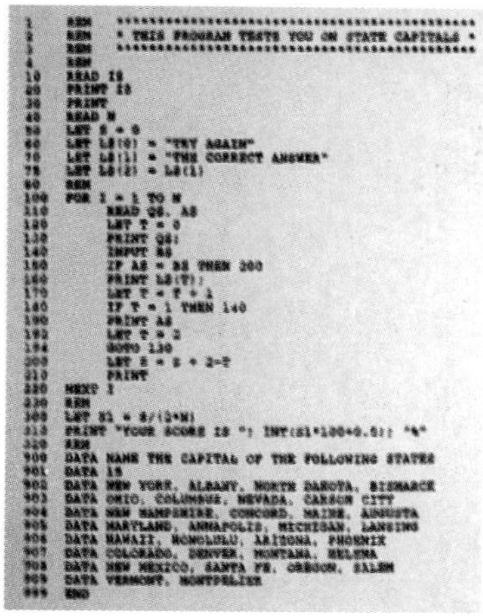

Fig. 22–22 A set of instructions, called a program, tells the microprocessor what to do.

RESEARCH IT
Research to discover the components used in making computers. Make a poster display of your findings.

Today computers do many things (fig. 22–23). They keep record of how much money your family has in the bank. They print bills for your telephone and electric company. They can answer the telephone and print newsletters. Astronauts use computers to control their spaceships. Large airplanes fly through bad weather and darkness safely with the help of computers. Police use computers to look for criminals. Schools use them for teaching. A personal computer was even used in the making of this book.

Computers are being used increasingly in business. Being familiar with computers is becoming a necessary part of any job. If you learn how to operate computers when you are a student, you will increase your job opportunities when you are older.

Fig. 22–23 Computers are already being used in many ways.

TRY THIS 22–4: Human Brain vs. Calculator

Materials:
 calculator

Procedure:
 1. With your partner, see who can do the following sets of problems faster. One partner uses a calculator. The other person either uses paper and pencil or does the problem in his or her head.
 2. After the first set, trade the calculator and repeat step 1.

   Set A   5 x 10, 3 + 9 + 4, 56/7, 2 x 6, 100/20

   Set B   185 x 283, 18 + 27 + 36, 600/24, 24 x 178, 1504/32

   • What conclusion can be made?

As wonderful as they are, even the most powerful computers can't match the complexity of the human brain. God designed your mind so that you can make choices, feel emotions, and enjoy life. Computers, on the other hand, are machines. They must be programmed before they can do anything. When computers make mistakes, it is usually because someone programmed them incorrectly. Scientists are working on ways to make computers think as people do, but so far their efforts have failed.

REVIEW IT

 1. What are some uses of home computers?
 2. What is a microprocessor?
 3. In what way is the human mind superior to the computer?

22–5 ELECTRICAL SAFETY

DID YOU KNOW?
Benjamin Franklin stood inside a shed and out of the rain during his experiment with lightning. Several people stood in the rain and tried Franklin's experiment. They died when the lightning came down their kite string. Ben was lucky!

OBJECTIVE

- Describe safety precautions with regard to electricity.

Electricity injures many people each year. These injuries could be avoided by following the simple safety precautions listed below and on the next page.

ELECTRICAL SAFETY RULES

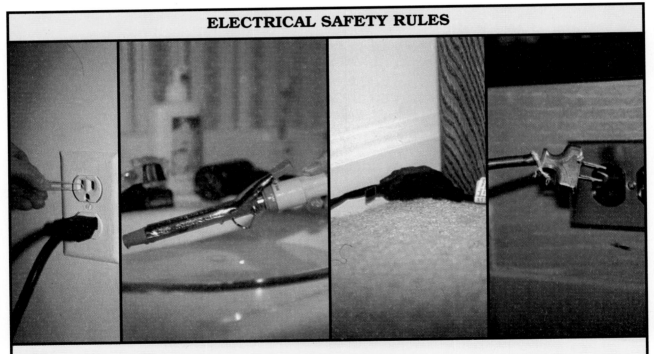

1. Put only electric plugs in electric outlets.

2. Touch electrical devices only when your hands are dry.

3. Keep electric cords and wires on top of rugs and carpets.

4. Replace broken or frayed wires.

ELECTRICAL SAFETY RULES

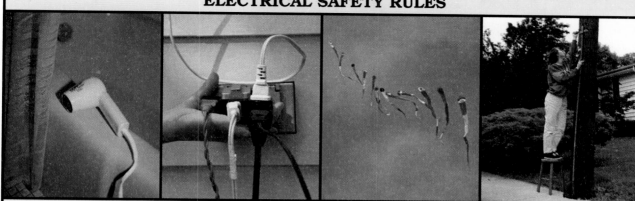

5. Keep electrical devices, such as hair dryers, radios, and telephones, away from the bathtub.

6. Plug no more than two plugs into one outlet.

7. Fly kites in open areas away from power lines.

8. Do not play on or around power poles, lines, or stations.

ELECTRICAL SAFETY RULES

9. Don't go near swimming pools or trees during a thunderstorm. Go indoors if possible.

10. *Never* touch a power line, whether it is in the air or on the ground.

11. Disconnect electrical devices before working on them or adjusting them.

REVIEW IT

1. Why is it important to follow the electrical safety rules?

CHAPTER 22 WRAP-UP
SKILLS DEVELOPMENT

THINKING SKILLS: COMPUTER SKILLS

Purpose: This program is designed to assist you in calculating your electric bill.

Procedure:
1. Contact your utility company to find out how much each Kwhr of power costs.
2. Determine how many Kwhrs of electricity your family used.
3. Enter the BASIC program (shown below) into a computer.
4. Start the program by typing "RUN" and then pressing the "Enter" key.
5. Enter the answer for question A, and press the "Enter" key.
6. Enter the answer for question B, and press the "Enter" key. NOTE: Enter the cost of a Kwhr as a decimal value.
      (Example: Use .05 not 5 or $.05.)
7. Record the cost of your utility bill.
8. If you wish to calculate another bill, answer Yes to question C.
9. If you wish to stop the program, answer No to question C.

BASIC Program:

```
10  REM Cost of Electricity
20  Input "A. How many Kwhrs of electricity were used?"; A
30  Input "B. What is the cost of 1 Kwhr?"; B
40  Let C = A * B
50  Print "The cost of your electric bill is $"; C
60  Input "C. Do you want to calculate another bill? Yes/No"; A$
70  If A$ = "Yes" GOTO 20
80  If A$ = "No" then print "ByeBye, from Mr. Kilowatt-hr.":End
90  GOTO 60
```

QUESTIONS AND PROBLEMS
1. Why is water used to make electricity?
2. Why are windmills and solar cells "clean" sources of electricity?
3. On average, how much electricity does your family use each day?
4. List five ways you personally can reduce the amount of electricity used in your home.
5. How are integrated circuits better than transistors?
6. What is the advantage of microchips over integrated circuits?
7. Why were early computers so large?
8. Identify three ways computers are used in schools.
9. What do you think is the most common cause of electrical fires at home? Why?
10. What do you think is the most common cause of electric shock at home? Why?

RESEARCH
1. Find out how electricity is used in your body. Write a report that explains your findings.
2. Write a story of what it would be like in your home if you had no electricity for a week. Include illustrations.
3. Interview someone who uses a computer at work. Find out what computer and programs he or she uses, what he or she feels are the advantages and disadvantages of the computer, and how important he or she thinks computer skills are.
4. Contact your utility company to find out when and why utility rates change during the year. Prepare an oral report that includes visual aids.
5. Find out if living near high-voltage power lines can affect you. Write a report on your findings.

Review

HIGHLIGHTS
1. Generators produce electricity as a wire coil is rotated between a set of magnets.
2. Coal and oil, nuclear energy, steam from geysers, flowing water, and wind are all sources of energy used to power generators.
3. Transformers lower the voltage of electricity so it can be used in our homes, appliances, and electronic equipment.
4. Electricity that is used in your house passes through a meter. A utility company employee reads the meter to determine how much electricity is used.
5. The watt is the unit used to measure electric power. The watt-hour measures the rate at which electric power is used. One thousand watt-hours equals one kilowatt-hour.

6. You can help conserve electricity by turning off lights when they are not needed, turning down heaters, and closing refrigerator doors.
7. Electronics is the study of electrons and how they move.
8. The first major electronic discovery was the vacuum tube, followed by the transistor. The next development was the integrated circuit, and finally the microchip was developed.
9. Electronics are used in toys, watches, calculators, computers, cameras, VCRs, and microwave ovens.
10. Computers have benefited society in many ways, including storage and retrieval of data, analysis of data, problem solving, education, printing, and entertainment.
11. The human mind is able to make choices, feel emotion, and enjoy life. Computers must first be programmed before they can do anything.
12. Following safety precautions when around electricity can help you avoid injury. These precautions are described on page 436, 437.

VOCABULARY LIST

electric power	microchip	vacuum tube
electronics	microprocessor	watt
generator	program	watt-hour
integrated circuit	transformer	
kilowatt-hour	transistor	

PRACTICE
Multiple Choice. Pick the best answer.
1. Why isn't solar power used more than it is?
   a. too expensive
   b. takes up too much space
   c. both a and b
   d. neither a nor b
2. Which is not used to generate electricity?
   a. wind
   b. coal
   c. steam
   d. kilowatts
3. What unit is used to measure the electricity used in your home?
   a. volt
   b. ohm
   c. kilowatt-hour
   d. kilogram
4. Being safe with electricity means avoiding
   a. swimming during a thunderstorm
   b. touching a power line
   c. running wire under carpets
   d. all of these

5. Which shows the order of development?
   a. ENIAC, microchip, transistor
   b. vacuum tube, transistor, microchip
   c. transistor, microchip, TV
   d. none of these
6. Which pair of meter readings shows the greatest amount of power usage?
   a. 261–312
   b. 417–508
   c. 933–1012
   d. 689–770
7. Which of the following businesses use computers?
   a. insurance companies
   b. police departments
   c. grocery stores
   d. all of these
8. Which is an advantage of the integrated circuit?
   a. gives off no heat
   b. saves space
   c. both a and b
   d. neither a nor b
9. Which of the following tasks are computers *not able to do*?
   a. think
   b. help airplanes to fly
   c. keep records
   d. teach students in bad weather
10. When does turning off lights save electricity?
   a. always
   b. sometimes
   c. never
   d. depends on the watts being used

Matching. Match each word with its definition or description.
1. electronic device developed in 1959
2. uses sunlight to produce electricity
3. labor-saving electronic device
4. first large computer
5. units used to measure electric power
6. very small electronic circuits
7. produces electricity
8. used to replace vacuum tubes
9. first electronic invention
10. changes the voltage of electricity

a. computer
b. ENIAC
c. generator
d. integrated circuit
e. microchips
f. solar cell
g. transformer
h. transistor
i. vacuum tube
j. watt-hour

MAGNETISM

INTRODUCTION

Most people who hike or camp in wilderness areas are careful to take a compass with them. When you're away from familiar landmarks, a compass can keep you oriented because no matter which way you turn, the compass needle always points in the same direction.

The special container shown in the picture is filled with iron filings floating in a liquid. When a magnet is placed in the opening, the filings become arranged in a pattern. How do magnets cause this pattern? Do all magnets work in the same way? Can you make your own magnets? By the time you complete this chapter, the special container may no longer be a mystery!

SECTION TITLES

A magnetic field is shown by the arrangement of iron filings in this liquid-filled chamber.

23–1 MAGNETS

VOCABULARY
lodestone
magnetic field
magnetite
pole

Fig. 23–1 Lodestones contain the mineral magnetite.

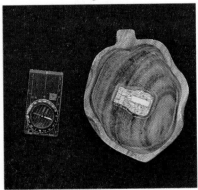

Fig. 23–2 Early explorers used floating magnets as compasses.

OBJECTIVES

- Describe the historical use of magnets.
- Describe the characteristics of magnets.
- Distinguish between magnets and magnetic fields.

You have probably learned something about magnets by playing with them. You know that magnets pick up paper clips, nails, and pins—but not pennies. You also know that a magnet will pick up other magnets.

What you may not know is that magnets have been in use for thousands of years. Originally, **lodestones** were the only magnets (fig. 23–1). Lodestones contain a mineral called **magnetite** that is able to pick up small pieces of iron.

Someone discovered that when a lodestone is hung with a piece of string, it always points in the same direction. From this discovery came the compass. A compass needle always points to the North Pole. Around the 1100s, sailors began placing a magnet on a piece of floating material, such as cork or straw, to navigate on the open seas (fig. 23–2).

Eventually people learned to make magnets from metal. Metal magnets can be molded into almost any shape or size.

Magnets have two magnetic **poles**, or ends. These poles are labeled "north" and "south" (fig. 23–3). A magnet has the greatest pull at the poles. If a magnet is cut in half, each piece still has a north and south pole. The north pole of one magnet attracts the south pole of another (fig. 23–4).

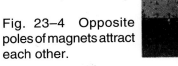

Fig. 23–3 Magnets always have a north and south pole.

Fig. 23–4 Opposite poles of magnets attract each other.

If you try to put the same poles together, like N to N or S to S, they push apart or repel each other (fig. 23–5).

Generally, if two magnets are made from the same material, the larger magnet will be stronger than the smaller magnet. Size, however, is not the only factor that affects a magnet's strength. For instance, magnets made from pure iron are not as strong as those made by mixing iron with other metals (fig. 23–6).

The area affected by a magnet is called its **magnetic field**. The stronger a magnet, the larger and stronger its magnetic field. It is easy to show a magnetic field. Place a magnet under a sheet of paper and sprinkle iron filings on the paper (fig. 23–7). The filings form curved lines that show the magnetic field. The filings are thickest at the poles because the magnetic field is strongest there. On paper the magnetic field appears to be flat. However, all magnetic fields are three-dimensional (see page 442).

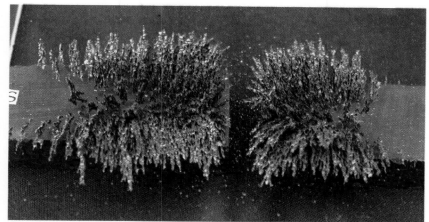

Fig. 23–5   Similar poles of magnets repel each other.

Fig. 23–6   Magnets made from mixing iron with other metals (left) are stronger than those made from only iron (right).

Fig. 23–7   The magnetic field of this magnet is illustrated by the arrangement of the iron filings.

TRY THIS 23–1: Compass Needle in Styrofoam

Materials:

bar magnet   styrofoam cup
sewing needle   water
styrofoam cube

Procedure:
1. Break off a small piece of styrofoam and insert a needle through it (fig. A).
2. Place the styrofoam with the inserted needle in a cup of water.
   • What happens?
3. Rotate the cup of water.
   • What happens?
4. Remove the needle from the styrofoam.
5. Magnetize the needle by rubbing the needle in one direction only with either end of a bar magnet as shown in B.
6. Insert the magnetized needle through the styrofoam as you did in step 1.
7. Repeat steps 2 and 3. Record what happens.

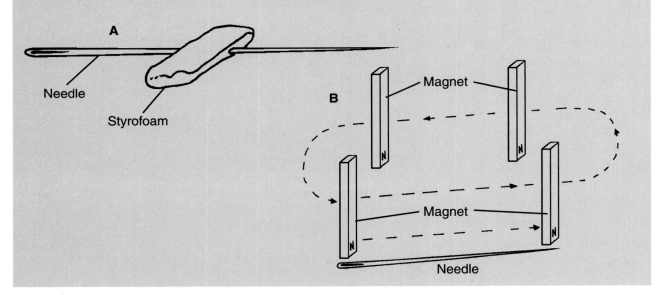

REVIEW IT

1. How have magnets been used in the past?
2. What determines the strength of a magnet?
3. What is the area affected by a magnet called?

23–2 HOW DOES A MAGNET WORK?

OBJECTIVES

- Explain what causes magnetism.
- Distinguish between permanent and temporary magnets.
- Identify substances from which magnets are made.

VOCABULARY
alloy
magnetic domain
permanent magnet
temporary magnet

In Fig. 23–8 (top) there are several small magnets. Each magnet can lift a small weight. In the next picture (bottom), the small magnets are placed together to form a large magnet. The large magnet's increased strength comes from combining the strengths of all the little magnets.

Just as the large magnet is made up of small ones, all magnets are made up of miniature magnetic areas called **magnetic domains**. The magnetism of each tiny domain is created by the spin of the atoms and electrons that make up the domain.

In a small piece of iron there are billions of domains. When most of these domains are lined up in the same direction, a magnetic field is created. The magnetic field is what causes the "pull" of a magnet.

A magnet can be made by placing a bar of iron in a strong magnetic field. When the iron comes into the magnetic field, all of the domains in the bar try to line up with the magnetic field. When most of the domains are lined up and stay that way, the bar is magnetized (fig. 23–9).

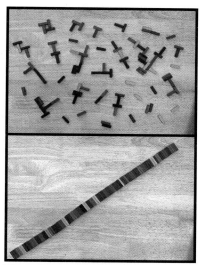

Fig. 23–8   Each small magnet can lift a small mass (top), but when put together, several small magnets can lift a much heavier mass (bottom).

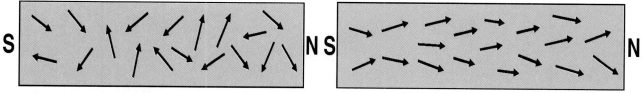

Fig. 23–9   In unmagnetized iron, the magnetic domains are not aligned (left). When magnetized, the magnetic domains of the iron align themselves (right).

TRY THIS 23–2: Magnetic Domains

Materials:
paper   ruler
pencil   scissors

Procedure:
1. Cut 20 rectangles about 1 cm x 2.5 cm (0.5 in x 1 in). Label one end of each rectangle "N" and the other end "S". (This will represent a domain within a bar magnet.)
2. Fold a full sheet of paper in half lengthwise. Label one side **MAGNETIZED** and the other side **NONMAGNETIZED**. (The sheet of paper represents an iron bar.)
3. Randomly place 10 of the rectangles (N–S domains) on the **NONMAGNETIZED** side of the paper (fig. A).
4. Place the remaining 10 rectangles (N–S domains) on the **MAGNETIC** side so that the majority of N–S domains point in the same direction (fig. B).
   • What is the difference between the **MAGNETIZED** and **NONMAGNETIZED** piece of iron?
   • What do you think determines the strength of a magnet?

A. Nonmagnetized

B. Magnetized

Permanent magnets remain magnetized for a long period of time. **Temporary magnets** are magnetic for only short periods of time. For example, when you pick up a nail with a magnet, it becomes a temporary magnet. As long as the nail touches the magnet, it will pick up paper clips (fig. 23–10). When removed from the magnet, the nail loses most of its magnetism.

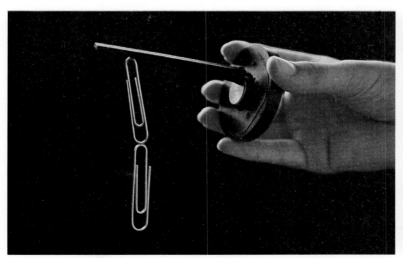

Fig. 23–10   A temporary magnet (nail) is magnetized only as long as it is in contact with a permanent magnet.

Fig. 23–11   Many magnets are made from magnetic metal mixed with plastics or ceramics.

Iron is not the only material from which magnets are made. Magnets are also made from mixtures of metals called **alloys** (al´ oiz). Steel is a magnetic alloy made mostly from iron and carbon. Other magnetic alloys contain nickel, cobalt, and aluminum. Many household magnets, such as those used to hold notes on refrigerators, are made from magnetic material mixed with plastics or ceramics (fig. 23–11).

DID YOU KNOW?
Computer disks and cassette tapes are magnetic.

REVIEW IT

1. What is a magnetic domain?
2. What causes the "pull" of a magnet?
3. What is the difference between temporary and permanent magnets?

CLASS ACTIVITY 23–2: How Strong Is It?

Question: How can the relative strength of magnets be determined?

Materials:
   magnet set (A–E)
   paper clips – 50

Procedure:
1. Obtain one of the five labeled magnets and several paper clips.
2. See how many paper clips the magnet can pick up. Record your results as "Trial 1" for the magnet on the data chart. Be sure to record the data in the correct column for the particular magnet.
3. Repeat step 2 two more times for the magnet. Record the results as "Trial 2" and "Trial 3."
4. Repeat steps 2–4 until all five magnets have been tested three times.
5. Determine the total number of paper clips held by each magnet by adding Trial 1, 2, and 3. Record the total on the chart.
6. Determine the average number of paper clips held by each magnet. (The average can be found by dividing the total number of paper clips by the number of trials.)

Data:

	A	B	C	D	E
Trial #1					
Trial #2					
Trial #3					
Total					
Average					

Questions:
1. What is the relationship between a magnet's strength and the number of paper clips it picks up?
2. Which magnet is the strongest? the weakest?
3. List the magnets in order of strength from strongest to weakest.

Conclusion: Write 3–5 sentences about what you learned from this activity.

23–3 ELECTROMAGNETS

OBJECTIVES

- Describe the relationship between magnetism and electricity.
- Identify uses of electromagnets.

VOCABULARY
electromagnet

In 1820, Hans Christian Oersted (ûr´ sted) accidentally discovered a new kind of magnetism. He had a coil of wire near a compass. When electricity ran through the wire, the compass pointed at the coil (fig. 23–12). Electricity running through the coil had turned it into an **electromagnet**. A coil can be a magnet only when electrons flow through it. When electrons stop flowing, the magnetic field disappears.

Fig. 23–12   Simply wrapping wire around a compass does not affect it (left). But when electricity is run through the wrapped wire, a magnetic field is created (right).

RESEARCH IT
Discover devices that use the principle of electricity and magnetism (electromagnetism). Make a poster to display your findings.

DID YOU KNOW?
Large electromagnets can lift
4000 kg (9200 lbs) of scrap
iron.

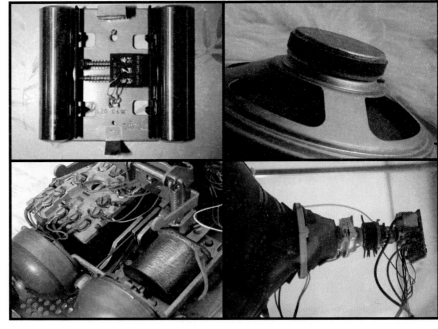

Fig. 23–13 Doorbells, stereo speakers, telephones, TVs, and other common devices use electromagnets.

Small electromagnets are used in motors, telephones, electric locks, doorbells, speakers, TVs, and stereos (fig. 23–13). Large electromagnets are used to move scrap metal. When the electromagnet is switched on, it lifts the metal. When the load is in the correct position, the magnet is turned off, and several tons of scrap metal drop (fig. 23–14).

Fig. 23–14 Some electromagnets are strong enough to lift heavy chunks of iron and steel.

DID YOU KNOW?
Maglev trains run with huge electromagnets. They float above their train tracks on a cushion of air at speeds of 250–300 mph.

REVIEW IT

1. How do electromagnets work?
2. How are electromagnets used?

23–4 MOTORS AND GENERATORS

OBJECTIVE

- Distinguish between the function of an electric motor and an electric generator.

VOCABULARY
coil
electric motor
generator

Figure 23–15 shows an electric motor and a generator. When electricity enters the **electric motor**, it causes the shaft to turn. In factories, motors run large, complex machines. At home, smaller motors run clocks, refrigerators, hair dryers, toys, VCRs, and tape recorders.

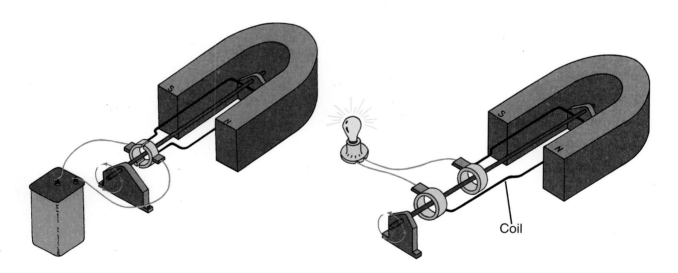

Fig. 23–15 Electric motors change electricity into motion (left); generators change motion into electricity (right).

Generators change motion into electricity. A generator has two major parts—a magnet and a coil. The **coil** is made of wraps of wire. When the coil of the generator rotates, it moves through the magnetic field, and electrons begin to flow through the wraps of wire. This flow of electrons is electricity.

RESEARCH IT
Find pictures from magazines that show electric motors and generators.

Fig. 23–16 This large windmill produces electricity for thousands of customers.

DID YOU KNOW?
Power plants at Niagara Falls can generate over 4 million kilowatts of power, enough electricity to supply about 1 million homes.

The United States and Canada are major producers and consumers of electricity. Some power plants have large generators that can produce 20 000 kilowatts of electricity, enough to supply about 5000 families. Some wind generators supply enough electric power for up to 50,000 homes (fig. 23–16).

REVIEW IT

1. Explain how an electric motor works.
2. How are electric motors and generators different?

FRONTIERS: LLU Proton Accelerator

The Loma Linda Proton Treatment Center opened on October 23, 1990, by treating a registered nurse from southern California for usually fatal cancer of the eye. After two years, the patient had no symptoms of disease, although it was too early to claim that she had been cured.

This $45-million facility, producing 250 million electron volts and weighing 400 tons, stands three stories high and is the only one of its kind in the world. It can deliver very large doses of protons, traveling up to 335 million miles per hour, to tumors (centers of cancer) within the body. This is done with accuracy down to 1 millimeter of precision and without the negative side effects usually associated with radiation therapy. It has three rotating gantries, which look like little Ferris wheels and aim the proton beam. Each gantry weighs 95 tons and is capable of rotating around the patient so that scientists can aim the proton beam from any angle.

The one-of-a-kind cancer treatment facility, spearheaded by James M. Slater, M.D., eventually will be able to treat more than 100 patients per day. Loma Linda University Medical Center has made it possible for scientists from

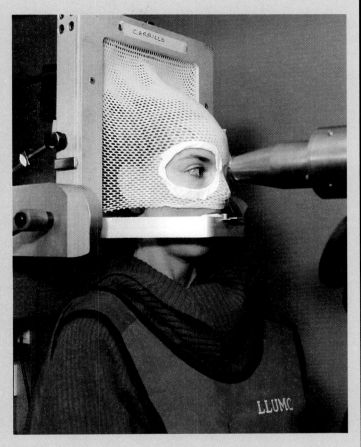

around the world to send their patients' computed tomography (CT) scans to Loma Linda by earth satellite. Loma Linda has the technology to receive those scans, to do treatment planning by computer simulation—in three dimensions and in color—and to send those scans back by satellite. Those scientists will be involved in deciding who comes to Loma Linda for treatments.

Questions:
1. What kind of cancer was first treated at the Proton Treatment Center?
2. What advantage does the Center have over other cancer treatment centers?
3. How do other scientists from around the world have access to this center?
4. This treatment center cost $45 million. Do you think it is worth that much money? Explain.

23-5 EARTH AS A MAGNET

VOCABULARY

aurora
aurora australis
aurora borealis
magnetosphere

OBJECTIVES

- Describe Earth's magnetic field.
- Explain how Earth's magnetic field helps us.
- Explain what causes auroras.

About 400 years ago scientists discovered that Earth acts like a giant magnet. Like all magnets, Earth has a magnetic field that spreads out in all directions (fig. 23-17). The core of Earth is mostly iron. Most scientists believe that as Earth spins, the core also spins and creates the magnetic field called the **magnetosphere** (mag nēt´ ō sfir).

DID YOU KNOW?

Our sun and all of its planets and all of their moons have magnetic fields.

On Earth's surface the magnetic field strength is about 200 times weaker than a toy magnet. But though Earth's magnetosphere is weak and hardly noticeable, it serves an important purpose. God created the magnetic field around Earth to shield us from radiation from the sun.

Earth has a magnetic north and south pole. However, these magnetic poles are not in the same location as the geographical North and South poles (fig. 23-18).

Fig. 23-17 Earth's magnetism creates a large magnetic field.

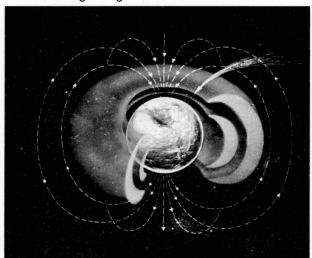

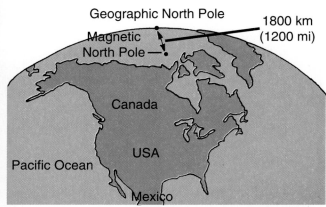

Fig. 23-18 Earth's magnetic north pole is located 1200 miles to the south of its geographic North Pole.

Geographic North Pole

Magnetic North Pole

1800 km (1200 mi)

Canada

USA

Pacific Ocean

Mexico

456

The arrangement of filings on a piece of paper shows the magnetic field of a small magnet. In a similar way, a display of light in the sky called an **aurora** (ô rôr´ ə) demonstrates the presence of Earth's magnetic field. This light is created by charged particles from the sun that are deflected toward the magnetic poles (fig. 23–19). Near the poles the particles collide with molecules in the atmosphere that give off red, green, and blue light. The auroras are brightest when the sun sends out more particles than usual.

The **aurora borealis** (bôr ē al´ is), or Northern Lights, occurs in the northern regions of Earth. The **aurora australis** (ô strā lis), or Southern Lights, glows in the southern areas of the world. Whenever there is a display in the north, there is also one in the south (fig. 23–20).

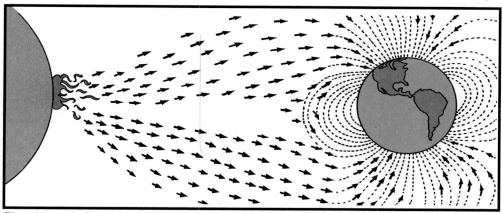

Fig. 23–19 The magneto-sphere deflects charged particles from the sun to the north and south poles.

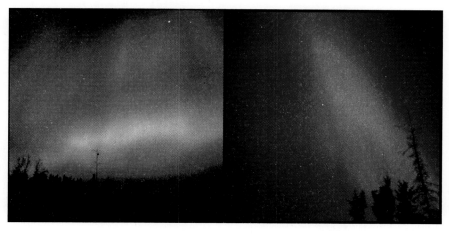

Fig. 23–20 The auroras create beautiful displays of light in the night sky.

REVIEW IT

1. How does our magnetic field protect us?
2. What causes the Earth's magnetic field?
3. What phenomenon shows that Earth has a magnetic field?

CHAPTER 23 WRAP–UP SKILLS DEVELOPMENT

THINKING SKILLS: READING TABLES

The following table shows the number of items picked up by an electromagnet under different conditions. The conditions that vary are the voltage and the number of wraps of wire around the nail.

NUMBER OF ITEMS PICKED UP BY AN ELECTROMAGNET

Number of Wraps of Wire

	0	5	10	15	20	25	30
Voltage Used (volts) 0	0	0	0	0	0	0	0
5	0	4	6	8	10	12	14
10	0	8	10	12	14	16	18
15	0	12	14	16	18	20	22
20	0	16	18	20	22	24	26

1. In general, what happens to the number of items picked up when the number of wraps of wire increases?

2. What two conditions will cause the strength of the electromagnet to be "0"?

3. In general, what happens to the number of items picked up when the voltage is decreased?

4. What three combinations of wraps and voltage will cause the electromagnet to pick up 14 items?

QUESTIONS AND PROBLEMS

1. Describe a magnetic field.
2. How did sailors tell direction before they discovered compasses?
3. Do auroras happen only at night?
4. Why isn't Earth's magnetic north pole located at the geographic North Pole?
5. Why does a temporary magnet work only when it touches a permanent magnet?
6. Why do you think magnets have two poles (north and south)?
7. What can be done to make an electromagnet stronger?
8. Why do electromagnets stop working when the electricity is turned off?
   Which do you think are more important, magnets or electric generators? Why?
10. Which devices in your home use magnetism?

RESEARCH

1. Research the aurora borealis. When is it most readily seen? What causes it? Write a report on your findings.
2. Find out whether all planets of our solar system have North and South poles. Draw a diagram showing what scientists know about each of the planets' magnetic fields.
3. Construct a small working generator that uses wind, sunlight, or water as a source of power. Demonstrate its use to the class.
4. Find out how animals use Earth's magnetism. Give an oral report on your findings. Include visual aids.
5. Ask your utility company how they generate their electricity. Make a graph of your findings.

Review

HIGHLIGHTS

1. Lodestones, natural magnetic rocks, were the first magnets to be used. Early sailors used lodestones as compasses for navigation. Later, metals, such as iron, were used as magnets. Today metal alloys, certain plastics, and ceramics are also used as magnets.
2. All magnets have a north and south pole and are surrounded by a magnetic field.
3. A magnet is any object that has magnetic properties. The magnetic field is an invisible, three-dimensional force field that surrounds every magnet.
4. Magnetism is created when the magnetic domains of an object line up. The magnetism of each domain is caused by the spin of its atoms and their electrons.

5. Permanent magnets are those that stay magnetized for a long time. Temporary magnets stay magnetized only for a short time.
6. Flowing electrons (electric current) always create a magnetic field. Magnets created by electric current are called electromagnets.
7. Electromagnets are used in motors, telephones, locks, doorbells, speakers, TVs, and stereos.
8. Electric motors change electricity into motion. Electric generators change motion into electricity.
9. Earth's magnetic field, called the magnetosphere, spreads out in all directions around Earth.
10. The magnetosphere protects us from harmful radiation from the sun.
11. The auroras are created when charged particles from the sun collide with molecules in the atmosphere, giving off light energy.

VOCABULARY LIST

alloy	electromagnet	magnetosphere
aurora	generator	permanent magnet
aurora australis	lodestone	pole
aurora borealis	magnetic domain	temporary magnet
coil	magnetic field	
electric motor	magnetite	

PRACTICE

Multiple Choice. Pick the answer that best completes the question.

1. The first magnets were
   a. man-made
   b. lodestones
   c. round
   d. all of these
2. Earth's magnetic field
   a. is very weak
   b. may be caused by iron
   c. helps protect us
   d. all of these
3. What determines the strength of a magnet?
   a. length
   b. weight
   c. material
   d. color
4. Which causes a magnet to work?
   a. domains
   b. size
   c. shape
   d. weight
5. How are electromagnets used?
   a. in telephones and motors
   b. in coils and transistors
   c. both a and b
   d. neither a nor b

6. When do temporary magnets work?
   a. when part of the aurora
   b. when pointed north
   c. when touching a magnet
   d. none of these
7. Which is not part of a generator?
   a. magnet
   b. coil
   c. source of power
   d. motor
8. Metal magnets
   a. can be shaped
   b. are used many ways
   c. came after lodestones
   d. all of these
9. Which of the following can change electric energy into motion?
   a. generators
   b. electromagnets
   c. doughnut-shaped magnets
   d. electric motors
10. What is the difference between an electric motor and a generator?
   a. they do opposite types of work
   b. the generator is larger
   c. the electric motor does not use magnetism
   d. generators have limited use

Matching. Match each word with its definition or description.
   1. produces electricity
   2. naturally occurring magnetic minerals
   3. area of force created by a magnet
   4. magnetic if touching another magnet
   5. displays of light in the sky
   6. a device having a magnetic field
   7. wraps of wire
   8. units that cause magnetism
   9. turns electricity into motion
   10. magnet created by electric current

   a. auroras
   b. coil
   c. electromagnet
   d. generator
   e. lodestone
   f. magnet
   g. magnetic domain
   h. magnetic field
   i. motor
   j. temporary magnet

CAREERS

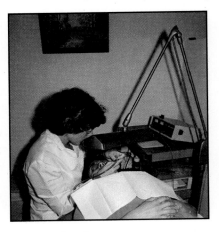

Robotics Technician

Description of Work
Robotics technicians work with other engineers to plan and develop robotic equipment. They must design and redesign equipment until it works. Robotics technicians hypothesize solutions to problems and experiment to see if the ideas work. They must keep accurate records of procedures and test results and compile data into charts and tables.

Personal Qualifications
Robotics technicians must have mechanical aptitude, like working with objects, and have inquiring minds. They must be well organized.

Requirements
A high-school diploma and completion of a college degree or approved program in robotics.

Career Information
Robotics Intl. of SME
P.O. Box 930
Dearborn, MI 48121

Electrician

Description of Work
Electricians work with electrical systems in homes, businesses, and factories. Some install electrical systems such as climate control systems, security systems, communication systems, and general wiring. Others maintain and repair motors, transformers, generators, or robots.

Personal Qualifications
Electricians must have good health and mechanical aptitude. They must also be able to solve problems, follow directions, and understand basic safety.

Requirements
A high-school diploma and the completion of a four-year apprenticeship program. Often they need a license.

Career Information
Intl. Brotherhood of Electrical Workers
1125 15th St., N.W.
Washington, DC 20005

Electrologist

Description of Work
Electrologists remove hair from the body by inserting a very fine filament in the opening of the hair follicle and touching the hair root. A small electric current is then passed through the filament, and the root is destroyed. Once the treatment is complete, the hair is removed permanently.

Personal Qualifications
Electrologists must have good eyesight, steady hands, and a great deal of patience. They must also be friendly and put their clients at ease.

Requirements
A high-school diploma and the completion of an approved program in electrolysis. Usually a license is required.

Career Information
Intl. Guild of Professional Electrologists
202 Boulevard, Suite B
High Point, NC 27262

Electronics Technician

Description of Work
Electronics technicians use various measuring and diagnostic devices to manufacture and service electrical and electronic equipment. This equipment may include radios, radar and sonar devices, televisions, industrial and medical measuring equipment, navigational equipment, and computers.

Personal Qualifications
Electronics technicians must have both mechanical ability and good problem-solving skills. They must be patient and willing to follow directions.

Requirements
A high-school diploma and completion of an approved technical training program.

Career Information
Intl. Society of Certified Electronics Technicians
2708 W. Berry, Suite #3
Fort Worth, TX 76109

Computer Programmer

Description of Work
Computer programmers write the software that makes computers work. Then they must test it and write a set of instructions so computer operators can run the program successfully. Programmers often work from descriptions prepared by systems analysts.

Personal Qualifications
Computer programmers must have good problem-solving skills and be able to think logically and creatively. They also need patience and good communication skills.

Requirements
A high-school diploma and a college degree or completion of an approved program in computer programming.

Career Information
Contact your state office of employment.

Electronics Assembler

Description of Work
Electronics assemblers represent the largest group of workers in the electronics industry. These workers put together all kinds of equipment, including televisions, radios, and computers. Thousands of parts may go into one device. Assemblers must do their work perfectly, or the device will not work well.

Personal Qualifications
Electronics assemblers must have mechanical ability and good hand coordination. They must be able to follow directions and work accurately.

Requirements
A high-school diploma and on-the-job training.

Career Information
Electronics Industry Assoc.
2001 Eye St., NW
Washington, DC 20006

ACKNOWLEDGMENTS

Special acknowledgment and appreciation are given to the following individuals who participated in the preparation of *Discover God's Creation*.

Dick Duerksen for collecting and producing photographic images.
Bonnie Casey for her technical assistance in preparing the materials for publication.
All the teachers and students who participated in field testing the components of this series.

Science/Health Steering Committee
Marion Hartlein, Associate Director, Office of Education, North American Division of Seventh-day Adventists
Marilyn J. Bauer, 6th grade teacher, Hinsdale, Illinois
Jerry Beem, Superintendent of Education, Oklahoma Conference
Henry Farr, Assoc. Superintendent of Education, Georgia-Cumberland Conference
Delano A. Gilliam, Assoc. Superintendent of Education, Atlantic Union Conference
Donald F. Hodder, academy science teacher, St. John's, Newfoundland, Canada
Joyce W. Hopp, Professor of Health Promotion and Education, School of Public Health, Loma Linda University
James D. Mason, principal/science teacher, Sandpoint, Idaho
Alyce J. Pudewell, Associate Director for Elementary Curriculum and Instruction, Pacific Union Conference
Gary E. Randolph, Associate Director of Education, Lake Union Conference
James Stephan, Superintendent of Education, Pennsylvania Conference

Technical Readers
Paul Buckheim, Ph.D., Loma Linda University
Kenneth Burke, Ph.D., Loma Linda University
Sue Dixon, Ph.D., Walla Walla College
Joyce Hopp, Ph.D., M.P.H., Loma Linda University
Patricia Johnston, Dr.P.H., Loma Linda University
Edwin Karlow, Ph.D., La Sierra University
John Lewis, Ph.D., Loma Linda University
Robert Ludeman, Ph.D., Andrews University
Norman Mitchell, Ph.D., La Sierra University
Gilbert Muth, Ph.D., Pacific Union College
Michelle Naden, Ph.D., Loma Linda University
David Steen, Ph.D., Andrews University
Roger Tatum, Ph.D., Loma Linda University

Pacific Press Development
Paul Hey, project coordinator
Ira Lee, designer
Pat McCoy, electronic publishing design assistant
Bonnie Tyson-Flyn, in-house editor

Credits for photos used in *Discover God's Creation*:

Most photos are listed by illustration number. Careers, Frontiers, and Minibiographies are listed by page number.

Front cover/USGS
Back cover/USFS

Adventist Community Services, 19–18
Craig Aldred, p. 152
American Automobile Association, 9–0
American Cancer Society, 18–10
American Honda-Acura, 17–0
David Apple, M.D., p. 212
ATT, 11–0
G. I. Bernard/Animals, Animals, 5–10
Bettman Archives, 16–0
Blackstar/Orlando Sentinel, 6–2
Ron Blakeley/Uniphoto, 4–17
Boeing Commercial Airplane Group, 22–0
Robert Bond, C–0, 13–10, 14–9, 15–4
Dr. Ernest Booth, 2–15, 7–13
Richard Boyd Photography, 2E
Richard Boyd Photography, Courtesy of 20/20 Optical Group, p. 273
California Institute of Technology/The Archives, p. 70, p. 410
P. Carrara/USGS, 4–14, 6–5, 6–14
Dr. Harold Coffin, 4–4, 5–8, 7–0, 7–5, 7–10
John Colletti/Uniphoto, 18–7
R. B. Colton/USGS, 6–14
Paul Conklin/Uniphoto, 22–23
James F. Conner, 23–20
D. R. Crandell/USGS, 6–14
DC Commission to Promote Washington, D.C., B–0
Glenn Dalby, 1–2, 18–1
Roy Doyle, 5–2, 17–5
D. A. Emmrich/Uniphoto, 22–23
Chris Falkenstein/Falkfhoto, 19–0
GE Canada, 22–3
Gemological Institute of America, p. 153
John Gerlach/Animals, Animals, 8–7
Stephen P. Ginsburg, M.D./Kensington Eye Center, 12–4
Grapes-Michaud/Photo Researchers, p. 279
Rafn Hafnfjord, 3–0, 4–0
W. B. Hamilton/USGS, 5–7, 6–12, 6–13
Dr. Robert Hessler, 2–3
Hewlett Packard Company, 11–9, p. 461
Hinsdale Hospital, 14–10, 15–10

Cliff Smith, 4-18, 8-4, 8-5, 8-8, 8-9, 8-12, 8-17, 8-20, 11-8, 13-1, 15-12, 17-10, 17-11, 17-12, 18-8, 18-11, 19-5, 21-2, 21-14.

Smithsonian Institution, 22–20, p. 12

Soil Conservation Service, p. 153

Southern Edison, 22–4, 22–10

D. R. Specker/Animals, Animals, 12–0

Trent Strickland, 4–3, 4–15, 5–1, 5–3, 5–5, 5–6, 5–12, 6–14, 7–6, 8–1, 8–18, 8–20, 8–22, 13–0, 13–3, 22–14, 23–0, p. 143

Jim Tuten/Animals, Animals, 12–0

Uniphoto 2–3, 14–0

USFS, 18–0

USGS, 3–12, 4–2, p. 77, p. 152, p. 153

USGS/Hawaii Volcano Observatory, 2–10

USGS/Menlo Park, p. 152, p. 153

US Library of Congress/Map Division, 2–0

Howard G. Whishire/USGS, Menlo Park, 19–9

D. E. White/USGS, 6–3

Bruce and Karlette Winters, M.D., 1–11

Dan Wyrick, 5-6, 5-9, 6-10, 8-0, 8-6, 8-8, 8-9, 8-11, 8-12, 8-14, 8-20, 12-1, 12-5, 16-9, 17-10, 17-12, 18-0, 22-12, 23-1, pp. 143, 144.

The Yakima Herald Republic, 6–16

All other photos from Mt. Goat Look, Dick Duerksen

Credits for illustrations used in *Discover God's Creation:*

Crystal Dutson, CA 10–4, p. 180; CA 15–3, p. 267; TS p. 300; 18–9; TS p. 368

Robert Knabenbauer, 9–3, 10–1, 10–2, 10–3, 10–4, 10–5, 10–6, 10–8, 10–10, 10–11, 11–1, 11–2, 11–3, 11–4, 11–5, 11–6, 12–2, 12–3, 12–6, 12–9, 12–10, 12–11, 13–2, 13–6, 13–9, 14–1, 14–2, 14–5, 14–6, 14–7, 14–12, 15–1, 15–2, 15–3, 15–6, 15–7, 15–8, 15–9, 16–1, 16–3, 16–4, 16–5, 16–6, 16–7, 16–8, 16–10, 16–11

Ira Russell Lee, Sec. Dev. 3–2, p. 51; Sec. Dev. 11–2, p. 191; Sec. Dev. 11–3, p. 193; TT 13–5, p. 235; Chap. Intro., p. 243; Sec. Dev. 14–1, p. 244; TT 14–1, p. 249; TT 16–4, p. 293; Sec. Dev. 19–2, p. 353; Demo. A, B, p. 395; Chap. Dev., p. 397; Sec. Dev. 21–1 A, B, p. 398; 21–1; 21–4; 21–6; 21–11; Sec. Dev. 21–4, A, B, p. 407; Chap. Intro., p. 443; 23–9; TT 23–2, A, B, p. 448

Pat McCoy, 2–2, Frontiers, p. 221, 14–13

Sheldon Van Etten, 1–4; TT 1–3B, p. 15; 1–12; 2–1; TT 2–1, p. 29; 2–4, 2–5, 2–6, CA 2–2, p. 33; 2–7, 2–9, 2–13, 2–15, 2–18, 2–19, 2–20, TS, p. 42; 3–1, 3–2, 3–3, 3–5, 3–6, 3–7, 3–8, 3–9, 3–13, 4–1, 4–12, 4–16, 4–19, 4–22, CA 4–3, p. 76; 6–1, CA 6–3, p. 109; 6–15, 7–2, 7–3, 7–4, 7–8, 7–11, 7–12, 8–23, TS, p. 166; TT 21–3 A, B, p. 406; 21–15, 21–19, 21–20, TT 21–6 A, B, C, p. 415; CA 21–6, p. 417; 22–2, 22–5, TT 23–1 A, B, p. 446; 23–15, 23–18, 23–19

GLOSSARY

Acid rain –A mixture of air pollution and rain that pollutes lakes and streams and dissolves the stone and metal of buildings and statues.

Acne –A skin disorder that can cause pitting and scarring of the skin.

Additive –Any chemical added to packaged foods to improve the taste and reduce spoilage.

AIDS –The abbreviation for Acquired Immune Deficiency Syndrome, a disease of the immune system that destroys lymphocytes.

Air sac –A tiny space in the lung where blood picks up oxygen and loses carbon dioxide.

Alloy (al´ oi) –A mixture of two or more metals.

Alluvial (ə lōō´ vē al) fan –A fan-shaped deposit of rock and gravel at the base of hills or mountains.

Alternating current (AC) –Electric current that changes direction many times per second.

Amperage –A measure of the number of electrons moving through a wire each second.

Anorexia nervosa (aɪə e reks´ ē a nar vō´ sə) –A serious eating disorder that involves starving oneself, sometimes resulting in death.

Antibody –The blood proteins that give immunity by killing microorganisms.

Anus –The opening at the lower end of the digestive tract.

Anvil–A small bone in the middle ear attached to the hammer.

Aorta –The large artery that comes out of the heart.

Aquifer –Underground water deposits.

Arteriosclerosis (är tir ē ō skla rō´ sis) –A disorder caused by fatty material sticking to the inner walls of arteries.

Artery–A thick-walled blood vessel that carries oxygenated blood from the heart back to the body.

Artificial respiration –A method of first aid used to help a person start breathing.

Athlete's foot –A skin infection of the foot caused by a fungus.

Atrium–One of two uper chambers of the heart that collect blood returning to the heart.

Auditory nerve–The nerve that takes impulses from the cochlea to the brain for processing.

Auricle–The visible outer part of the ear that collects sound waves.

Aurora (ô rôr´ə) –Light in the night sky created by charged particles from the sun striking gases in Earth's atmosphere.

Aurora australis (ô rôr´ ə ô strā´ lis) –Auroras that occur in the southern regions of Earth.

Aurora borealis (ô rôr´ ə bôr ē al´ is) –Auroras that occur in the northern regions of Earth.

Axis–The imaginary line running from the North Pole, through the center of Earth, and out to the South Pole.

Axon –The long fiber of the neuron that sends the electrical message along the neuron.

Balanced diet –A variety of food from each of the four food groups that supplies everything your body needs.

Battery –A set of connected electric cells.

Biceps –The muscle on the front of the upper arm.

Bile–A substance produced by the liver and stored in the gallbladder that helps to break down fat.

Bile duct –A small tube that carries bile from the liver to the small intestine.

Bladder–An organ that stores the urine.

Blood type –One of the kinds of human blood (such as A, B, AB, and O).

Body composition–The ratio of a person's fat compared to his lean tissue.

Brain –The master control center of the nervous system.

Bronchi –A tubelike structure that leads from the trachea to each lung.

Bulimia (byōo lē´ mē ə) –An eating disorder that involves overeating, followed by vomiting.

Calorie –The unit of measure of energy in food.

Capillary–The smallest blood vessel; it connects the arteries to the veins.

Carbohydrate–A nutrient present in grains, fruits, and vegetables that is easily digested. It provides most of the energy used in the body.

Carbonic acid –Acid in caverns that forms stalactites and stalagmites.

Cardiac muscle–The involuntary muscle that makes up the heart.

Carotene (kar´ ə tēn) –A pigment that turns the skin a yellowish color.

Cartilage –Connective tissue that covers the ends of bones and shapes the nose and outer ear.

Cavern –A large underground chamber in a cave.

Cell body–The main part of the neuron; it acts as the message center.

Central nervous system –The brain and the spinal cord.

Cerebellum (ser ə bel´ əm) –The part of the brain that controls balance.

Cerebral cortex –The outer layer of the cerebrum that allows people to see, hear, taste, smell, and feel.

Cerebrum (ser´ ə brəm) –The part of the brain that deals with intelligence, creativity, and voluntary movements.

Characteristic –A feature of an item such as color, size, shape, texture, smell, sound, speed, mass, volume, and temperature.

Chart –Data arranged into rows and columns.

Chemical weathering –The action of rocks turning into new substances.

Cholesterol (kə les´ tər ôl) –Animal fat that can stick to the inside walls of blood vessels.

Cilia –Tiny hairs that line the trachea and bronchi.

Cinder cone–The smallest type of volcano; it has very steep sides and forms when pieces of lava blow out the vent of a volcano.

Circuit –A pathway along which electricity can travel.

Circuit breaker –An automatic switch that shuts off when too much electric current flows through it.

Circulatory system –The transportation system that includes blood, blood vessels, and the heart.

Cirrhosis (se rō´ sis) –A disease of the liver that causes it to harden.

Cleavage –The ability of a material to split along a smooth, flat surface.

Coal –A dark-colored rock made from the remains of plants and animals.

Cochlea–A fluid-filled, coiled tube of the inner ear, which converts vibrations into nerve impulses.

Coil–The part of a generator that rotates between the magnets.

Colliding boundary–The type of boundary that occurs where two tectonic plates come together.

Combination food–A food that provides a variety of nutrients.

Composit cone–A volcano made up of alternating layers of lava and ash and characterized by explosive eruptions.

Compound –A substance formed when two or more elements combine chemically.

Concussion (kən kush´ ən) –A bruise of the brain caused by a fall or a blow to the head.

Conductor –Material through which electrons can flow.

Cone –The part of a volcano formed by material coming out of the volcano.

Cone cell –The type of nerve cell in the eye that allows an animal to see color.

Connective tissue–Tissue that holds other tissue together and forms bone, cartilage, fat, and blood.

Continental drift theory –The theory that the original landmass (Pangea) split apart into the continents, which drifted to their present positions.

Continental glacier–Very large glaciers that cover entire continents. Greenland and Antarctica are the only two continental glaciers.

Convection (kən vək´ shən) current –The motion of heated liquids and gases as they rise or sink.

Core –The innermost layer of Earth.

Cornea–The protective covering of the eye.

CPR–Cardiopulmonary resuscitation is a technique used to restore the heartbeat and breathing after they have stopped.

Cranium –The bones of the head and face, often called the skull.

Crater –A bowl-shaped pit formed at a volcano's vent.

Crust –The outer layer of Earth (averages 19 miles thick).

Current –A constant flow of electrons.

Dandruff –Loose skin cells from the scalp.

Data –Facts collected by observing and measuring.

Decibel –A unit used to measure the loudness of sound.

Delta –Land formed at the mouth of a river from material carried in the river water.

Dendrite–Short treelike fibers that branch out of the cell body of the neuron.

Depressant–A drug that slows down body processes.

Dermis–The second layer of skin, which contains the blood vessels, nerves, sweat glands, and oil glands.

Desirable weight –A person's ideal weight, determined by age, sex, height, and body build.

Diabetes (dī ə bēt´ ēz) –A disease caused by lack of insulin.

Dialysis (dī al´ ə sis) machine –A device that filters wastes from the blood.

Diaphragm (dī´ə fram) –The muscle that separates the chest from the abdomen and controls breathing.

Digestive system –The system that makes large food molecules small enough that they can enter the blood and be used by the body.

Direct current (DC) –A flow of electrons that moves in only one direction through a circuit.

Direct pressure –The method of pressing on a wound to stop bleeding.

Drug –Any chemical that changes the way the body works.

Dry cell –A device, such as a flashlight battery, that uses chemicals to create electricity.

Ear canal–The passageway that carries sound waves into the ear.

Eardrum–A thin membrane at the end of the ear canal that vibrates when sound waves hit it.

Earthquake–Shock waves created by the sudden movement of Earth's crust.

Electric motor –A device that changes electric energy into motion.

Electric power –The rate at which electric energy is used.

Electrical cell –A device that produces electricity.

Electromagnet –A magnet formed when electrons flow through a coil of wire.

Electron –The part of an atom that has a negative (-) charge.

Electronics –The study of electrons and how they move.

Electroscope –A device used to detect static charges.

Element –A substance, such as gold and silver, that normally does not change into other substances.

Energy input –The calories a person eats.

Energy output –The calories a person uses.

Enriched food –Processed food to which nutrients have been added.

Enzyme–A chemical that helps break down food.

Epicenter –The point on the surface of the ground directly above the focus of an earthquake.

Epidermis–The outer layer of skin cells that protect the body from infection and loss of fluid.

Epithelial tissue–Tissue that forms the skin and the mucous membranes in the lining of the mouth, throat, stomach, and intestines.

Equator –An imaginary line that circles Earth halfway between the North and South poles.

Erosion –The movement of pieces of weathered rock and soil.

Erratic boulder –A large boulder picked up and carried to a new location by a glacier.

Esker (es´ kər) –A long, winding ridge formed where water once flowed underneath a glacier.

Esophagus (i säf´ə gəs) –The tube that connects the mouth with the stomach.

Eustachian tube–The tube that connects the middle ear with the throat and helps regulate air pressure in the ear.

Excretory system –The body's waste-removal system, which includes the skin, kidneys, bladder, and small intestine.

Exhalation –Movement of air out of the lungs.

Extrusive –Rocks that form and cool above ground.

Fainting –A temporary loss of consciousness caused by inadequate blood to the brain.

Fat –A nutrient present in oils, which supplies energy and helps to store some vitamins.

Fat tissue –Groups of fat cells, often beneath the skin or around muscles and internal organs.

Fault –The area between two tectonic plates or at a crack in a plate.

Feces –The solid waste from the body.

Femur –The longest human bone, located between the hip and knee.

Fiber –The part of food that cannot be digested.

First aid –The first treatment for injuries.

Fissure (fish´ ər) –A crack from which lava flows.

Fixed joint –A joint between two bones that does not move.

Flash flood –A flood caused when great amounts of water flow suddenly and without warning.

Flood plain –The area covered by water when a river overflows its banks.

Fluorescent (flō res´ ənt) –Minerals that appear bright or colorful under ultraviolet light.

Focus –The underground location at which an earthquake starts.

Follicle –A structure in the skin from which a hair grows.

Food group –Foods that contain the same kind of nutrients.

Fortified food –Processed food to which vitamins and minerals have been added.

Fossil –Hardened remains of a plant or animal.

Fracture –A break or split in a mineral.

Frostbite –An emergency condition that occurs when an area of skin freezes.

Fuse –A thin metal strip that melts when too much electric current flows through it.

Gastric juice –Substance produced by the lining of the stomach, made up of water, hydrochloric acid, and enzymes.

Gateway drug –A drug that often encourages people to use stronger and more harmful drugs (example: marijuana).

Generator –A device that spins and turns motion into electricity.

Geologic (jē ə läj´ ik) column –A set of rock layers that contain fossils.

Geyser –A spring from which hot underground water bursts into the air.

Glacial polish –A very smooth rock surface caused by grinding action underneath a moving glacier.

Glacier –A large mass of thick ice.

Graph –A method used to display data in picture form.

Gravity –The pull of matter on matter (such as Earth's pull on people).

Ground water –Water that soaks into the soil.

Guyot (gē´ ō) –Underwater, flat-topped mountains found in the Pacific Ocean.

Hallucinogen –A drug that changes how the brain works.

Hammer –A small bone in the middle ear attached to the eardrum that moves when the eardrum vibrates.

Heat exhaustion –Overheating that causes a person to feel faint and nauseated.

Heatstroke –Overheating that causes the body to lose its ability to cool itself.

Heimlich (him´ lik) maneuver –A first-aid procedure that clears a choking person's air passageway.

Hemoglobin –A blood protein that carries oxygen and gives blood its red color.

Hormone –The chemical substances that help control the body's processes.

Hot spring –Heated underground water flowing out above ground.

Humus (hyoo´ məs) –Material formed from dead plants and animals.

Hypertension –Above-normal blood pressure.

Hypothermia –The condition that occurs when the human body gets too cold (can cause death).

Ice age –A period of time when Earth's climate was much colder, and huge glaciers formed.

Igneous rock –Rock that forms as magma cools.

Imagination –Creative thought.

Immune system –The body system that protects the body from disease.

Immunity –The body's ability to defend itself from infection and disease.

Immunization (im myoo niz ā´ shən) – The use of special drugs to help prevent disease.

Impulse –An electrical message that travels through neurons.

Ingredient –Any substance used to make a food product.

Inhalation –Movement of air into the lungs.

Insulator –A material that does not let electrons flow through it.

Insulin –A hormone that helps control the amount of sugar in the blood.

Insulin-dependent diabetes –A form of diabetes that can be controlled only by daily injections of insulin.

Integrated circuit –A complete miniature circuit made on a piece of silicon.

Integument (in teg´ yoo ment) –The outer covering of any object.

Integumentary (in teg´ yoo men´ ter ē) system –The system that covers the outside of the body and involves the skin, hair, and nails.

Interferon (in ter fir´ än) –A material produced by cells to prevent viruses from multiplying.

International Date Line –An imaginary line that lies 180 degrees from the Prime Meridian and is used to determine what day it is. If you are traveling west and cross the date line, you move forward one day. You move back one day when you travel east across this imaginary line.

Intestinal juice –A substance secreted by the walls of the small intestine that helps digest food not digested in the stomach.

Intrusive –Rocks that form and cool below ground.

Involuntary muscle –A muscle, such as the heart, that is automatically controlled by the brain.

Iris –The colored part of the eye, which controls the amount of light entering the eye.

Joint –A structure formed where bones come together.

Junk food –Any food that supplies little nutrition but contains large amounts of fats, salt, and sugar.

Kettle lake –Basins gouged out by a glacier and filled with water.

Kidney–One of a pair of organs that filters excess salt, water, and liquid waste out of the blood.

Kilowatt-hour–A unit used to measure large quantities of electrical power equal to 1000 watt-hours.

Landslide –An area where rock and soil slide downhill.

Large intestine –The last part of the digestive tract.

Larynx –The voice box.

Latitude –The distance north or south of the equator, measured in degrees.

Lava –Magma that reaches the surface of Earth.

Lean tissue –Tissue that makes up the skeleton, muscles, skin, and internal organs.

Lens–The structure that focuses the light on the retina.

Lichen (lī´ kən) –Plants that produce acids that help to weather rock.

Ligament –A tough band of tissue that holds a joint together.

Lightning –An electrical discharge that occurs between a cloud and the ground, or between two clouds.

Liver –The organ that produces bile, stores and recycles materials, and filters poisons from the blood.

Load –The material washed along by a river.

Lodestone –A magnetic rock; the original magnets.

Logic–The type of thinking that includes problem solving and decision making.

Longitude –Lines used to locate points east or west of the Prime Meridian, measured in degrees.

Lung –The organ in which oxygen enters the blood and carbon dioxide leaves the blood.

Luster –The ability of a mineral to reflect light.

Lymph –The liquid portion of the blood that passes through the capillary walls into the surrounding tissue.

Lymphocyte (lim´ fō sīt) –A special type of white blood cell that helps defend against infection.

Magma –Melted, underground rock.

Magnetic domain –Miniature magnetic areas that give a magnet its ability to be magnetic.

Magnetic field –The area affected by a magnet.

Magnetism –The force of attraction produced by a magnet.

Magnetite –The magnetic mineral that makes up lodestones.

Magnetosphere (mag nēt´ ō sfir) –Earth's magnetic field.

Mantle –The thickest of Earth's layers lies between the crust and the core.

Marrow –The soft tissue inside a bone that makes bone and blood cells.

Mass –How much matter, or atoms, an object contains.

Matter –Anything that has mass and takes up space (solid, liquid, or gas).

Measure –The amount of anything, such as the length, width, height, volume, mass, temperature, or speed.

Medulla–The connecting link between the brain and the spinal cord.

Melanin (mel´ ə nin) –A dark-brown or black skin pigment.

Memory–The storage and retrieval of information processed by the brain.

Meridian –Any imaginary line that runs from the North Pole to the South Pole and is used to locate points from east to west.

Metabolic rate –The rate at which a person uses energy.

Metabolism (me tab´ ə liz əm) –The use of energy by the whole body.

Metal –Any material that has luster and can be hammered into flat sheets or drawn into wire.

Metamorphic rock– Rock that forms as other rock is changed by heat and pressure.

Microchip –A microscopic-sized integrated circuit.

Microprocessor –The chip that is the "brain" of the computer and is controlled by a program.

Microscope –An instrument that enlarges the appearance of small objects so they can be studied more easily.

Midocean ridge –An underwater mountain range that circles Earth.

Mineral –Any of the elements or compounds that occur in Earth, such as gold, silver, and copper.

Mixture –A combination of two or more materials that are mixed together but are not combined with each other.

Mohs' scale –A scale used to decide the hardness of minerals.

Molecule–Particles of food that can be used by the body.

Moraine (mə rān´) –A pile or hill of gravel and soil left behind by a melting glacier.

Motor neuron –A nerve cell that carries messages from the brain to muscles and organs.

Mountain chain–A series of mountains.

Movable joint –Any joint that allows movement.

Mucous membrane –Lining of the mouth, nose, stomach, and small intestine that secretes mucus.

Mucus –A wet, sticky substance secreted by the mucous membrane.

Nasal passage –The pathway of air through the nose.

Natural disaster –Any destructive event caused by weather or movements of Earth.

Nervous tissue–Tissue that carries electrical messages throughout the body and forms the brain, spinal cord, and nerves.

Neuron –A nerve cell.

Neutron–The neutral particle present in the nucleus of an atom.

Non-insulin-dependent diabetes–A form of diabetes that can be controlled by diet and does not need daily injections of insulin.

Normal fault–The type of fault that occurs when a moving plate slips below a stationary plate.

Nostril–One of the openings in the nose.

Nutrient –A part of food that supplies the body with material needed for life.

Observation –The act of looking or watching.

Ohm (ōm) –The unit used to measure resistance of a material to the flow of electrons.

Oil gland–A gland in the skin that secretes oil to keep the skin soft and moisturized.

Olfactory (äl fak´ tə rē) nerve –A nerve that carries messages from the nose to the brain.

Optic nerve –A nerve that carries messages from the eyes to the brain.

Orbit –The path of a planet around the sun.

Organ –A group of tissues that performs a certain task.

Organ system –Two or more organs that work together to carry out a common task.

Osteoporosis (äs tē ō pə rō´ sis) –A weakening of a bone caused when too much mineral material dissolves out of a bone.

Oxide –Any material that has combined with oxygen.

Pancreas–A feather-shaped organ located just below the stomach.

Pancreatic juice–An enzyme produced by the pancreas that helps digest food.

Pangea (pan jē´ ə) –A large land mass believed to have existed when all of the continents touched.

Parallel –Imaginary lines that run east and west, parallel to the equator.

Parallel circuit–A circuit with more than one path through which current can flow.

Parent rock–The solid rock that lies below subsoil.

Pelvis–The bowl-shaped set of bones that form the hip area.

Perception–Interpretation of information processed by the brain.

Peristalsis (per ə stal´ sis) –Muscle contractions that push food through the digestive system.

Permanent magnet –A magnet that re-mains magnetized for a long period of time.

Pharynx (far´ inks) –The throat area between the mouth and larynx.

Physical weathering –Processes that break rock into smaller pieces.

Pillow lava –Lava that cools under water.

Pimple –A small swelling of the skin, caused by bacteria and filled with pus.

Pinch test–A simple way of checking one's percentage of fat tissue.

Pinkeye –An eye infection that causes redness and irritation.

Pipe–An underground pathway through which magma flows.

Plasma –The clear liquid part of the blood, which contains red cells, white cells, and platelets.

Plate –A large piece of Earth's crust that can move.

Plate tectonic (tek tän´ ik) theory – The belief that Earth's crust is broken into seven major movable plates.

Plateau–Flat, elevated land.

Platelet–A small particle in the blood that helps the blood to clot.

Plume –A column of hot magma that rises from the lower mantle.

Poison control center–A service that suggest emergency treament for victims of poisoning.

Pole –One end of a magnet.

Preservative –An additive used to prevent food from spoiling.

Primary wave–Also called a P-wave, this earthquake wave is created by the back-and-forth movements of the rock that makes up the crust.

Primary waves are the first to reach the seismograph. They *do not* cause damage on Earth's surface.

Prime Meridian –The line of longitude running through Greenwich, England, and assigned the value of zero degrees.

Principle of uniformity–The idea that events always happened at the same rate.

Program –A set of commands that tells the microprocessor what to do.

Protein–A nutrient present in nuts, legumes, and meat that helps build muscle, bone, and blood.

Proton –The part of an atom with a positive charge.

Pupil–The opening in the iris through which light passes.

RDA (Recommended Dietary Allowance) –The average amount of nutrients needed every day to operate the body properly.

Receptor cell –A cell in the skin that detects touch, pressure, heat, or pain.

Rechargeable cell –An electrical cell that can be recharged hundreds of times.

Rectum –The lower end of the large intestine.

Red blood cell–The most common blood cell; it carries oxygen throughout the body.

Reflex –A quick, nervous response controlled by the spinal cord.

Resistance –The opposition to the flow of electrons.

Respiratory system –The system made of the lungs and bronchi that gets oxygen into the blood.

Retina–The thin membrane that lines the back of the eye and converts light energy into nerve impulses. It works as the film to capture the images that are seen.

Revolution –Earth's movement around the sun.

Rib –One of the bones that shape the chest and protect the lungs.

Richter (rik´ tər) scale –The scale used to measure the strength of an earthquake.

Rift valley –A narrow valley running down the center of the midocean ridge.

Rock cycle–The continual process of rocks forming, changing, and forming again.

Rod cell –The type of nerve cell in the eye that allows animals to see white and gray light.

Rotation –Earth's spin on its axis.

Runoff water –Water that does not soak into the ground.

Saliva–An enzyme secreted by the salivary glands that keeps the mouth moist, aids swallowing, and begins the digestive process.

Saturated fat –The type of fat found in meat and dairy products.

Science –The process of asking questions and looking for answers.

Sea-floor spread –A widening of the ocean floor.

Secondary wave–Also called an S-wave, this earthquake wave is created by the up-and-down movements of underground rock. Secondary waves are the second earthquake waves to reach the seismograph. They *do not* cause earthquake damage.

Sediment (sed´ ə ment) –Material formed from small particles of rock, soil, dead plants, or animals.

Sedimentary rock–The most common surface rock; it is formed as sediments, usually laid down by water, and are cemented together to form rock.

Seismograph (siz´ mə graf) –An instrument used by geologists to record the shock waves created by an earthquake.

Seizure –An involuntary loss of muscle control.

Semicircular canal–A small coiled tube in the inner ear that aids balance and orientation.

Sensory neuron –The type of nerve cell that carries messages to the brain.

Septum –The dividing wall between the nostrils.

Series circuit –A circuit with only one pathway through which current can flow.

Shield volcano–The largest type of volcano; it has broad, gently sloping sides.

Shock –A dangerous drop of blood pressure and metabolism, as the body reacts to stress.

Sinkhole –A hole formed above ground as an underground space collapses.

Skeletal muscle–The voluntary muscle that moves the skeleton.

Sliding boundary–The type of boundary that occurs where two tectonic plates slide past each other.

Small intestine –The organ that completes digestion and absorbs most of the nutrients.

Smooth muscle–The involuntary tissue that forms the organs of the digestive system.

Sonar –A device that uses sound waves to locate underwater objects.

Spinal column –The set of bones that forms the backbone.

Spinal cord –The nerves located inside the spinal column.

Spiritual thinking–The type of thinking that allows one to experience emotion and to tell right from wrong. Spiritual thinking is unique to people.

Sprain –Damage to a joint caused by stretching during a twist or fall.

Spreading boundary–The type of boundary that occurs where two tectonic plates are pushed apart.

Static charge –A buildup of extra electrons.

Static discharge –The sudden movement of electrons from one area to another.

Sternum –The flat bone in the middle of the chest, between the ribs.

Stimulant–A drug that speeds up body processes.

Stirrup–A small bone attached to the anvil and inner ear.

Stomach –The digestive organ that lies between the esophagus and small intestine.

Streak –The color left by a rock or mineral when it is rubbed across a rough surface.

Strike-slip fault–The type of fault that occurs when a moving plate slides past a stationary plate.

Subsoil –The soil just below the topsoil.

Suffocation –The lack of oxygen caused when a person cannot breathe.

Sunscreen –Any skin lotion that helps block harmful sunlight from striking the skin.

Surface wave–Also called an L-wave, this earthquake wave is created on the surface of the ground. Surface waves make Earth's crust move and are the waves that cause earthquake damage.

Sweat gland–A gland in the skin that secretes perspiration, which helps to cool the body and get rid of liquid waste.

Synapse (sin′ aps) –The small gap between the end of one axon and the next neuron.

Taste bud –One of many sense organs on the tongue that responds to either sweet, salt, sour, or bitter flavors.

Technology–The applications of scientific principles, which improve our life.

Temporary magnet –A magnet that is magnetic for only a short time.

Texture –The appearance of soil based upon the size of its particles.

Thrust fault–The type of fault that occurs when a moving plate moves up and over a stationary plate.

Tissue –A group of similar cells that perform a certain task.

Topography (te päg′ rə fē) –The shape of the surface of land.

Topsoil –The upper layer of soil that is formed when humus mixes with subsoil.

Trachea (trā′ kē ə) –An air passageway between the larynx and the bronchial tubes.

Transformer –An electrical device that changes the voltage of a current.

Transfusion –The process of giving blood from one person to another.

Transistor –A small device that controls the flow of electrons.

Trench –A long, narrow canyon that forms the deepest parts of the ocean.

Triceps –The muscle on the back of the upper arm.

Tsunami (tsoo nä′ me) –A large wave caused by an underwater earthquake.

U–shaped valley –A rounded valley formed by a glacier.

Universal donor –A person who can give blood to anyone (Type O).

Universal recipient –A person who can receive blood from anyone (Type AB).

Unsaturated (un sach′ ə rāt id) fat –The type of fat found in vegetables, nuts, grains, fish, and poultry.

Urea –Waste from cells that is dissolved in the blood.

Urethra (yoo rē′ thrə) –A tube that leads from the bladder to the outside of the body.

Urine –Liquid waste (urea) filtered from the blood.

Vaccination (vak sə nā′ shən) –An injection of dead or weakened bacteria or virus that protects against disease.

Vacuum (vak′ yoo əm) tube –A device that works like a valve to control the flow of electrons.

Valley glacier–A small glacier that usually occurs in the high mountains and looks like a frozen river.

Vein–A thin-walled blood vessel that carries deoxygenated blood from the body back to the heart.

Vena cava (ve ne kā′ ve) –A large vein that returns blood to the heart.

Vent –An opening in a volcano through which gases and lava may escape.

Ventricle–One of two lower chambers of the heart that pump blood out of the heart.

Vertebra (vur´ te brə) –Any one of the bones that form the spinal column.

Villi (vil´ ī) –Small fingerlike projections on the wall of the small intestine that help absorb digested food.

Vitamin–A nutrient that builds new cells, helps to control body processes, and fights disease.

Vocal cord –Bands or folds in the larynx that vibrate when air passes over them.

Volcano –A hill or mountain formed when lava flows out of a vent and onto Earth's surface.

Volt –The unit of measure of voltage.

Voltage –The pressure that pushes electrons through a circuit.

Volume–The amount of space occupied by matter.

Voluntary muscle –Any muscle that can be controlled by a person.

Watt –The unit of measure of electrical power.

Watt-hour –The measure of the rate at which power is used.

Weathering –Any process that breaks up or changes rocks of Earth's crust.

Weight–The measure of the pull of gravity on matter.

Weight management–A plan that helps maintain the ideal body weight of an individual.

Wet cell –A device containing liquid acid that creates electricity.

White blood cell–A blood cell that fights infection by destroying harmful bacteria and by producing antibodies.

INDEX

F

K

Kettle lake, *see* glacier
Kidney, *see* excretory system
Kilowatt-hour 429
Krakatoa 67

L

Lake 100
Landslide 104
Large intestine, *see* digestive system
Larynx 266–268
    vocal cords 267
Latitude 40
Latrobe Valley 123
Lava, *see* volcano
Lean tissue 320
Lens, *see* eye
Lichen 88
Ligament 174
Lightning 400
Likens, Gene E. 88
Limestone 87, 144
Lines of defense, *see* immune system
Liver 165, 292, 296, 317
    bile 291, 292, 296
    bile duct 292
    cirrhosis 297
Load 101
Loamy soil, *see* soil
Lodestone, *see* magnetism
Longitude 41
Low-frequency sound, *see* sound
LSD 198, 339, 340
Lung, *see* respiratory system
Luster, *see* mineral
Lymph, *see* lymph system
Lymph gland, *see* lymph system
Lymph system 249, 293
    lymph 249, 293
    lymph gland 256
    lymphocyte 249, 256, 257
Lymphocyte, *see* lymph system

M

Magma, *see* volcano
Magnet, *see* magnetism
Magnetic domain, *see* magnetism
Magnetic field, *see* magnetism
Magnetism 37, 424–457
    electromagnet 451, 452
    lodestone 444
    magnet 37, 38, 424, 443–445
    magnetic domain 447, 448
    magnetic field 38, 445, 447–449, 456, 457
    magnetite 444
    magnetosphere 38, 456
    permanent 449
    pole 37, 444
    temporary 449
Magnetite, *see* magnetism
Magnetosphere, *see* magnetism
    magnitude 70
Mantle, *see* Earth
Marble 144
Mariana Trench 30
Marijuana 198, 333, 339, 340
Marrow, *see* bone
Mass 14, 37
Matter 134
Mauna Loa 66
Measure 13–15
measurement 13–15
Measurement, *see* measure
Medicine 332
    over-the-counter medicine 332
Medulla, *see* brain
Melanin 234
Memory 198, 199
Mendenhall Glacier 106
Mercali scale 70
Meridian 41
Metabolic rate 322
Metabolism 322
Metal 140
Meter, *see* electric meter
Metamorphic rock 144, 146
Mica, *see* mineral

Microchip 432, 433
Microprocessor 433
Microscope 20, 21
Mid-Atlantic Ridge 30
Midocean ridge 50, 53
Milk food, *see* food group
Mineral 133–142
    calcite 140
    calcium 176, 177
    cleavage 139
    features of 135
    feldspar 142
    fluorescent 140
    fracture 139
    galena 138
    luster 138
    mica 139, 142
    Mohs' scale 137
    quartz 142
    streak test 138
Mineral, *see* nutrient
Mississippi River 102
Mixture 141
Mohs' scale, *see* mineral
Molecule 284, 289, 457
Moraine, *see* glacier
Motor neuron, *see* neuron
Mt. Everest 30
Mt. St. Helens 66, 111
Mt. Stevens 117
Mt. Vesuvius 67
Mountain 39, 55
Mountain soil, *see* soil
Movable joint, *see* joint
Mucous membrane 158, 255, 265
Mucus 265, 268, 284
Muscle 162, 171, 178–181, 290
    biceps 181
    cardiac muscle 179
    involuntary muscle 179
    skeletal muscle 179, 181
    smooth muscle 179
    triceps 181
    voluntary 179, 194
Muscular system 162, 172–181
    care 178, 181
Muscular tissue, *see* tissue

Sprain, *see* first aid
Spreading boundary, *see* plate boundary
Spring 100
Starch 292
Static charge, *see* static electricity
Static discharge, *see* static electricity
Static electricity 397–402
    negative charge 400
    positive charge 400
    static charge 400–402
    static discharge 400
Sternum, *see* skeleton
Stimulant, *see* drug
Stirrup, *see* ear
Stomach, *see* digestive system
Streak, *see* mineral
Strike-slip fault, *see* fault
Stroke 253
Subsoil, *see* soil
Suffocate, *see* first aid
Sugar 292
Sulfur 138
Sunburn, *see* first aid
Sunscreen, *see* first aid
Surface wave, *see* earthquake wave
Surtsey 63
Sweat gland, *see* skin
Synapse, *see* neuron

T

Taste 218
Taste buds, *see* tongue
Tears, *see* eye
Technology 7, 8
Temporary magnet, *see* magnetism
Tendon 179
Texture 91
Thinking, types of 164, 199, 200
Thrust fault, *see* fault
Thunderstorm 367
Tidal wave 71

Tissue 158, 159, 162, 175
    connective tissue 158, 159, 162, 175
    epithelial tissue 158, 159
    fat tissue 158, 193, 320
    nerve tissue 158, 159
    muscular tissue 158, 159
Tobacco 271, 340
Tongue 218, 219
    taste buds 218
Topography 39
Topsoil, *see* soil
Tornado 365
Trachea, *see* respiratory system
Transformer 428
Transfusion, *see* blood
Transistor 432, 433
Trench 50
Triceps, *see* muscle
Tropical soil, *see* soil
Tsunami 71
Tundra soil, *see* soil
Turbine 425

U

U-shaped valley, *see* glacier
Ultraviolet light 140, 212
Universal donor, *see* blood
Universal recipient, *see* blood
Unsaturated fat, *see* fat
Urea, *see* excretory system
Urethra, *see* excretory system
Urine, *see* excretory system

V

Vaccination 256
Vacuum tube 431, 433
Valley glacier, *see* glacier
Vein, *see* blood vessel
Vena cava, *see* blood vessel
Vent, *see* volcano
Ventricle, *see* heart
Vertebrae, *see* skeleton
Villi, *see* digestive system
Virus 162, 256, 257

Vitamin, *see* nutrient
Vocal cords, *see* larynx
Volcano 36, 52, 54, 64–67, 77, 99, 127
    cinder cone 65, 66
    composite volcano 65, 66
    cone 65
    crater 65
    lava 36, 64, 65, 127
    magma 36, 64, 135
    pillow lava 50
    pipe 64
    shield volcano 65, 66
    vent 64
Volt 407
Volta, Alessandro 410
Voltage 407, 410, 428
Volume 14
Voluntary muscle, *see* muscle

W

Waste 9, 162, 164, 176, 228, 235–237, 248, 250, 294, 295, 307, 317
Water, *see* nutrient
Watt 429
Watt-hour 429, 430
Weather 31, 362, 365, 434
Weathering 83–93, 99, 146
    chemical weathering 84, 87, 88
    physical weathering 84–86
Wegener, Alfred 48, 49
Weight 14
    weight management 320, 323
Wet cell 410, 411
White blood cell, *see* blood
Wind 85, 103
Windmill 426
Wire coil 424

Y

Yosemite Valley 108